Elements of Abstract Algebra

A series of advanced mathematics texts under the editorship of CARL B. ALLENDOERFER

MEASURE AND INTEGRATION by *Sterling K. Berberian*

TOPICS IN HIGHER ANALYSIS by *Harold K. Crowder and S. W. McCuskey*

CONCEPTS IN MODERN ALGEBRA by *W. E. Deskins*

THEORY AND SOLUTION OF ORDINARY DIFFERENTIAL EQUATIONS by *Donald Greenspan*

RETRACING ELEMENTARY MATHEMATICS by *Leon Henkin, W. Norman Smith, Verne J. Varineau, and Michael J. Walsh*

INTRODUCTION TO MATHEMATICAL STATISTICS by *Robert V. Hogg and Allen T. Craig*

ELEMENTARY MATRIX ALGEBRA, Second Edition, by *Franz E. Hohn*

METHODS IN ANALYSIS by *Jack Indritz*

PROJECTIVE AND RELATED GEOMETRIES by *Harry Levy*

STATISTICAL THEORY by *B. W. Lindgren*

INTRODUCTION TO PROBABILITY THEORY by *James R. McCord, III, and Richard M. Moroney, Jr.*

ELEMENTS OF ABSTRACT ALGEBRA by *John T. Moore*

ELEMENTS OF
ABSTRACT ALGEBRA

JOHN T. MOORE
THE UNIVERSITY OF FLORIDA

THE MACMILLAN COMPANY   NEW YORK

Fifth Printing 1964

Library of Congress catalog card number: 61-17533

The Macmillan Company, New York
Brett-Macmillan Ltd., Galt, Ontario

Printed in the United States of America

To my Mother and Father

PREFACE

There are several fine books on the subject of modern abstract algebra, and there may be some serious doubt of the need for another book on this topic. Hence a brief explanation is in order.

The present text differs from most of its predecessors in at least three important respects: level of student audience, order of material, coverage of material. While the best of the established books in the area of modern algebra are directed principally to the beginning graduate student, this book is addressed to undergraduates—usually at the junior or senior level. The order of development which we have adopted is to proceed from the most simple algebraic system, the set, to systems with one binary composition, culminating with groups, and thence to systems with two binary compositions, such as rings, fields, vector spaces, and lattices. Some books introduce integral domains first, since one of our most familiar algebraic systems—the system of ordinary integers—is of this variety. While I recognize that there is some pedagogical merit in this introduction, the order adopted here has the advantage of being logically sequential. As for coverage, it is probably true that most of the topics in this book are to be found somewhere in one or more of the fine comprehensive texts to which reference has already been made. But it is difficult to make a satisfactory selection of material for a beginning one-semester course from one of these texts—excellent as it may be. It is possible to do so, of course, but it does take extreme care not to get too much involved in one topic to the exclusion of others. Moreover, if selections are made throughout a more comprehensive book, it is difficult to avoid making assignments of problems involving material which has not been covered in class. In addition, it is my opinion that students often feel unhappy about the omission of large portions of a textbook; and, although this is admittedly a shallow reason for complaint, I feel that the psychological approach of a student to a mathematical discipline is one which should not be ignored. There is a certain sense of accomplishment in covering substantially all of a book, even though the same material might have been covered by making a proper selection of material from a larger book. For these reasons, an attempt has been made in the present text to give a survey of the principal algebraic systems of modern abstract algebra without giving too exhaustive a treatment of any one of them. For example, Chapter 2 is devoted to the real numbers, but while a whole semester could be spent on this topic, there has been included here only enough material to indicate the modern algebraic point of view on the subject. Our limited coverage of the other topics has had a similar motivation.

An earlier form of the first six chapters has been used for several semesters with junior and senior students at the University of Florida. Experience there indicates that, if too much time is not spent on working problems in class, ample time remains to cover most of this material in a three-hour course in one semester. The last two sections of Chapter 5 may be omitted, as well as the whole of Chapter 7, unless the class is advanced or additional time is available. It is hoped that each section contains the proper amount of text for presentation in one usual class period, so that any of the problems immediately following the section can be assigned without fear that the background material has not been covered.

It probably should be pointed out that this is not primarily a book on linear algebra or matrix theory. Matrices are introduced to provide us with examples of a ring, and the connection between matrices and linear transformations of a vector space is explained in Chapter 6. However, a detailed development of matrix theory is left for a separate course, which could either follow or precede this one.

The reader will observe that many routine verifications of points in the theoretical development of the text have been relegated to the problem sets—for the student to complete. In every instance these proofs are quite elementary, and in many cases some of the steps have actually been included in the descriptive material. These problems, which constitute an integral part of the theory, have been indicated by *, and their solutions will be assumed in subsequent developments. I am aware that there are very few illustrative examples actually worked out in the text proper. However, the Appendix contains the detailed solution of one somewhat representative problem from each problem set. These illustrative problems have been identified by **, and the student is invited to refer to the Appendix to help him develop some of the techniques needed for the solution of problems.

There are many people to whom I am indebted for help in the course of getting this book ready for publication. I am particularly indebted to Professor Franz E. Hohn of the University of Illinois who read an early edition of the manuscript and made many valuable comments on it. I wish to thank several of my colleagues at the University of Florida, in particular Professors Edwin H. Hadlock, Walter P. Morse, and Henryk Minc, for assistance in reading and offering criticism on portions or all of the manuscript. In addition, I wish to acknowledge assistance from Mr. Arnold Insel, a graduate student at the University of Florida, who read the final manuscript and called attention to several points in need of revision. I would also like to recognize my colleague and friend Professor Dudley E. South who, while not directly involved in any phase of the book, has always been a source of inspiration and encouragement. Finally, to Mr. A. H. McLeod and other members of the staff of The Macmillan Company many thanks are due for their kind and friendly cooperation.

John T. Moore

Gainesville, Florida

CONTENTS

1 INTRODUCTORY CONCEPTS   *1*

1.1   Sets   1
1.2   The Cardinality of a Set   4
1.3   Product Sets and Mappings   6
1.4   Relations   10

2 AN AXIOMATIC APPROACH TO OUR NUMBER SYSTEM   *16*

2.1   The Natural Numbers   16
2.2   Order and the Second Principle of Induction   21
2.3   The Rational Integers   24
2.4   Theorems on Integers   28
2.5   The Rational and Real Numbers   32

3 *GENERAL ALGEBRAIC SYSTEMS*   *35*

   3.1 Groupoids and Semi-groups   35
   3.2 Monoids and Groups   39
   3.3 Isomorphism   41
   3.4 Homomorphism   44
   3.5 Fundamental Homomorphism Theorem   47

4 *GROUPS*   *50*

   4.1 An Equivalent Definition   50
   4.2 Some Simple Examples of a Group   53
   4.3 Two Important Groups   56
   4.4 Elementary Properties of Groups   60
   4.5 Subgroups   64
   4.6 Important Results on Permutation Groups   66
   4.7 The Uniqueness Theorem   70
   4.8 Cosets and Lagrange's Theorem   72
   4.9 Normal or Invariant Subgroups   76
   4.10 Normal Subgroups and Homomorphisms   78
   4.11 A Brief Survey   80

5 *RINGS*   *83*

   5.1 Definition and Examples   83
   5.2 Some Elementary Properties of Rings   89
   5.3 Types of Rings   91
   5.4 Two Important Rings   94
   5.5 The Quotient Field of a Commutative
       Integral Domain   98
   5.6 Ideals in a Ring   101
   5.7 Quotient or Difference Rings   105
   5.8 Prime Ideals in a Commutative Ring   108
   5.9 Further Results on Quotient Rings   111
   5.10 Gaussian and Euclidean Domains   114
   5.11 Noetherian Rings   118

6 *VECTOR SPACES*   *123*

   6.1 Introduction   123

6.2 Generalizations 127

6.3 Simple Properties of a Vector Space 131

6.4 Linear Dependence 135

6.5 Bases for a Vector Space 138

6.6 An Important Theorem 142

6.7 Linear Transformations 145

6.8 The Isomorphism Theorem 149

6.9 Systems of Equations 154

6.10 Cramer's Rule and Matrix Inversion 157

6.11 Solutions by Gauss Reduction 160

7 **LATTICES AND BOOLEAN ALGEBRA** 167

7.1 Introduction 167

7.2 An Alternate Definition 171

7.3 Sublattices and Isomorphism 174

7.4 Types of Lattices 176

7.5 A Brief Survey 179

7.6 Boolean Algebras 180

7.7 The Boolean Algebra of Propositions 184

APPENDIX 190

INDEX 201

Elements of Abstract Algebra

chapter 1

INTRODUCTORY CONCEPTS

1.1 SETS

A study of modern abstract algebra is an examination of certain algebraic systems which have been subjected to an axiomatic development. If we take a careful look at each of these systems, we find the notions of a *set* and certain *mappings* of sets as common ingredients. Accordingly, it is proper to give a brief survey of the theory of sets before we begin a detailed investigation of any one particular algebraic system.

A *set* (or *collection* or *class*) and its *elements* are basic undefined concepts of mathematics, but the notions are intuitively very simple. Thus, we may have a set S, the elements of which may be listed as $a, b, c, \cdots$, and indicate this symbolically by $S = \{a, b, c, \cdots\}$. The essential relationship between a set and its elements is that the latter

1

are members of or *belong to* the set. In particular, with reference to the above set, b is a member of or belongs to S, an assertion which may be conveniently abbreviated by $b \in S$. It is easy to think of many examples of sets: for instance, the set of points on a line, the set of books in the Library of Congress, the set of people now living in Florida, and the set $\{1, 2, 3, \cdots\}$ of all natural numbers. We emphasize that the nature of the elements of a set does not concern us at this time. To illustrate further the notation introduced: if L is a line segment, considered as a set of points, we could indicate that p is a point on the line by writing $p \in L$. (A stroke through this or any other symbol will indicate the denial of the symbolic assertion. Thus, if x is not a member of the set S, we may write $x \notin S$.)

It is easy for confusion to arise in designating the members of a set if we fail to distinguish between the *names* of the members and the *members* themselves. For example, the set $\{$John, Harry$\}$ could be a set of two proper names or a set of two people named John and Harry. The set of letters of the word "CALCULUS" could be a set of eight distinct—but not all distinguishable—symbols, an interpretation which we adopt in a study of the possible permutations of these letters in college algebra; or we could have in mind the set whose members are the five distinct letters of our alphabet symbolized by C, A, L, U, S. In our brief discussion here we shall always assume the second interpretation, i.e., our sets will comprise the *objects whose names are listed.* In line with this convention we shall say that two elements a and b of a set are *equal* and write $a = b$ whenever a and b are merely two different names for the same object. For example, in the set of natural numbers we might have occasion to state that $2 = $ II or $4 = $ IV. With reference to the preceding paragraph we have "named" the set $\{a, b, c, \cdots\}$ by identifying it with S and writing $S = \{a, b, c, \cdots\}$. In the sequel the notion of "equality" will be of frequent occurrence, and this particular usage to mean "identity" may be considered somewhat trivial. However, any two elements which are "equal" in the sense of identity will also be "equal" in any extended meaning of the notion of equality.

A *subset* of a set S is a set all the elements of which belong to S. If A is such a subset, A is *contained* in S, and we write $A \subseteq S$. If it is known that there are elements in S which are not in A, the latter is a *proper* subset of S, a fact which is indicated symbolically by $A \subset S$. Two sets A and B are *equal*, i.e., $A = B$, if each is a subset of the other. Thus, it follows from this definition of equality of sets that $A = B$ if $A \subseteq B$ and $B \subseteq A$, so that two sets are equal if they contain the same elements. In this case again A and B are merely different names for the same set.

The *intersection* $A \cap B$ of two sets A and B is the set of all elements common to both A and B. Thus, $A \cap B$ is the set of all elements x such that $x \in A$ and $x \in B$, a set which it is convenient to designate as $\{x \mid x \in A \text{ and } x \in B\}$. If $A = \{1, 2, 3, 4, 5\}$ and $B = \{2, 4, 6\}$, it follows that $A \cap B = \{2, 4\}$. If S is the set of all mathematics students in your college and T is the set of all coeds, $S \cap T$ is the set of all coed mathematics students in your college. This notion of intersection may, of course, be extended to include the intersection of any finite number of sets $A_1, A_2, A_3, \cdots, A_n$, in which case we use the notation $\overset{n}{\underset{i=1}{\cap}} A_i$ to designate the intersection.

A similar notion is that of *logical sum* or *union* of sets. Thus, $A \cup B$ is the set of all elements x such that $x \in A \text{ or } x \in B$ (or possibly both); i.e., in the notation introduced above, $A \cup B = \{x \mid x \in A \text{ or } x \in B\}$. For example, if $A = \{a, b, c, d\}$ and $B = \{b, d, e, f\}$, it follows that $A \cup B = \{a, b, c, d, e, f\}$. More generally, $x \in \overset{n}{\underset{i=1}{\cup}} A_i$, if $x \in A_j$ for some j on the range from 1 to n.

It is convenient to introduce the notion of the *empty* set $\emptyset$, i.e., the set with no members. For example, the set of all even prime integers greater than 2 is the set $\emptyset$. It is clear that if A and B are disjoint, i.e., they have no elements in common, it will follow that $A \cap B = \emptyset$.

Problems 1-1

**1. If S_1 is the set of letters of the word "ALTERNATE" and S_2 is the corresponding set for the word "ILLITERATE" list the members of the sets $S_1 \cup S_2$ and $S_1 \cap S_2$.

2. The *power set* of a set is the set of its subsets, including the whole set and the empty set. List the members of the power set of $\{a, b, c, d\}$.

3. If A, B, and C are the sets of points comprising the three sides of a triangle, describe the sets $A \cap B$, $B \cup C$, $A \cap B \cap C$, and $A \cup B \cup C$.
4. If R, S, and T are subsets of a set, prove that: (a) $(R \cup S) \cup T = R \cup (S \cup T)$; (b) $(R \cap S) \cup T = (R \cup T) \cap (S \cup T)$.
5. If S is a set of n elements, how many elements does the power set of S contain? (See **Problem 2.**)
6. Let A, B, and C be the sets of points inside or on three intersecting circles. Use crosshatched diagrams (known as Venn diagrams) to designate: **(a)** $A \cap B$; **(b)** $A \cap B \cap C$; **(c)** $A \cup C$; **(d)** $A \cup B \cup C$.

1.2 THE CARDINALITY OF A SET

In our everyday lives there occur many instances in which the elements of one set may be seen to *correspond* to the elements of another set. We do not define the word "correspond," but rather accept the fact that it has an intuitive meaning. For example, each telephone in operation in your city corresponds to a number in your local telephone directory; to each of the United States there corresponds a governor; to each cubic equation with real coefficients there correspond one or more real solutions; to each article in a store there corresponds a price. Another very familiar example of this intuitive notion of correspondence is that established between two sets of real numbers by means of an algebraic equation. Thus, the equation $y = x^3$ may be considered to establish a correspondence in which a real number x, of one set, corresponds to the real number y, which is equal to x^3, in the other.

If two sets S and T are so related that each element in S corresponds to a unique element in T, and each element in T is the correspondent of one and only one element in S, the two sets are said to be in *one-to-one correspondence*. For example, the set of fingers on one of your hands may be seen to be in one-to-one correspondence with the set of fingers on your other hand. Two sets whose members can be put in one-to-one correspondence are also said to be *cardinally equivalent*, or to have the *same cardinal number*. For example, if a theater is completely filled and there are no people standing, the set of people and the set of chairs in the theater have the same cardinal number. A set which is cardinally equivalent to the set $\{1, 2, 3, \cdots, n\}$ of natural numbers for some n is said to be *finite* with *cardinal num-*

ber n. This number n is familiarly known as the "number" of elements in the set. We note in passing that it is quite possible—as in the example of the theater above—to know that two sets have the *same* cardinal number without our knowing the cardinal number of either set. If a set is neither finite nor the empty set, it is said to be *infinite*. The most familiar example of an infinite set is the set $\{1, 2, 3, \cdots\}$ of all natural numbers, and any set which is cardinally equivalent to this set is said to be *denumerable*. A set which is either finite or denumerable may be said to be *countable*, though there is some variation in the usage of the words "denumerable" and "countable." We shall always use N to designate the set of all natural numbers.

It is a characteristic of finite sets—and one which can be proved —that no proper subset can have the same cardinal number as the whole set. It is easy to see, however, that this is not true for infinite sets. For example, the set of all even natural numbers has the same cardinal number as the set of all natural numbers, for it is possible to set up a one-to-one correspondence between the two sets so that each even number corresponds to the number half as large. This correspondence can be illustrated as follows:

It can also be shown that both the rational numbers **(Problem 3)** and the algebraic numbers **(Problem 4)** form denumerable sets. (It may be necessary for the student to look up the meaning of "algebraic" as applied to numbers.) The set of real numbers is not denumerable, however, as can be seen by a simple argument; for let us suppose that the real numbers between 0 and 1 do form a denumerable set and that R_k is the real number corresponding in the enumeration to the natural number k. We shall reach a contradiction by constructing a real number r between 0 and 1, such that $r \neq R_n$ for any $n \in N$. First we recall that the only real numbers with nonunique decimal representations are those involving a repeated 9 or

0; for example, $0.2999 \cdots = 0.3000 \cdots$. We then define the number r to be $0.r_1 r_2 r_3 \cdots$, where $r_n = 7$ if the nth decimal digit in the representation of R_n is 3, and otherwise $r_n = 3$. This number r cannot have two decimal representations, since it contains neither 9 nor 0; and since it differs in at least one digit from R_n for every n, it is in fact different from each R_n. Hence r is not included in any denumerable arrangement of the real numbers between 0 and 1, and so these numbers are not denumerable. The cardinal number of a denumerable set is considered the first infinite cardinal, and is usually designated $\aleph_0$ (read "aleph naught"), where $\aleph$ is the first letter of the Hebrew alphabet.

Problems 1–2

1. Show that the set of all positive integral multiples of 3 has cardinal number $\aleph_0$.

**2. Show that the cardinal number of the union of two finite disjoint sets is the sum of the cardinal numbers of the individual sets.

3. Prove that the set of all irreducible fractions a/b, where a and b are natural numbers, is denumerably infinite. (If necessary, look this up in some other text on abstract algebra.)

4. Look up the proof in some other algebra book that the set of all algebraic numbers is denumerably infinite.

5. Prove that the union of two denumerable sets is itself denumerable. (Hint: If m_{ik} is a typical element of a set M_i, there are only a finite number of elements with this designation such that $i + k = j$, for any j.) Generalize this result to include the union of a denumerable number of denumerable sets.

1.3 PRODUCT SETS AND MAPPINGS

If S and T are arbitrary sets, the *product set* $S \times T$ is defined to be the set of all ordered pairs (s, t), with $s \in S$ and $t \in T$. The pairs are "ordered" in the sense that (s, t) is considered distinct from (t, s) if $s \neq t$. We define the *equality* of two ordered pairs as *identity* by stating that $(s_1, t_1) = (s_2, t_2)$ provided $s_1 = s_2$ and $t_1 = t_2$. If $S = \{1, 2, 3\}$ and $T = \{1, 2\}$, it follows from the definition of a product set that $S \times T = \{(1, 1), (1, 2), (2, 1), (2, 2), (3, 1), (3, 2)\}$. If $S = \{s_1, s_2, \cdots, s_m\}$ and $T = \{t_1, t_2, \cdots, t_n\}$, the product set $S \times T$ consists of the mn elements (s_i, t_j), where $i = 1, 2, 3, \cdots, m$ and $j =$

$1, 2, 3, \cdots, n$. More generally, if $S_1, S_2, \cdots, S_r$ are any r sets, then $S_1 \times S_2 \times \cdots \times S_r$ or $\prod\limits_{i=1}^{r} S_i$ is the set of all r-tuples $(s_1, s_2, \cdots, s_r)$, where the ith component $s_i \in S_i$, $i = 1, 2, 3, \cdots, r$. It will turn out that product sets will play an important part in our future developments.

In elementary mathematics considerable attention is usually paid to the meaning of the statement that one quantity is "a function of" another quantity. This type of discussion attempts to make it clear, for instance, that a quantity y *is a function of* a quantity x whenever y *is associated with* or *corresponds to* x in some well-defined and unique way. The meaning of the word "function" itself is either ignored or defined in some nonmathematical and intuitive form as anything from a "rule" to a "meatgrinder"! While it is readily admitted that the abstract concept of a function is of secondary importance to a knowledge of the quantities which are associated by it, it seems to be nonetheless in good mathematical form to give an appropriate definition of this important concept. It is especially desirable for us to do so at this time, since we can accomplish this with the help of product sets. We have recalled that a "function"—whatever it may be—does determine a correspondence or association between pairs of elements. To be more precise, if $y = f(x)$ in the familiar symbolism of functions, the quantity y is associated with the quantity x, so that the ordered pair (x, y) is determined by the function. It should not be too farfetched, then, to choose to *define* the *function f* to be the set of *all* such ordered pairs. The following more formal definition does just this.

> **Definition.** A *mapping* (or *function*) α *of a set S into a set T* (*or on S to T*) is a subset of $S \times T$ such that each $s \in S$ occurs exactly once as the first component of a member of the subset.

Each ordered pair $(s, t) \in \alpha$ associates s with t, where t is known as the *value* of the function at s or the "image" of s under the mapping. It would be in harmony with long-established custom to denote this image element or function value by $\alpha(s)$; however, algebraists usually prefer $s\alpha$ to $\alpha(s)$, and we shall adopt this preferred usage. Our definition above defines what used to be referred to as a "single-valued" function or mapping, but it is customary now to restrict the use of the words "function" and "mapping" to this case. The set of all the first components s of the ordered pairs of a function comprise the *domain* of the function, while the set of function values y is its *range*.

To illustrate the notation which we are using, let α be the mapping of the set of real numbers into itself defined by $y = x^3$, so that $x\alpha = y$. Then $1\alpha = 1$, $2\alpha = 8$, $3\alpha = 27$, etc. (In the more usual notation of functions, with f replacing α, this is equivalent to writing $f(1) = 1$, $f(2) = 8$, $f(3) = 27$, etc.) As another illustration, let $S = \{a, b, c\}$ and $T = \{1, 2, 3, 4, 5\}$. Then, if θ is the mapping of S into T defined with obvious symbolism by $a \rightarrow 1$, $b \rightarrow 4$, $c \rightarrow 5$, we may write $a\theta = 1$, $b\theta = 4$, $c\theta = 5$. It is sometimes convenient to designate such a mapping in inexplicit form by $\theta: S \rightarrow T$.

We note that we have defined a mapping α of S into T as a subset of $S \times T$, this subset consisting of the totality of pairs $(s, s\alpha)$, where $s \in S$. It is customary to think of a "graph" as a pictorial representation of something. In particular, if both S and T are the set of all real numbers, we can identify their members with the points on the axes of a Cartesian coordinate system; the *graph* of $S \times T$ is then the set of all points on the plane. The *graph* of any *mapping* of a set of real numbers into a set of real numbers will then be a subset of these points, selected according to the rule of the mapping —a procedure which is familiar from analytic geometry.

A mapping α of a set S into a set T is said to be *injective* if distinct elements of S have distinct images in T, i.e., if $s_1\alpha = s_2\alpha$ implies that $s_1 = s_2$. If each $t \in T$ occurs as an image $s\alpha$, for some $s \in S$, the mapping is said to be *onto* T or *surjective*. A mapping which is both injective and surjective is said to be *bijective*. A bijective mapping determines and is determined by a one-to-one correspondence between the elements of the two sets, as discussed previously. While the words which we have just defined are not essential or in common use, they are convenient to have. The prefix "in-" suggests that it is possible that all the elements of T may not be image points; "sur-"—from the French for "on"—suggests that each element of T is an image point under α; and "bi-" has the usual interpretation of "both ways."

In a bijective mapping of S into T each element $t \in T$ is the image of some unique element $s \in S$. If we represent such a mapping by α, it is clear that we can reverse the mapping and map the elements of T onto elements of S, according to the rule that t maps onto s provided s is mapped onto t by α. We designate this mapping which is *inverse* to α by α^{-1}. The mapping α^{-1} is a bijective mapping of T into S and *exists as a mapping of T only if α is bijective.*

Inasmuch as we have defined mappings as sets, it is clear that two mappings are *equal* if they comprise the same set of elements. However, it is convenient to give an alternate but equivalent definition of equality of mappings. Thus, if α and β are two mappings of S into T, we make the *definition* that $\alpha = \beta$ if $s\alpha = s\beta$ for each $s \in S$. Now let S, T, and U be three sets, with α a mapping of S into T, and β a mapping of T into U. Then the mapping that sends $s \in S$ onto the element $(s\alpha)\beta$ in U is known as the *product* of the mappings α and β. We designate this product as $\alpha\beta$, so that by definition $s(\alpha\beta) = (s\alpha)\beta$.

A mapping of a set S into itself is known as a *transformation* of the set. Included among these mappings is the transformation that leaves each element of the set unchanged. We symbolize this transformation by 1 (or 1_S), so that $s1 = s$ for each $s \in S$. It is clear that $\alpha 1 = \alpha = 1\alpha$, for any transformation α **(Problem 1)**. Furthermore, if α is a bijective mapping of S into T, $\alpha\,\alpha^{-1} = 1_S$ and also $\alpha^{-1}\alpha = 1_T$ **(Problem 2)**. It may be appropriate to remark here that 0 and 1 will be used with many different meanings during the course of this book. However, in any given context it should be clear which meaning is to be understood.

Everyone is familiar with the "operations" of addition and multiplication in the set of real numbers. That is, everyone knows how to find the *sum* and *product* of any two such numbers. But what about the abstract concepts of "addition" and "multiplication" and of "operations" in general? Since both addition and multiplication determine a mapping of pairs of real numbers onto real numbers, the following more general definition should be easy in view of what has preceded.

Definition.   A (binary) *operation* or *composition* in a set S is a mapping of $S \times S$ into S.

For example, addition is the binary operation in the set of real numbers whose "rule of composition" is such that each pair (a, b) maps onto the real number $a + b$. Multiplication is a similar operation under which the pair (a, b) maps onto ab. For either of these compositions it is clear that the image of (a, b) is the same as the image of (b, a). This is not true for operations in general, however.

Problems 1–3

*1. Prove that if α is an arbitrary mapping of a set S, and 1 is an appropriate identity mapping, then $\alpha 1 = \alpha = 1\alpha$.

*2. If α is a bijective mapping of a set S into a set T, prove that $\alpha \alpha^{-1} = 1_S$ and $\alpha^{-1}\alpha = 1_T$.

3. Let the mappings α and β of the set of natural numbers into itself be defined, respectively, by $n\alpha = n^2$ and $n\beta = 3n - 2$, for each natural number n. Determine the mappings α^2, $\alpha\beta$, β^2, $\alpha\,(\beta\alpha)$, and $(\alpha\beta)\,\alpha$.

*4. Let S, T, U, V be sets, with α a mapping of S into T, β a mapping of T into U, and γ a mapping of U into V. Show that $\alpha\,(\beta\gamma) = (\alpha\beta)\,\gamma$.

**5. Let α be a mapping of S into T and β be a mapping of T into S, such that $\alpha\beta = 1_S$ and $\beta\alpha = 1_T$. Then, prove that:

    (a) α and β are injective mappings;

    (b) α and β are surjective mappings;

    (c) $\beta = \alpha^{-1}$.

6. If α is the mapping defined on the set of all real numbers by the equation $y = 2x^2 + 3$, with $x\alpha = y$, determine each of the following: (a) 2α; (b) $(-3)\alpha$; (c) $(1/2)\alpha$; (d) $(1/4)\alpha$.

7. If $S = \{1, 3, 5, 7\}$ and $T = \{0, 1\}$, list the members of the product set $S \times T$.

*8. Let α be a bijective mapping of a set S into a set T, and β be a bijective mapping of the set T onto a set U. Then prove each of the following assertions:

    (a) $\alpha\beta$ is a bijective mapping of S into U;

    (b) $(\alpha^{-1})^{-1} = \alpha$;

    (c) $(\alpha\beta)^{-1} = \beta^{-1}\alpha^{-1}$.

1.4 RELATIONS

If a and b are real numbers, the meanings of the statements "a is less than b" (written $a < b$) and "a divides b" (written $a\,|\,b$) are quite clear from the earlier mathematical experience of the reader.

If m and n are two lines in a plane, such statements as "m is parallel to n" (written $m \parallel n$) and "m is perpendicular to n" (written $m \perp n$) are of common occurrence in elementary geometry and are well understood in that context. In such cases we say that a "relation" has been defined in the associated set, and each ordered pair of elements of the set either is or is not "in the relation." It will be assumed that if a relation $\mathcal{R}$ has been defined in a set, the statement, "b is in the relation $\mathcal{R}$ to a" for any two elements a and b of the set, is meaningful—and true or false according to the choice of the elements. It is customary to write $b \mathcal{R} a$ if the statement is true and $b \not{\mathcal{R}} a$ if the statement is false.

At this point we are faced with another rather perplexing question. To illustrate: everyone knows what is meant by the statement, "2 is less than 4," or "6 is less than 10," but what do we mean by the "less than" *relation* itself? That is, how do we actually define the *relation* "less than" in, say, the set of real numbers? There are two simple courses open to us. One is to ignore the question—as is frequently done—and argue that after all the concept of "less than" is not of great importance, but that rather more significant is the ability to tell for any two distinct real numbers a and b whether $a < b$ or $b < a$. The other alternative is to give a definition which may not be completely satisfactory to all people. We have already encountered a very similar situation in connection with the "function" concept; in most elementary courses, the meaning of "a function of" is explained, but the notion of the function itself is left very vague. For our part we have defined a function or mapping in the preceding section as a certain set; and we again use this apparent panacea of sets to resolve our present difficulty. It is clear that the ordered pair (a, b) is determined whenever $b \mathcal{R} a$, and we *define* the relation $\mathcal{R}$ to be the set of *all* such ordered pairs. This is formalized by the following definition.

Definition. A *relation* in a set S is a subset of ordered pairs (a, b) of the product set $S \times S$. If $\mathcal{R}$ is a relation, and $(a, b) \in \mathcal{R}$, we say "b is in the relation to a" and write $b \mathcal{R} a$.

By this definition a relation $\mathcal{R}$ is a set of ordered pairs (a, b) such that $b \, \mathcal{R} \, a$. But even more important is the observation that *any* subset of ordered pairs constitutes a relation in an appropriate set. Sometimes—as is the case with the "less than" relation—the relation will have an obvious interpretation, but sometimes no such interpretation is apparent. It may be well to point out that while the order of the elements in a pair $(a, b) \in \mathcal{R}$ may seem to be unnatural if $b \, \mathcal{R} \, a$, it is this order rather than that of (b, a) which is preferred by mathematicians. Our definition makes it clear that we are considering a function as a special case of a relation, in which no two ordered pairs of the relation can have the same first component.

Thus, the relation "is less than" in the set of all real numbers is the set of all ordered pairs (a, b) of real numbers a and b such that $b < a$. The relation "is perpendicular to" in the set of all lines in a plane is the set of all ordered pairs (m, n) of lines m and n in the plane such that $n \perp m$. The relation "is the father of" in the set of all people is the set of all ordered pairs (p, q) of people p and q such that q is the father of p. In particular our definition of a relation identifies the relation "is a divisor of" in the set $\{1, 2, 3, 4, 5, 6\}$ with the set $\{(6, 6), (6, 3), (6, 2), (6, 1), (5, 5), (5, 1), (4, 4), (4, 2), (4, 1), (3, 3), (3, 1), (2, 2), (2, 1), (1, 1)\}$.

A relation $\mathcal{R}$ is known as an *equivalence* relation (and then the symbol $\mathcal{R}$ is replaced by $\sim$) if it satisfies the following conditions for arbitrary members a, b, c of the set in which the relation is defined:

1. $a \, \mathcal{R} \, a$ (reflexive property);
2. If $a \, \mathcal{R} \, b$, then $b \, \mathcal{R} \, a$ (symmetric property);
3. If $a \, \mathcal{R} \, b$ and $b \, \mathcal{R} \, c$, then $a \, \mathcal{R} \, c$ (transitive property).

There are many simple examples of an equivalence relation. The relation of "equality" ($=$) in the set of all real numbers is probably the most familiar and is undoubtedly the one to which the notion owes its origin. That "equality" is an equivalence relation follows immediately from the above conditions. In the set of all lines in a plane, the relation of "is parallel to" may also be seen to satisfy these conditions: for if m, n and s are arbitrary lines in a plane, it is clear that $m \parallel m$ (if we admit that a line is parallel to itself); $n \parallel m$ if $m \parallel n$; and if $m \parallel n$ and $n \parallel s$, it follows that $m \parallel s$. Hence "is parallel to" is an equivalence relation.

In order to give the next definition we need to extend our earlier concept of set union to include infinitely many sets. Thus, for any (finite or infinite) "index" set Δ, the set $\underset{i \in \Delta}{\cup} S_i$ is the set of elements which belong to *at least one* of the subsets S_i. An "index" set is merely a useful device to enumerate a collection of items. For example, if r is a rational number, S_r might be the set of rational numbers x such that $x < r$. If we wished to enumerate all such sets, the proper "index" set to use would be the set of all rational numbers. As another illustration S_n might be the set of all real numbers x such that $x^2 - n^2 < 1$, where n is an arbitrary real number. An enumeration of all such sets S_n would then require the use of an index set Δ, equal to the set of all real numbers. We note in this case that Δ is an uncountable set, so that there is no restriction on the cardinal number of an index set. In a similar manner it is easy to extend our earlier definition of set-theoretic intersection to include a collection of subsets which is indexed by an arbitrary set, so that $\underset{i \in \Delta}{\cap} S_i$ is defined.

> **Definition.**   A *partition* of a set S is a collection of subsets S_i of S, with i in some index set Δ, such that:
>
> 1. $S = \underset{i \in \Delta}{\cup} S_i$;
> 2. $S_i \cap S_j = \emptyset$, for $i \neq j$.

That is, a partition of a set is a collection of disjoint subsets whose union is the whole set. For example, a partition of the set of all living people might be the set whose two nonempty members are the subset of males and the subset of females. A partition of the set of all lines in a plane might be the set whose members are the subsets of parallel lines in the plane. In this geometric example the partition contains infinitely many elements.

If a is an element of a set in which an equivalence relation has been defined, the subset S_a of elements which are equivalent to the element a constitutes an *equivalence class*. In view of the reflexive property $a \in S_a$; and the symmetric and transitive properties imply that all elements of S_a are equivalent to each other. Moreover, if $b \in S_a$, the transitive property implies further that $S_a = S_b$, so that any equivalence class is merely the subset of elements which are equivalent to *any one* of its members. *Any* member of an equivalence class is then said to be a *representative* of the class. We are now able to derive our principal result on equivalence relations.

Theorem 1.41   If $\sim$ is an equivalence relation defined in a set S, the set of equivalence classes related to $\sim$ is a partition of S. Conversely, for any given partition of S, there exists an equivalence relation $\sim$ in S, such that the set of equivalence classes related to $\sim$ is the given partition.

Proof.   If a and b are nonequivalent elements of S, the classes S_a and S_b have only the empty set in common; for, if $c \in S_a$ and $c \in S_b$, it follows that $c \sim a$ and $c \sim b$, whence $a \sim b$, contrary to our assumption. It is clear that each element of S is in some equivalence class—namely the class of elements equivalent to it. Hence, if Δ is a subset of S consisting of one representative from each of the equivalence classes, it follows that $S = \underset{a \in \Delta}{\cup} S_a$, and $S_a \cap S_b = \emptyset$, for $a \neq b$ in Δ.

Conversely, if S is partitioned into a set of disjoint classes, we can define an equivalence relation in S as follows: $a \sim b$ if and only if a belongs to the same class as b. It is evident that the conditions **1, 2,** and **3** in the definition of an equivalence relation are satisfied **(Problem 1),** and the proof of the theorem is completed.

There is a close connection between equivalence relations and mappings. For, let $\bar{S}$ be a set of equivalence classes in a set S, the set $\bar{S}$ being known as the *quotient set* of S relative to the given equivalence relation. There is then a *natural* mapping ν of S onto $\bar{S}$ which is defined by the rule that an element $a \in S$ is mapped by ν onto the equivalence class of $\bar{S}$ that contains a. That is, for any $a \in S$, $a\nu = S_a$. On the other hand, if α is any mapping of the set S into a set T, we can use α to define an equivalence relation in S. Thus, for $a \in S$ and $b \in S$ we can define $a \sim b$ if $a\alpha = b\alpha$. In this case each equivalence class is a subset of elements of S which are mapped onto the same element of T **(Problem 2).**

Problems 1–4

***1.** Let a set S be partitioned into a set of disjoint subsets. Then, if we define $a\,\mathcal{R}\,b$, for $a \in S$ and $b \in S$, provided a lies in the same subset as b, prove that $\mathcal{R}$ is an equivalence relation.

****2.** Let α be a mapping of a set S onto a set T. Then, if we define $a\,\mathcal{R}\,b$, for $a \in S$ and $b \in S$, provided $a\alpha = b\alpha$, prove that $\mathcal{R}$ is an equivalence relation.

3. List the members of the relation "is less than" in the set $\{1, 2, 3, 4\}$.

4. List the members of the relation "is prime to" in the set $\{2, 3, 4, 5\}$.

5. We have noted that "is parallel to" is an equivalence relation in any set of lines in a plane. Consider the relation "is perpendicular to" in the same set, and decide whether it is also an equivalence relation.

6. If c is replaced by a in condition **3** of an equivalence relation, it would appear that condition **1** follows from conditions **2** and **3**! Is this so? Explain your answer.

7. Give two illustrations of an equivalence relation not previously mentioned.

8. Give an illustration of a relation which is symmetric and reflexive but not transitive.

9. Give an illustration of a relation which is reflexive and transitive but not symmetric.

REFERENCES

HALMOS, P.: *Naive Set Theory* (Princeton, N.J., Van Nostrand, 1960).

JACOBSON, N.: *Lectures in Abstract Algebra*, Vol. 1, pp. 1–6 (Princeton, N.J., Van Nostrand, 1951).

KAMKE, E.: *Theory of Sets* (New York, Dover, 1950).

McCOY, N.: *Introduction to Modern Algebra*, Chap. 1 (Boston, Allyn and Bacon, 1960).

NORTHROP, E. P., and STAFF: *Fundamental Mathematics*, Vol. 1, Chaps. 1–5, (Chicago, University of Chicago Press, 1948).

chapter 2

AN AXIOMATIC APPROACH TO OUR NUMBER SYSTEM

2.1 THE NATURAL NUMBERS

The so-called system of real numbers is the system that under-lies the whole of elementary mathematical analysis. Although it is generally treated in an intuitive fashion at the elementary level, this system has in fact a very complex structure, as is evidenced by the numerous books devoted to the subject. The real number system contains the subsystems of rational numbers, integers, and natural numbers. The subject of discussion in this and the section immedi-ately following is the natural numbers, but reference will be made to the other number systems at the appropriate time.

There are many reasons why the set N of natural numbers is an important one in any study of abstract algebra. It is, of course, a very familiar set and, as we shall see, is one which is frequently used in the construction of examples of other algebraic systems. We have already used these numbers in many illustrations of the basic concepts in Chapter 1, and *in that chapter we assumed complete familiarity with them.* The natural numbers are also useful as an index source in labeling the numbers of an ordered set. Thus, we often have occasion to refer to an ordered set or "sequence" such as $(a_1, a_2, a_3, \cdots)$, the natural number subscripts playing the role of an indexing device. In addition, if an associative multiplication is defined in an algebraic system, the natural number powers a^n of any element a of the system occur, and so the mapping $n \rightarrow a^n$ of N into the system is defined.

It is well known from the study of Euclidean geometry in high school that the theorems and results of this discipline can be derived from a few simple axioms and postulates. Unfortunately, however, it is not so generally recognized that algebra has a similar axiomatic development. In order to illustrate our meaning, in these first two sections we shall give a partial development of the natural numbers from this point of view. Our purpose is *not* to establish any properties of natural numbers which are not already well known, but rather to show that it is *possible* to use a simple set of axioms to derive some of these familiar properties. In other words we wish to show that all these properties *need* not be merely accepted as intuitive, but are logical consequences of a very few basic assumptions. If this objective is not clearly understood, it is probably inevitable that most of the material of this chapter will appear quite inconsequential to the student.

The axiomatic development of the system of natural numbers is quite recent and dates back to G. Peano in 1899, with the so-called *Peano postulates.* All the properties of N that will concern us can be seen to be consequences of these postulates, which we now give in a form slightly different from what is found in Peano's work. In this discussion we should think of N as an abstract set, whose elements may be called "natural numbers," but which possesses only those properties which are postulated or which follow from these postulates.

The Peano Postulates

1. N is not empty.
2. There is an injective mapping $a \rightarrow a^+$ of N into itself, a^+ being known as the "successor" of a.
3. The collection of successors is a *proper* subset of N.
4. Any subset of N which contains a nonsuccessor, and which contains the successor of each element of the subset, is the whole set N. This is known as the *Axiom of Induction*.

We now illustrate the use of these axioms with a proof of a very familiar result.

Theorem 2.11   There is a unique nonsuccessor in N.

Proof.   For, let e be a nonsuccessor in N. Then, the subset consisting of e and all successors in N satisfies the conditions of Axiom 4. Hence this subset is the whole set N, and so e is the only nonsuccessor in N.

This unique nonsuccessor is designated 1. Furthermore, the successor 1^+ is written 2, the successor 2^+ is written 3, etc. It is Axiom 4 which is the basis of proofs by the First Principle of Induction.

First Principle of Induction

Let us suppose that E_n is a statement involving a natural number n. Then, if E_1 is true, and E_{k^+} is true whenever E_k is true, the statement E_n is true for every natural number n.

It can be readily seen that this principle is a direct consequence of the Axiom of Induction. Thus, let S be the subset of natural numbers s for which E_s is true. Then, $1 \in S$, and $k^+ \in S$ whenever $k \in S$. By the Axiom of Induction, $S = N$, and so E_n is true for every $n \in N$.

While it is possible—and perhaps more natural—to describe the basic operations and relations in the set of natural numbers by means of sets, it is in harmony with our present axiomatic approach to introduce them by means of *recursive* definitions. By the term "recursive" we mean that the notion has been defined for the number n^+ whenever it has been defined for n. We illustrate with the following definition.

Definition of Addition. With every pair of natural numbers m and n there is associated a unique natural number $m + n$, such that:
1. $m + 1 = m^+$;
2. $m + n^+ = (m + n)^+$.

In the sequel we shall usually write $m + 1$ for m^+, as is allowed by this definition. It can be seen by a simple argument that the sum $m + n$ of *any* two numbers m and n has now been defined. For, if m is any natural number, let E_n be the statement that $m + n$ is defined for the number n. By the first part of the definition above, E_1 is true. Moreover, the second part states that $m + k^+$ is defined whenever $m + k$ is defined, which is to say that E_{k^+} is true whenever E_k is true. It follows from the First Principle of Induction that E_n is true for every natural number n, which means that $m + n$ is properly defined. Inasmuch as m was also arbitrary, the sum $m + n$ of *any* two natural numbers m and n has been defined by the recursive definition given above.

We can give a similar definition of multiplication in N.

Definition of Multiplication. With every pair of natural numbers m and n there is associated a unique natural number mn, such that:
1. $m1 = m$
2. $mn^+ = mn + m$.

The proof that this definition does in fact define the product mn of *any* two natural numbers m and n is quite like the corresponding proof for the case of addition.

As a result of these definitions we can derive the familiar *Laws of Arithmetic* which we now list as a theorem.

Theorem 2.12. The following assertions are valid for arbitrary numbers $k, m, n \in N$.
1. *Associative Laws.*
   $k + (m + n) = (k + m) + n; \ k(mn) = (km)n.$
2. *Commutative Laws.*
   $m + n = n + m; \ mn = nm.$

3. *Distributive Law.*

$(k + m)n = kn + mn.$

4. *Cancellation Laws.*

If $m + k = n + k$, then $m = n$; if $mk = nk$, then $m = n$.

We do not wish to burden our present discussion by presenting a complete proof of the above theorem, with all its component parts. These proofs, if they are desired, can be found in some of the references cited at the close of this chapter. However, we do wish to illustrate what can be done with our postulates, and with this objective in mind we shall give a proof of the commutative law of addition. The proof which we give requires use of the associative law of addition, and for the purposes of the present proof we shall *assume* that this associative law has already been established.

> **Proof of Commutative Law of Addition.** For an arbitrary $m \in N$, let E_n represent the statement that $m + n = n + m$, where $n \in N$. We must first show that $m + 1 = 1 + m$, a fact not immediately evident from the definition of addition. In order to establish this preliminary fact, we use an inductive argument and let F_m be the statement that $m + 1 = 1 + m$. It is clear that F_1 is true, and let us assume that F_k is true, i.e., $k + 1 = 1 + k$. Then, $k^+ + 1 = (k + 1) + 1 = (1 + k) + 1 = 1 + (k + 1) = 1 + k^+$, where we have used the associative law of addition, and so F_{k^+} is true. By the First Principle of Induction, it follows that F_m is true, i.e., $m + 1 = 1 + m$ for any natural number m, which is to say that E_1 is true. To continue our original proof, let us assume that E_k is true, i.e., $m + k = k + m$, for the arbitrary— but considered fixed—natural number m, and arbitrary $k \in N$. Then, $m + k^+ = (m + k)^+ = (k + m)^+ = k + m^+ = k + (m + 1) = k + (1 + m) = (k + 1) + m = k^+ + m$, which means that E_{k^+} is true. It follows from the First Principle of Induction that E_n is true for every natural number n. Since m was also arbitrary, we have shown that $m + n = n + m$ for *any* numbers $m, n \in N$, as asserted.

Problems 2–1

*1. Prove the associative law of addition in N.

2. How could you characterize any statement or theorem whose truth might possibly be established by means of the First Principle of Induction?

**3. Prove that $n^+ \neq n$, for each $n \in N$. (Hint: Let S be the set of natural numbers n such that $n^+ \neq n$.)

4. Use the First Principle of Induction to establish the familiar calculus formula: if $f(x) = x^n$, for any real number x and any natural number n, then $f'(x) = nx^{n-1}$. (Assume the formula for the derivative of a product of two functions.)

5. Use the First Principle of Induction to establish the following summation for any natural number n:

$$1^2 + 2^2 + 3^2 + \cdots + n^2 = \frac{n(n+1)(2n+1)}{6}.$$

6. Prove that $n + m \neq n$, for arbitrary $m, n \in N$. (Hint: For any m, let S be the set of natural numbers such that $n + m \neq n$.)

2.2 ORDER AND THE SECOND PRINCIPLE OF INDUCTION

In the preceding section we have shown how the operations of addition and multiplication can be defined recursively in the set of natural numbers. The third basic concept in this system N is that of *order*, which can be defined now in terms of addition.

Definition.   The order relation "is less than" ($<$), in the set N, can be defined as follows: for $m, n \in N$, $m < n$ (or $n > m$) if and only if $m + k = n$ for some $k \in N$.

It can be shown that the following properties of this relation follow from the definition:

1. For any natural numbers m and n, either $m = n$, $m < n$, or $m > n$. (*Trichotomy Law*)

2. If k, m, n are natural numbers such that $k < m$ and $m < n$, it follows that $k < n$. (*Transitive Law*)

3. In any nonempty set of natural numbers, there exists a *least* number, i.e., a number l such that $l \leq s$, for each s in the set. (*Well-ordering Principle*)

Since the Well-ordering Principle is the basis for the Second Principle of Induction, to be given shortly, we shall include a proof of 3.

Proof of the Well-ordering Principle. Let S be the given set of natural numbers and T be the subset of N, such that $t \leq s$ for each $s \in S$ and $t \in T$. It is clear that $1 \in T$ **(Problem 1)**. If s is any element of S, $s^+ > s$, and so $s^+ \notin T$. Hence $T \neq N$, i.e., T is a proper subset of N. If $t^+ \in T$, for each $t \in T$, the Axiom of Induction would imply that $T = N$. Since $T \neq N$, there must exist some natural number $l \in T$, such that $l^+ \notin T$. This number l is the required number: because $l \leq s$, for each $s \in S$, since $l \in T$; and $l \in S$, since otherwise $l < s$, for each $s \in S$, and so $l^+ \leq s$ **(Problem 2)** in contradiction to the fact that $l^+ \notin T$.

We are now in a position to state the Second Principle of Induction.

Second Principle of Induction

Let us suppose that E_n is a statement involving a natural number n. Then, if E_m is true provided E_k is true for each $k < m$, it follows that E_n is true for every natural number n.

Proof.   Let F be the set of natural numbers t such that E_t is not true. If F is not the empty set, let q be its least element. Then E_q is not true, but E_p is true for each $p < q$. This contradicts our inductive assumption on the statement, and so F must be empty. Hence E_n is true for every natural number n as asserted.

The following theorem lists some well-known properties of the relation "is less than" in the set N.

Theorem 2.21 If m and n are natural numbers such that $m < n$, then: **(i)** $m + k < n + k$, and **(ii)** $mk < nk$, for each $k \in N$. Conversely, if either **(i)** or **(ii)** holds for some $k \in N$, then $m < n$.

Proof.   Let $m < n$, so that $m + t = n$, for some $t \in N$. Then $(m + k) + t = (m + t) + k = n + k$, so that $m + k < n + k$, as required by **(i)**. Also $mk + tk = (m + t)k = nk$, so that $mk < nk$, establishing **(ii)**. For the converse, we use the Trichotomy Law. Let us assume that $m + k < n + k$, for some

$k \in N$. By the Trichotomy Law either $m = n$, $m < n$, or $m > n$ If $m = n$, then $m + k = n + k$, which contradicts our assumption. If $m > n$ (or $n < m$), it follows from the first part of the theorem that $m + k > n + k$, which is again in contradiction with our assumption. Hence $m < n$, as alleged. We leave the proof of the multiplicative part of the converse to the student **(Problem 3)**.

The set N of natural numbers, along with the operations of addition and multiplication, the order relation "is less than," and the "equality" relation, comprises the algebraic *system* of natural numbers. We shall see in subsequent chapters that this system contains certain subsystems, which provide us with simple examples of general systems of algebraic significance. Before we leave the set N, however, it may be well to emphasize again what we have been trying to do in these two sections. We have *not* tried to derive any new properties of the natural numbers. Our purpose has been to show how the *already familiar* properties of these numbers *can* be derived from a set of simple postulates and definitions, for it is this spirit which characterizes the axiomatic approach to modern mathematics.

Problems 2–2

*1. Prove that 1 is the least natural number, i.e., $1 < n$, for each natural number $n \neq 1$. (Hint: If $n \neq 1$, n is a successor.) Also show that $n < n^{+}$, for each $n \in N$.

**2. If m and n are natural numbers such that $m < n$, show that $m^{+} \leq n$.

*3. If $mk < nk$, for natural numbers, k, m, and n, prove that $m < n$, as required in the converse of **Theorem 2.21**.

4. Look up the Axiom of Choice in another book and decide whether you are prepared to agree with the validity of this axiom. (For example, see Wilder in the references to this chapter.)

5. Find the fallacy in the following inductive "proof": *All numbers in a set of n numbers are equal to each other.*

Proof. If we let E_n be the proposition, it is clear that E_1 is true. Let $n_1, n_2, \cdots, n_k, n_{k+1}$ be an arbitrary set of $k + 1$ numbers. Then if we assume that E_k is true, it follows that $n_1 = n_2 = \cdots = n_k$ and also $n_2 = n_3 = \cdots = n_{k+1}$. Since "things equal to the same thing are equal to each other," we have $n_1 = n_2 = \cdots = n_k = n_{k+1}$, and so E_{k+1} is true. Hence, by the First Principle of Induction, E_n is true for every natural number n.

2.3 THE RATIONAL INTEGERS

It is quite likely that the *rational integers*—or *integers* as they are usually called—are just as familiar to the student as are the natural or "counting" numbers. However, it may be of interest to know that it is also possible to develop them axiomatically, using the foundation of the natural numbers. It is again not our purpose to derive any new results which are not already familiar, but merely to indicate what *can* be done. It is very easy to burden a discussion such as this with too complete a collection of proofs. And while this is necessary, of course, in any comprehensive development of our number system, our intention here is rather to point out the way and leave the details for more intensive courses on the subject. In this section it is appropriate that we accept the natural numbers N as a fully developed system, even though we left out many important steps in our brief development.

The need for the numbers which we call "integers" is apparent when we consider that all equations of the form $m + x = n$, with $m, n \in N$, are not solvable for $x \in N$. For example, the equation $5 + x = 2$ has no solution for x as a natural number. It is well known that the introduction of "signed" or "positive" and "negative" integers overcomes this deficiency in N, and the solution of the above equation would then be $x = -3$. In order to introduce these new numbers, we use the product set $N \times N$ and define the operations and relations in this set of ordered pairs of natural numbers.

In our previous discussion of product sets, we defined two ordered pairs (m, n) and (r, s) to be "equal" provided $m = r$ and $n = s$. This has been referred to as the somewhat trivial use of "equality" in the sense of "identity." For our present purposes, however, we must define a more inclusive equality relation so that many more ordered pairs will be considered "equal." Intuitively, what we have in mind is that there are many ways to represent, say, the integer 6, a few of which are $7 - 1$, $8 - 2$, $9 - 3$, etc.; and the integer -4 can be represented by $1 - 5$, $2 - 6$, $3 - 7$, etc. Of course, we have not as yet defined such a thing as subtraction, and so these representations are not really to be used—except as a guide to see what is going on. With this preview, we now give the definition of equality in $N \times N$, to which we have made reference.

Definition. If (m, n) and (r, s) are elements of $N \times N$, we define $(m, n) = (r, s)$ if and only if $m + s = n + r$.

If $m = r$ and $n = s$, it is immediate that $(m, n) = (r, s)$, so that pairs which are identically equal remain equal in the extended sense—as would be desired. Intuitively, we may think of (m, n) as $m - n$ and (r, s) as $r - s$ so that, of course, $m - n = r - s$ if and only if $m + s = n + r$. Hence our above definition is reasonable from this intuitive viewpoint. This definition implies, for example, that such pairs as $(7, 1)$, $(8, 2)$, $(9, 3)$, $\cdots$ are equal to each other; and likewise such pairs as $(1, 5)$, $(2, 6)$, $(3, 7)$, $\cdots$ are equal to each other. However, since we must not depend on our intuition, it is essential that our relation of equality satisfy the three requirements of any other equivalence relation. It is a simple matter to prove that this is the case. For example, if $(m, n) = (r, s)$, then $m + s = n + r$ and $r + n = s + m$, so that $(r, s) = (m, n)$ and hence the relation is symmetric. We leave the verification of the other two requirements to the student **(Problem 1).**

Inasmuch as "equality," as we have defined it, is a *bona fide* equivalence relation, it follows from **Theorem 1.41** that $N \times N$ is partitioned by it into disjoint subsets of equivalent or "equal" elements. We now identify each of these subsets with a new number called an *integer*. In other words, an *integer* is a subset of ordered pairs of $N \times N$ which are *equal* in our present sense of the word. It may appear that the elements or "representatives" of each class should more properly be called the integers, but it should cause no confusion if we identify an integer with its complete class of representatives. For example, the equivalence class $\{(7, 1), (8, 2), (9, 3), \cdots\}$ is the integer which we familiarly express as $+6$ or 6; the class $\{(1, 5), (2, 6), (3, 7), \cdots\}$ is the integer regularly designated as -4. It is clear that each of the integers—as we know them—can be easily identified with one of these equivalence classes of "equal" pairs in $N \times N$. Since an equivalence class is uniquely determined by *any one* of its members, it is appropriate that the class containing—i.e., the integer represented by—the pair (a, b) be designated $\overline{(a, b)}$. In the sequel we shall use I to refer to the set of integers.

We now assume the "natural" ordering of the natural numbers and order the integers according to the following definition.

Definition.   If $\overline{(m, n)}$, $\overline{(r, s)} \in I$, $\overline{(m, n)} < \overline{(r, s)}$ if and only if $m + s < n + r$.

Before we can accept this as a valid definition, we must show that it is independent of the representatives used. However, if (m', n') and (r', s') are elements from the same classes as (m, n) and (r, s), respectively, we know that $m' + n = m + n'$ and $r' + s = r + s'$. Now $m + s < n + r$ implies that $m + s + m' + r' < n + r + m' + r'$. But then $m + m' + r + s' < r + r' + m + n'$ and so, on cancellation of $m + r$, we obtain $m' + s' < r' + n'$. We have shown that $\overline{(m, n)} < \overline{(r, s)}$ implies that $\overline{(m', n')} < \overline{(r', s')}$, so that our definition of order is independent of the representatives selected from the classes.

The equivalence class in $N \times N$, all of whose members have the form (m, m) for some $m \in N$, defines the integer 0, a number which can be easily shown to have its familiar properties **(Problem 4)**. Now $(m, n) + (n, m) = (m + n, m + n) = 0$, from definition of 0. Hence if $x = \overline{(m, n)}$, it will be in keeping with our intuition to let $-x = \overline{(n, m)}$. It follows from this that $-(-x) = x$. An integer x such that $0 < x$ is said to be *positive*, while x is *negative* if $x < 0$. The Trichotomy Law for N carries over to I, so that every integer is either zero, positive, or negative. Moreover, it is easy to show that $x < y$ for any negative integer x and any positive integer y.

It can be shown that the positive integers, as we have defined them, are in every way quite similar to the natural numbers, and so it is customary not to distinguish between these two kinds of numbers. For example, the number 2 can be regarded as either a natural number or a positive integer. We realize that what we mean by "quite similar" is somewhat vague at this point, but we leave it to your imagination! In the next chapter, under the topic of isomorphism, our meaning will become more transparent. If we allow this identification of the natural numbers with the positive integers, the natural numbers can be considered a subsystem of the system of integers, and the latter an extension of the former.

Now that we have the integers—zero, positive, and negative—at hand, the next thing to do is to define in this system the familiar operations of addition and multiplication. We assume that such operations have been defined in N and extend these definitions to I as follows:

Definition. If $x = (\overline{m, n})$ and $y = (\overline{r, s})$ are arbitrary integers,
1. $x + y = (\overline{m + r, n + s})$ and
2. $xy = (\overline{mr + ns, ms + nr})$.

If we keep in mind our intuitive notion of (m, n) and (r, s) as $m - n$ and $r - s$, respectively, it is clear that these definitions are reasonable and in agreement with our familiar concept of these operations. However, for theoretical reasons, as for the "less than" relation we must show that the above operations have been "well defined" or independent of the representatives used for the classes. It would certainly be disastrous if we got different sums or products by using different representatives for the various integers! Thus, suppose $(m, n) = (m', n')$ and $(r, s) = (r', s')$, so that $m + n' = n + m'$ and $r + s' = s + r'$. Then, $m + r + n' + s' = m + n' + r + s' = n + m' + s + r' = n + s + m' + r'$, from which our definition of equality implies that $(m + r, n + s) = (m' + r', n' + s')$, so that $(\overline{m + r, n + s}) = (\overline{m' + r', n' + s'})$. Our operation of addition is then well defined, and we leave a similar verification for the case of multiplication to the student **(Problem 2).**

We complete this rather brief and sketchy development of the rational integers with definitions of two familiar notions. While "subtraction" is not essential in any discussion of numbers, it is nonetheless convenient to use, and we can define the *subtraction* of two integers x and y as follows: $x - y = x + (-y)$. The notion of *absolute value* $|x|$ of an integer x can be made precise in the following way: $|x| = x$, if $x \geq 0$; and $|x| = -x$, if $x < 0$. The absolute value of a non-zero integer is then defined to be a positive integer, or a natural number. In the following section we shall discuss several important properties of integers and show how the system of integers can be extended to the system of rational numbers.

Problems 2-3

*1. Prove that "equality," as we have defined it in $N \times N$, is an equivalence relation.
*2. Prove that multiplication has been well defined in I.
3. Prove that $-|x| \leq x \leq |x|$, for any $x \in I$.
**4. Use the definition of 0 to prove that $0 + x = x = x + 0$, for $x \in I$.
*5. Prove the associative law of addition for arbitrary integers.
*6. With the integer 1 defined as (n^+, n), prove that $1x = x1 = x$, for arbitrary $x \in I$.
*7. Prove that $0x = x0 = 0$, for any $x \in I$.
*8. Prove that $(-x)y = -(xy)$, for arbitrary elements $x, y \in I$.

2.4 THEOREMS ON INTEGERS

We have in mind two principal undertakings in the present section. One is to recall three very important and probably quite familiar theorems about rational integers. The other is to illustrate again the axiomatic method, which we have been emphasizing in the preceding sections, in the proof of these theorems. The theorems that we shall review are important tools in what is generally known as the *arithmetic* of integers. In view of our identification of the natural numbers with the positive integers, we shall feel entirely free to use, in our discussion of the positive integers, the axioms and any results that we have previously obtained for natural numbers. In particular, we shall use either principle of induction if it is useful in connection with the proof of any theorem about positive integers.

The elementary fact that any integer can be divided by any positive integer to yield a quotient and a positive remainder is formally stated as Theorem 2.41.

Theorem 2.41 (*The Division Algorithm*). For any given integers a and b, $b > 0$, there exist unique integers q and r such that $a = bq + r$, where $0 \leq r < b$.

Proof. Consider the subset of integers $S = \{a - bx \mid x \in I,\ a - bx \geq 0\}$. This subset contains at least one nonnegative integer, namely $a - b|a|$ or $a + b|a|$ (**Problem 1**). Now either $0 \in S$, or all elements of S are positive and the Well-ordering

Principle assures us of the existence in S of a least element. In either event, S contains a least element r such that $r \geq 0$. By definition of S, $r = a - bq$ for some $q \in I$, so that $a = bq + r$. We know that $r \geq 0$; but if $r \geq b$ it follows that $r - b = a - bq - b = a - b(q + 1) \geq 0$, while it is true that $a - bq - b < a - bq$. This is contrary to our choosing q so that r is the least element in S; hence $0 \leq r < b$, as desired. In order to establish uniqueness, suppose $a = bq + r = bq' + r'$, where $0 \leq r < b$ and $0 \leq r' < b$. Then $bq + r - bq' - r' = 0$, and so $b(q' - q) = r - r'$. This implies that $r - r'$ is a multiple of b, but smaller in absolute value than b **(Problem 2)**. It follows that $r - r' = 0$ and $r = r'$, whence $q = q'$ and the proof is complete.

If an integer a can be expressed in the form $a = bc$, we have been using the familiar language that b and c are "divisors" of a or "divide" a (written $b|a$ and $c|a$), and a is a "multiple" of b and c. We have seen before **(Problem 6 of Problems 2-3)** that 1 is a divisor of every integer, and a similar result could be established for -1. If an integer p is neither 0, 1, nor -1 and has no integral divisors except 1, -1, p, and $-p$, it is said to be *prime*. The *greatest common divisor* (g.c.d.) of two integers is a *positive* divisor which is "greatest" in the sense that it is divisible by any other common divisor. That is, if d is the g.c.d. of a and b while c is an integer such that $c|a$ and $c|b$, it follows from the definition that $c|d$. We shall have occasion in the sequel to refer to the "*Euclidean g.c.d.*" process, the existence of which is asserted in the following theorem.

Theorem 2.42 Any two nonzero integers a and b have a greatest common divisor d, where $d = sa + tb$ for $s, t \in I$.

Proof. The proof of this theorem involves a nice application of the Well-ordering Principle. Thus, let D be the set of all integers that can be expressed in the form $xa + yb$, with $x, y \in I$. This set certainly contains some positive integers, and the Well-ordering Principle assures us that there is a least positive integer $d = sa + tb$ in the set. By the Division Algorithm, $a = qd + r$ for integers q and r, $0 \leq r < d$. Hence $r = a - qd = (1 - qs)a + (-qt)b$, so that $r \in D$. Since d is the least positive integer in D, we must have $r = 0$ so that $d \mid a$. In a similar way we can show that $d \mid b$, so that d is a common divisor of a and b. To show that d is the g.c.d., let us suppose that some other integer c divides both a and b. Then $c \mid sa$ and $c \mid tb$, whence $c \mid (sa + tb)$ or $c \mid d$. It follows that $d = sa + tb$ is the greatest common divisor of a and b, as asserted.

If a and b are positive integers (where we can assume that $a > b$), the Division Algorithm asserts that there exist integers q and r such that $a = qb + r$, where $0 \leq r < b$. It can be seen quite easily **(Problem 3)** that the g.c.d. of a and b is also the g.c.d. of b and r. This fact can be readily utilized to derive a *process* for obtaining the g.c.d. of any two positive integers, as outlined below for the integers 63 and 720. In this process the larger number is divided by the smaller, followed by the division of the divisor by the remainder, and this procedure is repeated until a remainder 0 is obtained. The last divisor, which is 9 in the illustration, is then the desired g.c.d. **(Problem 7)**.

$$
\begin{array}{ccccc}
 & & 3 & 2 & 11 \\
9 & \overline{)27} & \overline{)63} & \overline{)720} & \\
 & 27 & 54 & 63 & \\
 & \overline{0} & \overline{9} & \overline{90} & \\
 & & & 63 & \\
 & & & \overline{27} &
\end{array}
$$

It is possible to write the g.c.d. in the form $sa + tb$, if the successive remainders are expressed in terms of the original numbers a and b. In the above illustration, if we represent these remainders by r_1 and r_2, we see that:

$$r_1 = 27 = 720 - 11(63) \text{ and}$$
$$r_2 = 9 = 63 - 2(27).$$

Hence $9 = 63 - 2[720 - 11(63)] = 23(63) + (-2)720$, which expresses 9 in the desired form with $s = 23$ and $t = -2$.

Our final theorem on integers is another very familiar one. We offer the proof of it as an illustration of the use of the Second Principle of Induction.

Theorem 2.43 (*Fundamental Theorem of Arithmetic*). Any positive integer a is either 1, a prime, or can be expressed as a product of positive primes, this expression being unique except for the order of the prime factors.

Proof. Let P_a be the assertion that the integer a is either 1, a prime, or can be expressed as a product of positive primes. If a is either 1 or a prime number, P_a is trivially true. On the other hand, if a is neither 1 nor prime, $a = bc$ for integers b and c such that $b < a$ and $c < a$. The inductive assumption of the Second Principle of Induction allows us to assume that P_b and P_c are true; i.e., $b = p_1 p_2 \cdots p_r$ and $c = q_1 q_2 \cdots q_s$, for prime integers $p_1, p_2, \cdots, p_r, q_1, q_2, \cdots, q_s$ with $r \geq 1$ and $s \geq 1$. But then $a = bc = p_1 p_2 \cdots p_r q_1 q_2 \cdots q_s$, so that P_a is true. An application of the Second Principle of Induction then allows us to conclude that P_n is true for every $n \in N$, i.e., every positive integer greater than 1 is either prime or can be expressed as a product of positive primes. In order to prove the uniqueness of the factors, we need the following result.

Lemma. If a prime integer p divides the product ab of two integers a and b, then p divides either a or b.

Proof. By definition of a prime, the only positive divisors of p are 1 and p. If p does not divide a, the only common positive divisor of p and a is 1, so that **Theorem 2.42** asserts the existence of integers s and t such that $1 = sa + tp$. On multiplication of both members of this equation by b, we obtain $b = sab + tbp$. Inasmuch as p is a divisor of both terms on the right side of this equation, p is also a divisor of the left member, i.e., $p \,|\, b$, as desired.

Now, to complete the proof of **Theorem 2.43,** let us suppose that $a = p_1 p_2 \cdots p_m = q_1 q_2 \cdots q_n$ are two factorizations of the positive integer a into primes $p_1, p_2, \cdots, p_m, q_1, q_2, \cdots, q_n$. Since $p_1 \,|\, a$, p_1 must divide $q_1 q_2 \cdots q_n$, and a repeated application of the lemma assures us that $p_1 \,|\, q_j$, where q_j is one of $q_1, q_2, \cdots, q_n$. But since both p_1 and q_j are primes, we must have $p_1 = q_j$. On "cancellation" of this common factor from both members of the

equation above, there results the equation $p_2 p_3 \cdots p_m = q_1 q_2 \cdots$
$q_{j-1} q_{j+1} \cdots q_n$. If we repeat the above process with p_2, p_3, $\cdots$, p_m
in succession, the left member will be reduced to 1, and so must
also the right member. (Why?) Hence $n = m$ and each of the
"p-factors" is equal to one of the "q-factors," so that the two
factorizations differ at most in the order of the factors. This
completes the proof of the theorem.

Problems 2-4

**1. If $a, b \in I$, with $b > 0$, prove that $a + b|a| \geq 0$.

*2. If $0 \leq r < b$ and $0 \leq r' < b$, prove that $0 \leq |r - r'| < b$.

*3. If a, b, q, r are positive integers such that $a = qb + r$, prove that
the g.c.d. of a and b is also the g.c.d. of b and r.

4. Use the g.c.d. process illustrated in this section to determine the
g.c.d. of each of the following pairs of numbers, and express each
g.c.d. in the form $sa + tb$ of **Theorem 2.42:**
    (a) 4078, 814;   (b) 982, 363;   (c) 48, 128.

5. Prove that the only integer divisible by every positive integer is 0.

6. Prove that if a and b are positive integers such that $a|b$ and $b|a$,
then $a = b$.

*7. Prove that the "last divisor" in the g.c.d. process illustrated in this
section is actually the g.c.d. of the original pair of numbers.

2.5 THE RATIONAL AND REAL NUMBERS

The discussion which we have given for the integers can be
imitated to give a development of the *rational numbers*, i.e., numbers
usually written in the form a/b, where a and $b \neq 0$ are integers. This
time we use the product set $I \times I_0$, where I_0 is the subset of nonzero integers, for our basic set, and define the operations and relations in an appropriate manner. In this development, we should
think intuitively of each ordered pair $(m, n) \in I \times I_0$ as "really"
being the fraction m/n, and with this in mind the following definition of *equality* will be reasonable.

Definition.   If (m, n), $(r, s) \in I \times I_0$, then $(m, n) = (r, s)$ provided $ms = nr$.

The equivalence classes in $I \times I_0$, determined by this equality relation, will then define the set of *rational numbers*. (It is easy to check

that this relation is an equivalence relation.) As was the case with the integers, the equivalence class that contains the pair (m, n) is uniquely determined by this pair, and so we can designate this class or *rational number* by $\overline{(m, n)}$. Intuitively this means, for example, that we are identifying the *set* of all fractions of the form $2/4$, $3/6$, $4/8$, etc., with the rational number $1/2$ or—if preferred—with $0.5000\cdots$. In the sequel, we shall use R to designate the set of rational numbers.

The operations of *addition* and *multiplication* are defined in R in a way which is consistent with our concept of a rational number as a fraction.

Definition. If $\overline{(m, n)}$, $\overline{(r, s)} \in R$, then
1. $\overline{(m, n)} + \overline{(r, s)} = \overline{(ms + nr, ns)}$ and
2. $\overline{(m, n)}\,\overline{(r, s)} = \overline{(mr, ns)}$.

Before introducing the relation "is less than" in R, we should make the following preliminary definition: The rational number $\overline{(m, n)}$ is *positive* if $mn > 0$. In order to show that the concept of being "positive" is well defined, consider another representative $(r, s) \in \overline{(m, n)}$. Since (m, n) and (r, s) are representatives of the same rational number, $ms = rn$; thus $(rn)^2 = (rn)(ms) = (rs)(mn) > 0$. Inasmuch as $mn > 0$, it follows that $rs > 0$, and our verification is complete. We can now proceed with the definition announced above.

Definition. If $\overline{(m, n)}$, $\overline{(r, s)} \in R$, then $\overline{(m, n)} < \overline{(r, s)}$ if $\overline{(r, s)} - \overline{(m, n)}$ is positive.

In a full treatment, it would be necessary to show that the operations of addition and multiplication are also well defined, and that the elements of R possess all the familiar characteristics of rational numbers. However, in view of our desire to be brief on this somewhat lengthy subject, we shall be content with merely recalling to mind two important properties. If a and $b \neq 0$ are rational numbers, it is possible to solve the equation $bx = a$ for $x \in R$. Finally, it can be shown that the rational numbers of the type $\overline{(m, 1)}$ perform in every way just like the integers m, and so if we agree to identify the numbers of these two types, we can say that $I \subset R$.

The *real* and *complex* numbers are also capable of an axiomatic development, but this requires the use of some new concepts which we prefer not to introduce here. So now we accept as completely familiar the systems of real and complex numbers, systems which we shall designate as R^* and C, respectively. The systems of natural numbers, integers, rational, real, and complex numbers can be ordered by set-inclusion so that $N \subset I \subset R \subset R^* \subset C$. Many of the illustrations of the abstract systems of later chapters will be drawn from these number systems.

REFERENCES

BIRKHOFF, G., and MacLANE, S.: *A Survey of Modern Algebra*, Revised Edition (New York, Macmillan, 1953).

EVES, H., and NEWSOM, C.: *An Introduction to the Foundations and Fundamental Concepts of Mathematics* (New York, Holt, 1957).

JACOBSON, N.: *Lectures in Abstract Algebra*, Vol. 1, pp. 7–14 (Princeton, N.J., Van Nostrand, 1951).

JOHNSON, R.: *First Course in Abstract Algebra*, Chap. 2 (Englewood Cliffs, N.J., Prentice-Hall, 1953).

WILDER, R.: *An Introduction to the Foundations of Mathematics* (New York, Wiley, 1952).

chapter 3

GENERAL ALGEBRAIC SYSTEMS

3.1 GROUPOIDS AND SEMI-GROUPS

We have already characterized an *algebraic system* as a set of elements in which certain operations and relations have been defined. The fewer there are of these operations and relations, and the smaller the number of other requirements to be satisfied, the simpler the system is. However, it should be recognized that the simplest systems are not necessarily the most familiar.

We recall that a binary operation or composition in a set S is a mapping of the product set $S \times S$ into S. Thus, with any two (distinct or equal) elements of S taken in a definite order there is associated a third, well-defined element of S. In systems with one algebraic operation, it is customary to use multiplicative terminology and symbolism; that is, we refer to the operation as "multiplication" and the image under the mapping of any pair (a, b) as their "product" ab. It happens sometimes, however, that additive notation is more convenient, in which case we refer to the operation as "addition" and designate the "sum" of a and b by $a + b$. It is to be understood, of course, that these operation symbols do not of necessity have any of the properties familiarly associated with them in ordinary arithmetic.

It is part of the definition which we have given for a binary operation that it is single valued and maps *any* ordered pair of elements of the set S in which it has been defined. Moreover, it should be noted that the image elements under such a mapping are all in S. If a and b are elements of a subset H of S, it may or may not happen that $ab \in H$. But if $ab \in H$, for arbitrary elements $a, b \in H$, the subset is said to be *closed* under the operation. We wish to point out that it is implicit in our definition of an operation defined in a set S, that S itself is always closed under the operation. From our point of view, if the underlying set is not closed, the "operation" has not been properly defined in the set, although it may be in some subset. Inasmuch as $S \times S$ is a set of *ordered* pairs, the order of the elements in such a pair is usually of importance in stating the rule of composition for any operation in S. That is, if a and b are elements of S, the mapped image of (a, b) may be different from that of (b, a). In the symbolism adopted, we are saying that ab (or $a + b$) may be different from ba (or $b + a$). If it is known that ab (or $a + b$) is the same as ba (or $b + a$) for arbitrary elements a and b of the system, the operation is said to be *commutative* and the system is known as a *commutative* system; otherwise, the operation and the system are *noncommutative*.

Definition. A set of elements in which an operation has been defined is known as a groupoid.*

Although an algebraic system is not to be identified with the underlying set of elements, we shall often find it convenient to use the same symbolism for both. For example, we may speak of an algebraic system S and also of an element $a \in S$. In the latter case,

---

*Some authors use this word for a different concept. See page 31 of the book by Zassenhaus listed under References in Chapter 4.

we are in reality referring to the elements of the system, but this
duplication of meaning should cause no confusion.

It is easy to find examples of a groupoid, though most of the
familiar ones are also examples of more complex systems. The
natural numbers, with either ordinary addition or ordinary multiplication as the operation, form a groupoid. However, the set of odd
natural numbers with ordinary addition and the set of real numbers
with ordinary division do not satisfy the definition. (Why?) The
set of integers with the operation of ordinary subtraction provides
us with an example of a groupoid with a noncommutative operation
or a *noncommutative groupoid*. A subset of a groupoid, which is
closed under the operation of the groupoid, is a *subgroupoid*. It is
important to understand in this definition—as in the definition of
any subsystem—that the same rule of composition applies to the
subset as to the set. It may be possible to define an operation in a
subset so that the rule of composition is quite different from that of
the operation in the set. Under such a circumstance, the subset
would comprise an algebraic system but *would not be a subsystem*
of the original.

The definition of a groupoid does not require that the operation
be *associative*. That is, for arbitrary elements a, b, c of the set, it is
not necessarily true that $(ab)c = a(bc)$ or $[(a + b) + c = a + (b + c)]$. However, the groupoid of natural numbers under either ordinary
addition or ordinary multiplication is easily seen to be both associa-
tive and commutative. We have noted previously that the groupoid
of integers under subtraction is not commutative, and it can also be
seen that it is not associative. Anyone who is familiar with the
multiplication of vectors in physics will note that this system of
vectors, with the operation of vector multiplication, provides us
with another example of a nonassociative groupoid.

Definition.   An associative groupoid is known as a *semi-group*.

The set of natural numbers under either ordinary addition or
ordinary multiplication is a familiar example of a (commutative)
semi-group. In Chapter 1 we gave a brief discussion of the idea of
a mapping of a set S into itself, as well as the products of such
mappings. If α, β, and γ are three mappings of a set S into itself, it

will be recalled that the definition of a product of mappings requires that $\alpha(\beta\gamma) = (\alpha\beta)\gamma$, and so the set of mappings of a set into itself under the product operation for mappings is an example of a semi-group.

For a semi-group, it is unambiguous to speak of the product abc of any three elements a, b, c of the system; but for a general groupoid, this could mean either of the products $(ab)c$ or $a(bc)$. It is somewhat intuitive—and we omit the proof—that if the Associative Law holds for any three elements, it will hold for an arbitrary finite number: i.e., the product $a_1a_2a_3\cdots a_n$ will have an unambiguous meaning, regardless of how the elements in the product are grouped. In this case, if $a_1 = a_2 = a_3 = \cdots = a_n = a$, we may designate the product conveniently by a^n. (If additive notation is used, we designate the sum of n elements, each of which is a, by na; i.e., $na = a + a + a + \cdots + a$, where there are n summands.) If a subset of a semi-group is closed under the operation, the subset comprises a *subsemi-group*.

Problems 3–1

1. If a and b are elements of the groupoid of integers under ordinary multiplication, determine ab where **(a)** $a = 5$, $b = -6$; **(b)** $a = -2$, $b = 8$.

2. Apply the directions of **Problem 1** to the groupoid of integers under ordinary addition.

3. Apply the directions of **Problem 1** to the groupoid of integers under ordinary subtraction, where we identify the abstract product ab with $a - b$.

**4. Let us define a binary composition in the set I of ordinary integers as follows: $a \circ b = a + b - ab$, for arbitrary $a, b \in I$. (This composition is known as the *circle composition*.) Show that I is a semi-group under the circle composition.

5. Let us define a binary composition in the set N of natural numbers as follows: $a * b = a + b + ab$, for arbitrary $a, b \in N$. Show that N is a semi-group under this *star composition*.

6. In the set P_S of all subsets of a set S, let set-theoretic union be the composition. Show that P_S is a semi-group under this composition.

7. If union is replaced by intersection in **Problem 6,** is the resulting system a semi-group?

3.2 MONOIDS AND GROUPS

It sometimes happens that an algebraic system has a *neutral* or *identity* element, i.e., an element e such that $ae = ea = a$, for an arbitrary element a in the system. However, if there is an identity element, this element is the only one that can be characterized in this way. For if f is another identity element, we must have $ef = e$ and also $ef = f$ from the definition of an identity element, so that $e = f$. It is customary to designate this unique identity element as 1 in the multiplicative notation and as 0 in the additive notation. To re-emphasize a point which we made earlier, however, these elements should not be confused with integers, though in special cases they may actually be these familiar numbers.

Definition. A semi-group with an identity element is known as a *monoid*.

The set of integers under either ordinary addition or ordinary multiplication provides an example of a monoid, with 0 or 1 playing its familiar role of identity element in the system. The semi-group of mappings of a set S into itself is also a monoid, the identity mapping—in which each element maps onto itself—being the identity element. The set of integers under subtraction is an example of a groupoid which is not associative (as we noted before), nor does it have an identity element. The integer 0 is not an identity element because while $a - 0 = a$, for any integer a, it is not true in general that $0 - a = a$. The semi-group of natural numbers under ordinary addition and the semi-group of even integers under ordinary multiplication are other examples of a semi-group without an identity element. A subset of a monoid is, of course, a *submonoid* if the subset contains the identity and is closed under the operation of the monoid.

We now introduce the notion of an "inverse" operation. It is customary to think of subtraction as the inverse of addition and of division as the inverse of multiplication. More specifically we ask the following question: for arbitrary elements a and b in an algebraic system, do there exist elements x and y in the system such that both $ax = b$ and $ya = b$? If there does *exist* a *unique* solution for both x and y in every case, we say that the operation (designated multiplication) of the system *has an inverse*. For example, in the monoid of integers under ordinary addition, the equations $a + x = b$ and $y + a = b$ have unique solutions for x and y with a and b arbitrary integers. In this case the solutions for x and y are the same and equal to $b - a$, which means in effect that we can subtract in the system. For a noncommutative system the solutions for x and y will not, in general, be the same.

Definition.   A monoid whose basic operation has an inverse is known as a *group*.

It is clear that the equation $ax = b$ is not always solvable in the monoid of non-negative integers under addition. In this case the more usual form of the equation would be $a + x = b$ and, for instance, there exists no non-negative number x such that $5 + x = 2$. A similar situation arises in the monoid of integers under multiplication.

In this book we are going to be concerned only with associative systems, although a great deal of study has recently been devoted to nonassociative systems. We merely remark, in passing, that a *quasi-group* is a (nonassociative) groupoid whose operation has an inverse; if the quasi-group has an identity element, the system is known as a *loop*.

Problems 3–2

1. Solve the equation $ya = b$ for y in the monoid of natural numbers under multiplication if: **(a)** $a = 2$, $b = 10$; **(b)** $a = 1$, $b = 4$. Could you solve the equation for y if $a = 4$ and $b = 2$?
2. In the groupoid of integers under subtraction, solve the equation $ya = b$ for y if ya is identified with $y - a$ and **(a)** $a = 2$, $b = 5$; **(b)** $a = 8$, $b = -4$.
3. In the groupoid of integers under subtraction, solve the equation $ax = b$ for x if ax is identified with $a - x$ and **(a)** $a = 2$, $b = 5$; **(b)** $a = 8$, $b = -4$. Compare the results of **Problems 2 and 3**.
**4. In our definition of a group, show that the existence of an inverse operation may be replaced by the weaker condition that the solutions of the equations $ax = b$ and $ya = b$ are *unique*, if such solutions exist, provided the group is finite.
5. Let a, b, c be elements of a group. Prove that the equation $axba = bc$ has a unique solution for x in the group.
6. What algebraic system is formed by the set of **(a)** rational numbers under addition, **(b)** irrational numbers under addition, **(c)** irrational numbers under multiplication?

3.3 ISOMORPHISM

It has happened in the past that independent studies have been made of two or more algebraic systems, and later these systems have been recognized to be "algebraically" the same. We refer to such systems as being "isomorphic" or say that we have established an "isomorphism"—a particular type of mapping—between them. Let us first consider the notion from an intuitive viewpoint. A set may be considered an algebraic system in which we have defined no operations or nontrivial (i.e., different from the identity) relations. In this simple case the idea of isomorphism is the same as that of cardinal number, which means for finite sets that they have the same number of elements. Notice that we do not consider any of the properties which the elements of either set may have—and these may well be different for the two sets—but we consider merely the question of cardinality. For instance, a set of 10 points on a line, a set of 10 people in a room, and a set of 10 words are isomorphic sets.

The situation is a little more complex in the case of systems in which we have defined operations and (or) nontrivial relations. However, the basic idea is still the same: two systems are isomorphic if their associated sets are isomorphic and—in very loose language— any deduction in one of the systems can be translated into an equally correct deduction in the other. As we have already noted, the elements of the two sets may be different, the rules of composition may be different, and the relations may be defined in entirely different ways; but if the systems are isomorphic they are algebraically indistinguishable. We are now ready to give a precise definition of the concept, for the case of algebraic systems with one operation and no nontrivial relations.

Definition. Let S and S' be two algebraic systems, each with one operation for which we shall use the same multiplicative notation. Then these systems are *isomorphic*, and we write $S \cong S'$ if:

1. there is a one-to-one correspondence between the elements of S and of S', this correspondence being conveniently indicated by $a \leftrightarrow a'$, for $a \in S$ and $a' \in S'$; and

2. the operation is "preserved" by the correspondence, i.e., if $a \leftrightarrow a'$ and $b \leftrightarrow b'$, with $a,\ b \in S$ and $a',\ b' \in S'$, it follows that $ab \leftrightarrow a'b'$.

It is sometimes helpful to represent the above conditions pictorially, as shown in the arrangement below

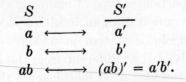

$$
\begin{array}{ccc}
S & & S' \\
\hline
a & \longleftrightarrow & a' \\
b & \longleftrightarrow & b' \\
ab & \longleftrightarrow & (ab)' = a'b'.
\end{array}
$$

The groupoid of even natural numbers under addition is isomorphic to the groupoid of all natural numbers N under addition. For, let us establish a one-to-one correspondence—as required by **1**—whereby each even number $2k$ corresponds to the number $k \in N$. It is immediate that this correspondence is one-to-one. Furthermore, in addition to $2k \leftrightarrow k$, let us assume that $2m \leftrightarrow m$, so that $2k + 2m = 2(k + m)$ and $2(k + m) \leftrightarrow k + m$. But this means that the correspondent of the sum of $2k$ and $2m$ is the sum of their respective correspondents, which is the statement (in additive notation) that **2** is satisfied. Hence the two groupoids are isomorphic.

A slightly less elementary example of an isomorphism is provided by the groupoid of positive real numbers P under multiplication and the groupoid of all real numbers R^* under addition. In this case, we can set up a one-to-one correspondence by associating each positive real number in P with its common logarithm in R^*. Each positive real number has a unique, well-defined, common logarithm, and each real number—positive, negative, or zero—is the common logarithm of some unique, well-defined, positive number. Hence the correspondence is one-to-one as desired. If a and b are arbitrary positive real numbers, the following correspondences show that the systems are isomorphic.

$$
\begin{array}{ccl}
P & & R^* \\
\hline
a & \longleftrightarrow & a' = \log a \\
b & \longleftrightarrow & b' = \log b \\
ab & \longleftrightarrow & (ab)' = \log ab = \log a + \log b = a' + b'
\end{array}
$$

It should be noted in this example that not only are the two sets distinct, but the operation in one case is addition, and in the other it is multiplication.

It is sometimes convenient to use a slightly different language in discussing isomorphic systems. Thus, the one-to-one correspondence or bijective mapping that is associated with two isomorphic systems may be said to define an *isomorphism* of one system with the other. In the language and terminology of mappings, we may say that a mapping ψ of a groupoid S onto a groupoid S' is an *isomorphism* if the following conditions are satisfied:

1. ψ is a bijective mapping of S onto S'.
2. If $a\psi = a'$ and $b\psi = b'$, then $(ab)\psi = a'b'$, i.e., $(ab)\psi = (a\psi)(b\psi)$ for arbitrary $a, b \in S$.

Let us re-emphasize a point which we noted above, that the elements and rules of composition for the operations and relations of two isomorphic systems can be quite different, and yet the two systems are not to be distinguished as to their algebraic structures. This means that any result which can be proved about one of the systems and which does not refer to the nature of its elements, operations and relations, remains valid for the other system. Hence it is not necessary to make independent studies of isomorphic systems. Only in examples will it be desirable to speak of sets of specific elements and operations that depend on the properties of these elements.

It can be shown that if two groupoids are isomorphic, the validity of the associative or commutative law in one system entails its validity in the other **(Problems 1, 2)**. Moreover, if one system S has an identity element 1, the correspondent of 1 in the other system S' is the identity element of S'. For let $1'$ in S' be the correspondent of 1 in S. Then, if a' is an arbitrary element of S', the correspondent of which is a in S, the equation $a1 = 1a = a$ in S implies that the equation $a'1' = 1'a' = a'$ is valid in S'. But this means that $1'$ is the identity element of S', as asserted. It can also be shown that if the operation in one of two isomorphic systems has an inverse, the same is true of the operation in the other system **(Problem 3)**. This should be expected, of course, along with the other properties just mentioned, in view of our algebraic identification of isomorphic systems.

An isomorphism of a system S with a system S' is said to be an *automorphism* if S and S' are the same system. Intuitively, we can think of an automorphism as a shuffling of the elements of a system, but with the operations and relations in the system remaining unaltered. We caution that it is quite possible for two systems to have the same elements—and so be equal as sets—but be different algebraic systems. Such systems may possibly not even be isomorphic. For an example of an automorphism, consider the system of complex numbers $a + bi$, where $a, b \in R^*$. If we think of this system as an additive group—i.e., with addition as the group operation—it is easy to verify that the mapping $a + bi \to a - bi$ of every complex number onto its conjugate is an automorphism of the system **(Problem 7).**

Problems 3-3

1. Prove that if one of two isomorphic groupoids is commutative, so is the other.

2. Prove that if one of two isomorphic groupoids is associative, so is the other.

3. Prove that if the operation in one of two isomorphic groupoids has an inverse, so has the operation in the other.

4. Prove that "is isomorphic to" is an equivalence relation in the set of all groupoids.

5. Use the definitions of §2.3 to prove that the additive groupoid of positive integers is isomorphic to the additive groupoid of natural numbers.

6. Let G be the groupoid of positive integers and G' the groupoid of positive even integers, with ordinary addition as the operation in each case. If the elements of these groupoids are ordered by the usual "is less than" relation, prove that G and G' are isomorphic as *ordered* groupoids. (Hint: Is the order relation preserved by the mapping?)

7. Prove that the mapping $a + bi \to a - bi$ of each complex number onto its conjugate is an automorphism of the additive group of complex numbers.

3.4 HOMOMORPHISM

The notion of isomorphism or isomorphic mapping, which we discussed in the preceding section, is a special case of the more general idea of *homomorphism*. In the case of a homomorphism or homomorphic mapping we do not require that the mapping be bijective. To be specific, we give the following definition.

> **Definition.**   Let S and S' be two algebraic systems, each with one operation for which we shall use the same multiplicative notation. A *homomorphism* of S into S' is a mapping $\psi : S \to S'$ such that $(ab)\psi = (a\psi)(b\psi)$ for each $a, b \in S$.

A comparison with the definition of the preceding section shows that an isomorphism is a homomorphism in which the mapping is one-to-one. If S and S' are the *same system*, a homomorphism of S into S' (i.e., into itself) is known as an *endomorphism*. In general, if ψ is a homomorphism of S into S', the set of image elements in S' is a *proper subset* of S'. In case every element of S' is the image of some element in S — i.e., ψ is a surjective mapping—we may say that S' is a *homomorphic image* of S, and ψ maps S *onto* S'.

While homomorphic images share many of the properties of the original system, they cannot be identified with or considered equivalent to the original system unless the homomorphism is an isomorphism. We shall consider a few examples of homomorphic mappings.

Let G be the groupoid of integers under addition, and G' the groupoid consisting of the two integers 1 and -1 with multiplication as the operation. Then, if $a\psi = 1$ or -1 according as a is even or odd, the mapping ψ is a homomorphism of G onto G'. For, if both a and b are even, $a' = a\psi = 1$ and $b' = b\psi = 1$, while $(a + b)' = (a + b)\psi = 1$ since $a + b$ is even; and so $(a + b)' = a'b'$, as required. If a is odd and b is even, $a' = a\psi = -1$, and $b' = b\psi = 1$, and so $(a + b)' = (a + b)\psi = -1$, since $a + b$ is odd. But then $(a + b)' = -1 = (-1)(1) = a'b'$, as before. Similar arguments for the other cases (a even and b odd, both a and b odd) will completely establish the fact that $(a + b)' = a'b'$, as is required in the definition of a homomorphism.

Another example of a homomorphism is supplied by the ordinary plane line-vectors of physics and the projections of these vectors on a straight line. In this case we let G be the groupoid of the plane vectors emanating from the origin, with ordinary vector addition as the operation; and we let G' be the groupoid of all horizontal vectors emanating from the origin. If ψ maps G onto G' so that $x\psi$ is the horizontal projection of x, for any x in G, we see that ψ is a homomorphism of G onto G'. For the projection of the sum of two vectors is the sum of their projections; and this is the same thing as saying that $(x + y)' = (x + y)\psi = x\psi + y\psi = x' + y'$ for arbitrary $x, y \in G$, as required in the definition.

It can be shown, just as in the case of an isomorphism, that if an operation in a system is associative or commutative, these properties are inherited by any homomorphic image of the system. It is also true that if a groupoid has an identity element, so has any homomorphic image. These remarks are equivalent to the statement that any homomorphic image of a (commutative) semi-group or monoid is, respectively, a (commutative) semi-group or monoid. If an operation in a system has an inverse, however, it cannot be inferred that the corresponding operation in a homomorphic image has this same property: for it is not possible to prove that the defining equations for an inverse have unique solutions as required in the definition of an inverse. We can prove, however, that these equations do have solutions in the image system. For suppose ψ is a homomorphic mapping of a system S onto a system S', with the operation in each system indicated as multiplication. If a' and b' are arbitrary elements of S', we must consider the existence of solutions of the equations $a'x = b'$ and $ya' = b'$ in S'. Since ψ is a surjective mapping, there exist elements a and b in S such that $a' = a\psi$ and $b' = b\psi$. We are assuming that the equation $ax = b$ has a solution $x = c \in S$, and the definition of a homomorphism implies that $a'c' = b'$, where $c' = c\psi$. Hence c' is a solution of $a'x = b'$, as alleged. However, inasmuch as a and b are not necessarily unique, it cannot be inferred that c and c' are unique. A similar argument applies to the solution for y of the equation $ya' = b'$. We shall prove in the next chapter that any homomorphic image of a group is a group, and so for this important type of algebraic system the "inverse" property of an operation *is* carried over to the image system.

While we have seen that most properties of a groupoid are inherited by a homomorphic image, there is very little that we can say in the other direction. It is quite possible for the associative law or the commutative law to be valid in a homomorphic image without either being satisfied in the original system. Neither can we infer the existence of an identity element or an inverse operation in a system from their existence in a homomorphic image.

Problems 3–4

1. Prove that a homomorphic image of a semi-group is a semi-group.
*2. Prove that a homomorphic image of a monoid is a monoid.
3. Let M be a commutative additive monoid, n a positive integer. Show that the mapping α on M defined by $x\alpha = nx$, for each $x \in M$, is an endomorphism of M.
**4. Prove that if α is a homomorphism of a groupoid A into a groupoid B, and β is a homomorphism of B into a groupoid C, then $\alpha\beta$ is a homomorphism of A into C.
5. Prove that the inverse of an isomorphism is an isomorphism.
6. Let α and β be mappings of the set I of integers into I, defined by $x\alpha = x + 1$ and $x\beta = 2x$, for each integer x. Then show that:
   (a) α is not a homomorphism of the additive monoid of integers;
   (b) β is a homomorphism of the additive monoid of integers;
   (c) $\alpha\beta \neq \beta\alpha$.

3.5 FUNDAMENTAL HOMOMORPHISM THEOREM

While a given groupoid G may have many distinct homomorphic images, it is possible to use the notion of a partition to obtain *all* of these—except for isomorphic duplicates. We shall call a partition "regular" if the class to which a product ab belongs depends only on the classes to which the elements a and b of G belong. The following definition makes this notion precise.

Definition.   A partition of a set comprising the elements of a groupoid is *regular* if, for arbitrary elements a_1 and a_2 of one class and arbitrary elements b_1 and b_2 of another class, the elements a_1b_1 and a_2b_2 belong to the same class.

It is now easy to define an operation in the quotient set—also known as the *factor set*—of G as follows: if A and B are any two classes of a regular partition, we define AB to be the class which contains the product ab, for any elements $a \in A$ and $b \in B$. The factor set with this operation is a groupoid $\overline{G}$, and the mapping that associates each element of G with its class in $\overline{G}$ is a homomorphism. This mapping is known as the *natural* homomorphism of G onto $\overline{G}$, where $\overline{G}$ is known as the "factor groupoid" or "quotient groupoid" of G with respect to the regular partition. That the factor groupoids with respect to various regular partitions exhaust all possible homomorphisms of G, up to an isomorphism, is the content of the following theorem.

Theorem 3.51 For each homomorphic image G' of a groupoid G, there exists a regular partition of G, such that G' is isomorphic to the factor groupoid $\overline{G}$ of G with respect to this partition.

Proof. If ψ is the homomorphism that maps G onto G', we obtain the desired partition of G by collecting into the same class all elements of G whose images under ψ coincide. This partition is regular, for suppose a_1 and a_2 are in one class while b_1 and b_2 are in another. Then $a_1\psi = a_2\psi = a' \in G'$, and $b_1\psi = b_2\psi = b' \in G'$, and the definition of a homomorphism requires that $(a_1b_1)\psi = (a_1\psi)(b_1\psi) = a'b' = (a_2\psi)(b_2\psi) = (a_2b_2)\psi$. Hence a_1b_1 and a_2b_2 are in the same class, and so the partition is regular. We now construct the factor groupoid $\overline{G}$, as described above, and assert that $G' \cong \overline{G}$. If a' is an arbitrary element of G', let $A \in \overline{G}$ be the set of elements $a \in G$ such that $a\psi = a'$. The definition of A assures us that the correspondence $a' \leftrightarrow A$ between G' and $\overline{G}$ is one-to-one. Now let a_1', a_2' be elements of G' which are associated by this correspondence with A_1 and $A_2 \in \overline{G}$, respectively. Then if $a_1 \in A_1$ and $a_2 \in A_2$, so that $a_1\psi = a_1'$ and $a_2\psi = a_2'$, the class A_1A_2 contains the element a_1a_2 and so $a_1'a_2' \leftrightarrow A_1A_2$, as required by the definition of an isomorphism. This completes the proof.

Problems 3–5

1. Explain why it is important that a partition of a groupoid be regular if a factor groupoid is to be constructed.
2. We have seen before (§3.4) that the mapping $\psi: I \to I$, such that $a\psi$ is 1 or -1 according as a is even or odd, is a homomorphism of the additive groupoid of integers onto the multiplicative groupoid of the set $\{1, -1\}$.

   (a) Describe the partition of G that is associated by **Theorem 3.51** with ψ.
 **(b) Prove that the partition described in (a) is regular.
   (c) What elements of the partition in (a) correspond to 1 and -1 in the isomorphism asserted by **Theorem 3.51**?
 3. Consider the homomorphism of the plane vectors, as discussed in §3.4, and prove that the associated partition of the basic groupoid of vectors is regular.

REFERENCES

BRUCK, R. H.: *A Survey of Binary Systems* (Berlin, Springer-Verlag, 1958).
CHEVALLEY, C.: *Fundamental Concepts of Algebra*, Chap. 1 (New York, Academic Press, 1957).
KUROSH, A.: *Theory of Groups*, Vol. 1, pp. 21–31 (New York, Chelsea, 1955).

chapter 4

GROUPS

4.1 AN EQUIVALENT DEFINITION

We have defined a group to be a monoid whose basic operation has an inverse. If it so happens that $ab = ba$, for arbitrary elements a and b of the group, the system is commutative and is known as a *commutative* or *abelian group*—the latter name in honor of the great mathematician Abel (1802–1829). It is possible, of course, that $ab = ba$ for certain elements a and b of a nonabelian group, and in such cases we say that these particular elements *commute* or *are permutable*. The *order* of a group is the number of its elements, and a group is *finite* if its order is a finite number. If a subset of a group is closed under the group operation and also satisfies all the other requirements of a group by itself, this subset comprises a *subgroup*. It would be possible at this time to establish the existence of groups of any order and discover many other interesting properties of a group, but we prefer to postpone this study until we have presented an equivalent set of postulates for a group.

Our postulate that a group be a monoid requires the existence of an identity element, and this has been shown to be unique. The fact that the basic operation of a group has an inverse allows us to establish the existence of other very important *unique* elements, known as *inverses*. For, if 1 is the identity element of a group, it follows from the inverse property that for each a in the group there exist *unique* elements a' and a'' (known as *right* and *left inverses* of a, respectively), such that $aa' = a''a = 1$. Actually, the elements a' and a'' are the same: for $a''aa' = a''(aa') = a''1 = a''$, and also $a''aa' = (a''a)a' = 1a' = a'$, whence $a'' = a'$. It follows that there is associated with each element a of a group a unique element, which is known as the *inverse* of a and designated as a^{-1}, such that $a^{-1}a = aa^{-1} = 1$.

We have seen that our group postulates have implied the existence of a unique identity element, and of a unique inverse element for each element of the group. These results characterize a group so completely that we can use them, along with the Associative Law, to make up a new, and frequently more useful, set of postulates. In fact, we do not actually require the uniqueness of the elements whose existence is to be postulated—though this uniqueness can be inferred.

Definition.   A *group* is an algebraic system G, with one binary operation indicated as multiplication for convenience, such that the following postulates are in effect:

1. *Closure.* The product $ab \in G$ provided $a, b \in G$. (This is actually assumed in our definition of a binary operation in G.)
2. *Associative Law.* For arbitrary $a, b, c \in G$, it is true that $(ab)c = a(bc)$.
3. *Existence of an Identity Element.* There exists an element $e \in G$ such that $ae = ea = a$, for each $a \in G$.
4. *Existence of Inverses.* For each $a \in G$ there exists an inverse element $a^* \in G$, such that $aa^* = a^*a = e$.

In testing whether a given system is a group, it will be found that this set of postulates is usually much easier to use than those given earlier. Furthermore, the fact that uniqueness is not postulated in 3 and 4 is another attractive feature of this set of postulates.

In order to see that the above postulates do imply the earlier ones, we must show that the existence of inverses in **Postulate 4** allows us to solve the equations $ax = b$ and $ya = b$ for unique x and y, where all elements involved are in the group. We note first that the inverse elements postulated in 4 are unique. For, if we suppose that there are two such inverses for any given group element, each of these is both a right and a left inverse, and the proof given in the second paragraph of this section shows that these two inverses are identical. Now let us consider the equation $ax = b$, where a and b are in a group G as defined by our new postulates. Since $a(a^{-1}b) = b$, it is clear that $x = a^{-1}b$ in G is a solution of the equation for x. Moreover, if x is any solution of the given equation, it follows that $a^{-1}(ax) = a^{-1}b$ or $x = a^{-1}b$, so that this solution for x is unique. In a similar manner it is possible to prove that $y = ba^{-1}$ is the unique solution in G of the equation $ya = b$. Hence the equations $ax = b$ and $ya = b$ can be solved uniquely in G for x and y, which means that the group operation has an inverse. We have shown that a group, as defined in this section, is also a group as defined in Chapter 3. Since we have noted that the earlier definition implies the validity of the postulates of this section, the two definitions are equivalent.

The first three group postulates of this section assert that a group is a monoid, and the proof given in Chapter 3 shows that the identity element postulated in 3 is unique. We shall continue to designate this unique, identity element by 1 in a multiplicative group, and by 0 if the group is additive.

Problems 4–1

1. Explain why the "closure" condition is actually redundant in the defintition of a group as given in this section.
**2. If we assume the existence of a left identity and left inverses in a semi-group, show that the left cancellation law holds (i.e., show that $ab = ac$ implies that $b = c$, for arbitrary group elements a, b, c).
3. Use the conditions and result of **Problem 2** to prove that a left identity is also a right identity.

4. Use the conditions of **Problem 2** and the results of **Problems 2** and 3 to prove that any left inverse is also a right inverse.

*5. Combine the results of **Problems 3** and 4 to see that **Postulates** 3 and 4 for a group may be weakened to assume the existence of only left (or right) inverses and a left (or right) identity.

*6. Prove that if e is a left (or right) identity for a given element a of a group, then e is the identity element of the group. (That is, show that $ae = a$ or $ea = a$ implies that $e = 1$.)

*7. An element a of a group is *idempotent* if $a^2 = a$. Show that the only idempotent element of a group is the identity element.

8. Express the results of **Problems 6** and 7 in additive notation.

4.2 SOME SIMPLE EXAMPLES OF A GROUP

In this section we shall collect some simple examples of a group, though in most cases we shall leave to the student most of the verification that the system actually is a group. This verification can be accomplished most conveniently with the help of the four postulates given in the preceding section.

1. The set of all integers forms a group under ordinary addition, the so-called *additive group of integers*. Since the sum of any two integers is an integer, and addition is an associative operation, **postulates 1** and **2** are satisfied. The identity element is 0, while the inverse of any integer n is $-n$, so that **postulates 3** and 4 are satisfied, and the system is a group. (What is the inverse of $-n$ in this group?) The sets of rational numbers, real numbers, and complex numbers also provide familiar examples of an additive group, and each of these contains the additive group of integers as a subgroup.

2. By an *integral multiple* of a given number a we shall mean na, where $na = a + a + \cdots + a$ (n summands). If we assume the familiar properties of such multiples, including $n(a+b) = na + nb$, it can be seen that all integral multiples of a given number form a group under addition. (What is the identity element of such a group?) However, the set of all odd integers and the set of all non-negative integers do not form additive groups. (Why?)

3. The set of all nonzero rational numbers forms a group under

multiplication, the so-called *multiplicative group of nonzero rational numbers*. The identity element of this group is the integer 1 (or 1/1), while the inverse of the rational number m/n is n/m. The subset of *positive* rational numbers also forms a multiplicative group, a subgroup of the larger group.

4. An example of a finite group is provided by the set $\{1, -1\}$ of integers, with ordinary multiplication as the operation. This group is also a subgroup of the principal group in **Example 3**.

5. The complex nth roots of unity form a group under ordinary complex multiplication. In order to see this, it should be recalled that if ω is a primitive nth root of unity, a complete set of nth roots is $\omega, \omega^2, \omega^3, \cdots, \omega^n = 1$. (A primitive nth root of unity has the property that its nth power, but not any smaller positive integral power, is 1.) Since n is an arbitrary positive integer, and there are n complex nth roots of unity, this example shows that there exists at least one group with any finite order.

6. The set of complex numbers with absolute value 1 is a group under ordinary complex multiplication. These numbers can be associated with points on a unit circle, and in the verification of the group postulates it will be helpful to recall the polar representation of a complex number.

7. The rotations of a plane figure, through multiples of 45° about a point, form a group, in which the *product* of two rotations is the rotation resulting from *performing in succession* the two rotations. If we consider two rotations to be *equal* if all points of the figure are in identical positions after each rotation, it is easy to see that there are only 8 distinct elements in the set of rotations. These may be designated, with an obvious symbolism, as: $R_0, R_{45}, R_{90}, R_{135}, R_{180}, R_{225}, R_{270}, R_{315}$. The identity element of this group is R_0, the rotation through 0°, and it should be noted that the inverse of each element is in the set. For example, the inverse of R_{45} is R_{315}, since $R_{45}R_{315} = R_{315}R_{45} = R_0$. Rotations through negative multiples of 45° are present in the set, in the form of equivalent positive rotations. For instance, a rotation through $-45°$ is equivalent to the rotation designated as R_{315}.

8. Consider a square so oriented that its center is at the origin and its sides are parallel to the axes of a rectangular coordinate sys-

tem. The square can be carried into itself as the result of any of the following 8 rigid motions:

I: the identity "motion" in which the square remains fixed.

H: the reflection of the square in the horizontal axis.

V: the reflection of the square in the vertical axis.

D: the reflection of the square in the diagonal of quadrants 1 and 3.

D': the reflection of the square in the diagonal of quadrants 2 and 4.

R: a clockwise rotation of the square about the origin through 90°.

R': a clockwise rotation of the square about the origin through 180°.

R'': a clockwise rotation of the square about the origin through 270°.

As in **Example 7,** we shall consider two rigid motions to be equal if each point of the square is carried into an identical position by the two motions. If we again define the *product* of two rigid motions to

Table 1

	I	R	R'	R''	H	V	D	D'
I	I	R	R'	R''	H	V	D	D'
R	R	R'		I				H
R'	R'		I	R				D
R''	R''			R'				V
H	H	D'	V	D	I	R'	R''	R
V	V			D'	I	R	R''	
D	D			V	R''	I	R'	
D'	D'	V	D	H	R''	R	R'	I

be the resultant of the motions performed in succession, it can be shown that the set of "symmetries" just listed comprises a group, known as the *group of symmetries of the square*. This group is nonabelian since, for instance, $VD = R$ while $DV = R''$. If we border a square mesh with the 8 symmetries of a square, as shown in Table 1 on page 55, and place the product ab of two elements a and b opposite a on the left and below b, the result is the *multiplication table* of the group. An array like this, which gives the complete multiplication table of a group, is also known as a Cayley square, in honor of the mathematician A. Cayley (1821–1895). The student is urged to fill in the spaces left blank in the Cayley square on page 55.

Problems 4–2

1. Use a Cayley square to exhibit the complete multiplication table of the group in **Example 1.

   2. Use the directions of **Problem 1** for the group in **Example 5** with $n = 4$.

   3. Show that the system in **Example 6** is closed under the operation.

   4. In the symbolism of **Example 7,** how would we represent a rotation of (a) $450°$; (b) $-270°$; (c) $-135°$; (d) $-360°$?

   5. Fill in the blank spaces of the multiplication table in **Example 8.**

   6. With reference to **Example 8,** use Table 1 to determine each of the following products: (a) $R(VD')$; (b) $(HV)D$; (c) $(R'D)(R''H)$.

   7. With reference to **Example 7,** express each of the following products as one of the basic set elements:

$$(a)\ R_{45}R_{180};\ (b)\ R_{180}R_{270};\ (c)\ R_{225}(R_{135}R_{270}).$$

 *8. Explain why the rule $n(a + b) = na + nb$, for any natural number n and arbitrary elements a, b of an algebraic system, is valid only if the system is both commutative and associative.

4.3 TWO IMPORTANT GROUPS

In this section we conclude our list of examples of a group with two very important types. One of these is of the abelian variety and one is not. A group of permutations on a finite set of elements, which we list as **Example 1,** is so basic that it illustrates the very beginning of the theory of groups.

1. A *permutation* is a *bijective mapping of a finite set onto itself,* and it is customary to describe a permutation by actually designating the image of each element under the mapping. For example, the permutation on the first n natural numbers such that each number i is mapped onto the number a_i, can be indicated by $\begin{pmatrix} 1 & 2 & 3 & \cdots & n \\ a_1 & a_2 & a_3 & \cdots & a_n \end{pmatrix}$. The *identity element*—or *identity permutation*—is the permutation in which every element is mapped onto itself, and can be designated as $\begin{pmatrix} 1 & 2 & 3 & \cdots & n \\ 1 & 2 & 3 & \cdots & n \end{pmatrix}$ or more simply as (1) or 1. The inverse of a permutation is simply the reverse mapping, so that if α is the permutation $\begin{pmatrix} 1 & 2 & 3 & \cdots & n \\ a_1 & a_2 & a_3 & \cdots & a_n \end{pmatrix}$, the *inverse* α^{-1} of α is the permutation $\begin{pmatrix} a_1 & a_2 & a_3 & \cdots & a_n \\ 1 & 2 & 3 & \cdots & n \end{pmatrix}$. In particular, if α is the permutation on the first five natural numbers designated as $\begin{pmatrix} 1 & 2 & 3 & 4 & 5 \\ 4 & 1 & 5 & 2 & 3 \end{pmatrix}$, it follows that $\alpha^{-1} = \begin{pmatrix} 1 & 2 & 3 & 4 & 5 \\ 2 & 4 & 5 & 1 & 3 \end{pmatrix}$. It should be noted that the order in which the elements are listed on the top line of an indicated permutation is of no importance. For example, the permutation α, just cited, could also have been designated as $\begin{pmatrix} 3 & 1 & 5 & 4 & 2 \\ 5 & 4 & 3 & 2 & 1 \end{pmatrix}$ and in many other ways, for it is only the mappings which matter in the description of a permutation. Moreover, in the description of a permutation, it is customary to omit any symbols that are left unchanged. For instance, the permutation $\begin{pmatrix} 1 & 2 & 3 & 4 & 5 \\ 1 & 3 & 4 & 2 & 5 \end{pmatrix}$ would generally be designated more simply as $\begin{pmatrix} 2 & 3 & 4 \\ 3 & 4 & 2 \end{pmatrix}$. If we define the *product* of two permutations to be the *resultant* of the two mappings, it can be seen quite readily that the set of all permutations on a finite set forms a group. This group has order $n!$, if there are n elements in the set, and is known as S_n—the *symmetric group of degree n*. That is, the symmetric group of degree n is the group of all permutations on n symbols. It is easy to see that the symmetric group is, in general, nonabelian. For example, consider the elements $\begin{pmatrix} 1 & 3 & 4 \\ 3 & 4 & 1 \end{pmatrix} = \alpha_1$ and $\begin{pmatrix} 3 & 5 & 6 \\ 6 & 3 & 5 \end{pmatrix} = \alpha_2$ of S_6. With $\alpha_1\alpha_2$ defined as the resultant of first α_1 and then α_2, the permutation $\alpha_1\alpha_2$ maps 1 onto 3 and 3 onto 6, so that $1(\alpha_1\alpha_2) = 6$. Similarly, $\alpha_1\alpha_2$ maps 2 onto itself, while 3 is mapped onto 4 by α_1, and 4 is unchanged by α_2, so that $2(\alpha_1\alpha_2) = 2$ and $3(\alpha_1\alpha_2) = 4$; and in like manner, $4(\alpha_1\alpha_2) = 1$, $5(\alpha_1\alpha_2) = 3$, $6(\alpha_1\alpha_2) = 5$. We have shown that $\alpha_1\alpha_2 = \begin{pmatrix} 1\ 3\ 4\ 5\ 6 \\ 6\ 4\ 1\ 3\ 5 \end{pmatrix}$, whereas a similar analysis will show that $\alpha_2\alpha_1 = \begin{pmatrix} 1\ 3\ 4\ 5\ 6 \\ 3\ 6\ 1\ 4\ 5 \end{pmatrix}$, so that $\alpha_1\alpha_2 \neq \alpha_2\alpha_1$.

Our final example of a group, to be introduced at this time, is an especially important one, since it arises in connection with many different topics of mathematics. It is the basis for what is usually known as a study of *congruences*.

2. The group to be introduced here is the *group of integers modulo m*, where m is any positive integer different from 1. In the arithmetic of this group, we essentially ignore multiples of m, i.e., we identify all multiples of m with the 0 of the system. For example: if $m = 5$, since $3 + 4 = 7 = 5 + 2$ we say that "$3 + 4$ is congruent to 2 modulo 5" and write $3 + 4 \equiv 2(\text{modulo } 5)$, or more simply $3 + 4 \equiv 2(\text{mod } 5)$, or even to $3 + 4 \equiv 2(5)$.

A more proper description of this arithmetic modulo m is to say that it is simply the familiar arithmetic of the additive group of integers, *but with a new definition of the equality relation* ($=$); and in this environment this "equality" relation is usually called a "congruence" and designated $\equiv$. This definition requires that two integers a and b are to be considered *equal* or *congruent* if they have the same remainder on division by m, and we write $a \equiv b(\text{mod } m)$. That this "equality" or "congruence mod m" relation is an equivalence relation can be readily checked, and there results a partition of the integers into m equivalence classes. The integers in each equivalence class are not be distinguished in this type of modulo arithmetic, and each integer in any class is "equal" or "congruent" to its smallest non-negative member—a *representative* of the class. In the case where $m = 5$, there are five equivalence classes with representative elements 0, 1, 2, 3, 4, and so every integer is "equal" or "congruent mod 5" to one of these five integers. For instance, $0 \equiv 5 \equiv 10 \equiv 15 \cdots (\text{mod } 5)$, $1 \equiv$

$6 \equiv 11 \equiv 16 \cdots \pmod{5}$, $2 \equiv 7 \equiv 12 \equiv 17 \equiv \cdots \pmod{5}$, $3 \equiv 8 \equiv 13 \equiv 18 \equiv \cdots \pmod 5$, $4 \equiv 9 \equiv 14 \equiv 19 \equiv \cdots$ (mod 5), and such equations as $4 + 4 \equiv 3 \pmod 5$ and $1 + 4 \equiv 0$ (mod 5) would be valid. If the nature of the system is clearly understood, it would be permissible to use the symbol $=$ in place of $\equiv$, so that the above equations would become $4 + 4 = 3$ and $1 + 4 = 0$. However, in view of the established usage of $\equiv$ for this type of equality, it is probably better to continue to use $\equiv$ for this purpose.

The system of integers modulo m consists of only m really distinct (i.e., not congruent) integers, which we can list as $0, 1, 2, \cdots, m-1$, and it is easy to check that this system is a group. As for the postulate of *closure*, the ordinary sum of any two integers is another integer and so is congruent to one of the integers in the above set. What we are saying is that *addition has been defined* in this algebraic system. The *associative* property follows from the same property in ordinary arithmetic. The *identity element* is 0—to which all multiples of m are congruent—while the *inverse* of an integer t is $m - t$, since $t + (m - t) = m \equiv 0$ (mod m). For example, if $m = 5$ the inverse of 3 is 2, and the inverse of 4 is 1. In the customary notation of additive inverses this means that $-3 \equiv 2 \pmod 5$ and $-4 \equiv 1 \pmod 5$.

We have described this example with considerable care, because of its importance in mathematical literature, but we could have been brief! For in the language of Chapter 3, the group of integers modulo m is simply the quotient or factor groupoid of the additive groupoid of ordinary integers, with respect to the congruence equivalence relation, and this factor groupoid has been shown to be a group. The classes of congruent integers are the "equivalence classes" of the earlier discussion, and in the earlier notation we would designate them as $\bar{0}$ (or 0), $\bar{1}, \bar{2}, \bar{3}, \bar{4}$.

Problems 4–3

1. Use a Cayley square to exhibit the complete addition table for the group of integers mod 5, discussed in **Example 2**.
2. Perform each of the following additions within the additive group of integers mod 7: **(a)** $4 + 4$, **(b)** $6 + 4$, **(c)** $5 + 6$, **(d)** $4 + 4 + 4$.

3. Determine the inverse of each of the following elements in the additive group of integers mod 7: (a) 4, (b) 2, (c) 0, (d) 6.

4. List all the members of the symmetric group S_3, and associate each of these with its inverse.

5. Show that $\alpha\beta \neq \beta\alpha$, where α and β are members of S_5 defined as follows:

$$\alpha = \begin{pmatrix} 1 & 3 & 4 \\ 4 & 1 & 3 \end{pmatrix} \quad \text{and} \quad \beta = \begin{pmatrix} 1 & 2 & 3 & 4 & 5 \\ 3 & 4 & 1 & 5 & 2 \end{pmatrix}.$$

6. If we use multiplication in **Example 2,** and assume m prime, the set of *nonzero* integers becomes the multiplicative group of nonzero integers mod m. (Why must 0 be excluded from the system?) Show that the additive group of integers mod 6 is isomorphic to the multiplicative group of nonzero integers mod 7. (Hint: Since no mapping is prescribed, you must *find* one which is satisfactory.)

**7. If $\alpha = \begin{pmatrix} 1 & 3 & 4 \\ 4 & 1 & 3 \end{pmatrix}$, $\beta = \begin{pmatrix} 1 & 2 & 3 & 6 \\ 3 & 6 & 1 & 2 \end{pmatrix}$, and $\gamma = \begin{pmatrix} 1 & 4 & 5 & 6 \\ 5 & 6 & 4 & 1 \end{pmatrix}$ are elements of S_6, determine each of the following products:
(a) $\alpha(\beta\gamma)$, (b) $\alpha(\gamma\beta)\alpha$, (c) $\alpha^2\beta$, (d) $\gamma^2\beta$.

8. Use the notation of **Problem 7** to determine each of the following:
(a) $\alpha^{-1}\beta^{-1}$, (b) $\gamma^{-1}\alpha^2$, (c) $\beta^2\gamma^{-1}$.

4.4 ELEMENTARY PROPERTIES OF GROUPS

In this section we discuss some of the very elementary but basic properties of groups, and we list them as theorems for the sake of future reference. The first two have been established earlier, but we repeat them in the interest of completeness.

Theorem 4.41   A group has *only one* identity element, usually designated 0 or 1 according as the additive or multiplicative notation is used.

Theorem 4.42   A group has *only one* inverse associated with each element of the group. The inverse of an element a will be designated $-a$ in the additive notation, and a^{-1} in the multiplicative notation.

Theorem 4.43   The inverse of a product of elements from a group is the product of the inverses of the elements in reverse order.

Proof.   For consider the product $a_1a_2a_3\cdots a_n$, with each element a_i in a group. Then it is clear that $(a_1a_2a_3\cdots a_n)\,(a_n^{-1}a_{n-1}^{-1}a_{n-2}^{-1}\cdots a_1^{-1}) = (a_1a_2\cdots a_{n-1})(a_na_n^{-1})(a_{n-1}^{-1}a_{n-2}^{-1}\cdots a_1^{-1}) = (a_1a_2\cdots$

$a_{n-1})(a_{n-1}{}^{-1}a_{n-2}{}^{-1}\cdots a_1{}^{-1}) = \cdots = a_1 a_1{}^{-1} = 1$. Inasmuch as the inverse of any group element is unique, by **Theorem 4.42**, it follows that $(a_1 a_2 a_3 \cdots a_n)^{-1} = a_n{}^{-1} a_{n-1}{}^{-1} a_{n-2}{}^{-1} \cdots a_1{}^{-1}$, as desired. We note in passing that in the additive notation, this theorem asserts that $-(a_1 + a_2 + \cdots + a_n) = -a_n - \cdots - a_2 - a_1$.

Theorem 4.44 (Cancellation Law). If a, b_1, and b_2 are elements of a group, such that $ab_1 = ab_2$ or $b_1 a = b_2 a$, it follows that $b_1 = b_2$.

Proof. For we can multiply both members of the first equation on the left, or of the second equation on the right, by a^{-1} and the result follows immediately.

Theorem 4.45 Any homomorphic image of a group is a group.

Proof. A group G is a monoid, and if G is mapped homomorphically onto a system G' we have seen before that G' is a monoid. Hence G' has an identity element, and we must show that each element $a' \in G'$ has an inverse. If a is an element of G that is mapped onto a' (Why does such an a exist?), there exists $a^{-1} \in G$ such that $aa^{-1} = a^{-1}a = 1$. It follows from the basic property of a homomorphic mapping that $a'(a^{-1})' = (a^{-1})'a' = 1'$, where $1'$ is the identity element of G'. Hence $(a^{-1})'$ is the inverse of a', and the postulates of a group (as given in this chapter) then imply that G' is a group.

It may be recalled that we were not able to prove the uniqueness of solutions of the characteristic equations for an inverse, in a homomorphic image of a groupoid, even though this uniqueness was assumed in the original system. In view of **Theorem 4.45**, however, solutions *are* unique in a homomorphic image if the groupoid is in fact a group. We have seen earlier that the factor groupoid of any groupoid with respect to a regular partition is a homomorphic image of the groupoid. It then also follows from **Theorem 4.45** that any factor groupoid of a group G, with respect to a regular partition, is a group known as a *factor* or *quotient* group of G. Our earlier result then implies that *every homomorphic image of a group is isomorphic to one of its factor groups.*

We have previously used the notation a^n for the product of n elements each equal to a. That is, $a^2 = aa$, $a^3 = aaa$, etc., and such products are unambigously defined in view of the associative property of the group operation. We now *define* negative powers of a to be the inverses of the corresponding positive powers, i.e., $a^{-n} = (a^n)^{-1}$. Inasmuch as $(aaa\cdots a)(a^{-1}a^{-1}a^{-1}\cdots a^{-1}) = 1$, where each of the indicated factors contains the same number of elements, it follows that $(a^n)^{-1} = (a^{-1})^n$, and so $a^{-n} = (a^n)^{-1} = (a^{-1})^n$. If we *define* $a^0 = 1$, we have given meaning to every integral power of a group element. In case the notation is additive, we write multiples na instead of a^n and $(-n)a$ instead of a^{-n}; so we have shown that $(-n)a = -(na)$, which we can designate more simply by $-na$. It is now easy to verify the following theorem.

Theorem 4.46   For any group element a and arbitrary integers m and n, we have $a^m a^n = a^{m+n}$ and $(a^m)^n = a^{mn}$. (In case the notation is additive, this becomes $ma + na = (m + n)a$ and $n(ma) = (mn)a$.)

We leave the verification of this result to the student.

If all powers of an element a are distinct elements of the group to which it belongs, a is said to be of *infinite* order. On the other hand, if $a^m = a^n$ where $m > n$, it follows that $(a^m)(a^{-n}) = a^{m-n} = 1$, as a result of **Theorem 4.46** and the definition of an inverse. Hence some power of a is equal to the identity element. If n is the smallest positive integer such that $a^n = 1$, we say that a is *of finite order* with *order n*.

If a group element a has order n, the elements $a^0 = 1$, $a^1 = a$, a^2, a^3, $\cdots$, a^{n-1} are all distinct, by definition of order. Moreover, every power of a is equal to one of these, for suppose m is an arbitrary integer. Then $m = nq + r$, for integers q, r such that $0 \leq r < n$, and so $a^m = a^{nq}a^r = (a^n)^q a^r = a^r$, as asserted. In particular, we see that if $a^m = 1$, it follows that m is divisible by its order n. We note that the inverse of a is a^{n-1}, since $aa^{n-1} = a^{n-1}a = a^n = 1$.

It is clear that every element of a finite group must have finite order, or the group could not be finite. If every element of a group has finite order, the group is said to be *periodic*. There are also groups whose elements—apart from the identity element—all have infinite order, and these are known as *torsion-free* or *locally infinite* groups. The ordinary additive group of integers is an example of a torsion-free group, while any group of permutations is a periodic group.

Problems 4–4

*1. Show that the multiplication table for a finite group contains each group element once, and only once, in each of its rows and columns.

2. Use the result of **Problem 1** to prove that there is only one possible multiplication table for a group of order 3.

3. Construct all possible abstract groups of order 4, using the result of **Problem 1**. (Note that the existence of a multiplication table does not in itself establish a group, for there are 4 postulates for a group! Moreover, two multiplication tables may seem to be different, whereas the associated groups may actually be isomorphic.)

4. If a and b are elements of a finite abelian group, prove that the order of ab is a divisor of the l.c.m. of the orders of a and b.

5. The integers 1, 3, 5, 7 comprise a group under multiplication and reduction modulo 8. (See **Example 2** of §4.3.) Exhibit the proper mapping to show that this group is isomorphic to one of the groups discovered in **Problem 3**.

6. Prove that a group is abelian if every element except the identity has order 2.

**7. For the purposes of this problem, we recall that a *function* was defined in Chapter 1 as a *mapping*. The *sum* $f + g$ of two functions f and g is defined so that $x(f + g) = xf + xg$, for each x in the common domain of f and g. Show that the set of all real-valued continuous functions on R^* is a group with this additive operation.

8. Use the definition of addition given in **Problem 7**, and show that the set of all real-valued differentiable functions on R^* comprises an additive group.

9. Prove that the mapping α, where $n\alpha = i^n$ for any integer n, is a homomorphism of the additive group of integers. Describe the homomorphic image, and identify its elements with those of the isomorphic quotient group whose existence was asserted following **Theorem 4.45**.

10. Let the mapping β of the additive group G of real numbers be defined by $x\beta = e^{2\pi i x}$, for each real number x. Show that β is a homomorphism of G onto a group G', and describe G'.

11. Which of the following mappings of the multiplicative group of all

nonzero real numbers into itself are homomorphisms? In each of these cases, describe the homomorphic image.

(a) $x \to -x$; (b) $x \to |x|$; (c) $x \to 1/x$;

(d) $x \to 3x$; (e) $x \to x^2$; (f) $x \to -1/x$.

4.5 SUBGROUPS

If a subset of a group is closed under the group operation and satisfies all the other requirements of a group in its own right, we have previously referred to the subset as a *subgroup*. It is perhaps conceivable that the identity element of a subgroup might be different from that of the original group. However, if we note that the identity element of a group must also serve as an identity element for any of its subgroups, and that the identity element of a group or subgroup is unique, this conceived possibility is untenable. The identity element of a group must coincide with the identity element of any of its subgroups. The uniqueness of the inverse elements in a group also implies that the inverse of any element *in a subgroup* must be the same element as the inverse in the whole group. The following theorem is a convenient criterion for deciding whether a subsystem of a group is a subgroup.

Theorem 4.51 A nonempty subset H of a group G is a subgroup if and only if $ab^{-1} \in H$ ($a - b \in H$, if group additive), for arbitrary $a, b \in H$.

Proof. Suppose that H is a subgroup with $a, b \in H$. Then $b^{-1} \in H$, and the "closure" postulate requires that $ab^{-1} \in H$. On the other hand, let us consider H to be a subset of G, such that $ab^{-1} \in H$ for arbitrary $a, b \in H$. Then, if $a \in H$, we have $aa^{-1} = 1 \in H$, where 1 is the identity element of G. Also, if $b \in H$, we have $1b^{-1} = b^{-1} \in H$. Hence, if $a, b \in H$, our assumption is that $a(b^{-1})^{-1} = ab \in H$, which gives us the "closure" property. Thus H is a subgroup, as alleged.

We now consider the notion of a *cyclic* group. If a is any element of a group G, the set K of elements $\{ \cdots, a^{-3}, a^{-2}, a^{-1}, a^0 = 1, a^1 = a, a^2, a^3, \cdots \}$ comprises a subgroup. For let $x = a^m$ and $y = a^n$ be arbitrary elements of K, where m and n are integers. We recall that all integral powers of a group element have been defined in §4.4, and that **Theorem 4.46,** requires that $a^m a^n = a^{m+n}$, for arbitrary integers m and n. Then $y^{-1} = (a^n)^{-1} = a^{-n}$, and so we have $xy^{-1} = a^m a^{-n} = a^{m-n} \in K$. It then follows from **Theorem 4.51** that K is a subgroup of G, as asserted. The element a is said to be a *generator* of K; and K is said to be the *cyclic* subgroup generated by a, and may be designated by $[a]$. Of course, it can happen that $K = G$, and in this case the whole group G is cyclic with a as a generator.

If G is finite, not all powers a^t of any of its elements a are distinct. In fact, the order of a must be some positive integer n, so that $a^n = 1$, and it is clear that $(a^t)^{-1} = a^{n-t}$. Hence, in this case, the subgroup generated by a must contain only the set $\{a^0 = 1, a, a^2, \cdots, a^{n-1}\}$ of n elements. A cyclic group is always abelian, and so we see that it is quite ordinary for a nonabelian group to contain abelian subgroups.

Theorem 4.52 If S is any collection of subgroups of a group G, the intersection of these subgroups is also a subgroup of G.

Proof. For let a and b be elements of the intersection. Then a and b are in each subgroup of the collection and, by **Theorem 4.51,** it follows that ab^{-1} is in each of these subgroups. But then ab^{-1} is in the common intersection and so this intersection is a subgroup of G, as asserted.

We are now able to generalize the notion of a cyclic subgroup. For if M is *any* nonempty subset of a group G, let H be the set of subgroups of G that contain M. Since H contains G, it is not empty, and by **Theorem 4.52** the intersection of all subgroups in H is a subgroup of G. This group is known as the subgroup *generated by the set M*, and will be denoted by $[M]$; the elements of M will be referred to as the *generators* of the subgroup. It is clear that $[M]$ can be characterized as the "smallest" subgroup of G that contains M, in the sense that any other subgroup of G that contains M also contains $[M]$. The elements of $[M]$ are just the finite products $a_1 a_2 a_3 \cdots a_n$, where each a_i is either an element of M or the inverse of such an element. For let K be the collection of all these products, for all positive integers n. Then, if $a = a_1 a_2 a_3 \cdots a_m \in K$ and $b =$

$b_1 b_2 b_3 \cdots b_n \in K$, we have $b^{-1} = b_n^{-1} b_{n-1}^{-1} b_{n-2}^{-1} \cdots b_1^{-1} \in K$, and it follows that $ab^{-1} = a_1 a_2 a_3 \cdots a_m b_n^{-1} b_{n-1}^{-1} b_{n-2}^{-1} \cdots b_1^{-1} \in K$. Hence, by **Theorem 4.51**, K is a subgroup of G which contains M. But any subgroup that contains M must contain every element of K, and so $K = [M]$. If $M = \{a\}$, the group $[M]$ is the cyclic group $[a]$, as discussed before.

Problems 4–5

*1. Prove that a finite semi-group is a group if the cancellation law is assumed to hold.

*2. Prove that any finite subsemi-group of a group is a subgroup.

**3. If g is a fixed element of a group G, the set N_g of all elements of G which commute with g is known as the *centralizer* of g. Prove that N_g is a subgroup of G.

4. The subset C of all elements of a group G which commute with all elements of G is known as the *center* of G. Prove that the center of a group is a subgroup.

5. If H is a subset of any group G, prove that the subset K of all elements of G such that $k^{-1}Hk = H$, for $k \in K$, is a subgroup of G. (By $k^{-1}Hk$ we mean the set of all elements $k^{-1}hk$, where h is an arbitrary element of H.) K is known as the *normalizer* of H in G.

6. Prove that any subgroup of a cyclic group is cyclic.

7. Determine the subgroup of the symmetric group S_4 which leaves **(a)** one symbol invariant; **(b)** a set of two symbols invariant.

8. Show that the elements of finite order in any commutative group form a subgroup.

9. Determine the center of the group of symmetries of the square. (See **Problem 4**.)

10. Determine all subgroups of S_4.

11. Prove that a nonempty subset H of a group G is a subgroup of G if and only if $Hh = H$ (or $hH = H$), for every element $h \in H$. (By Hh we mean the set of all products xh, with $x \in H$.)

12. Prove that if a and b are elements of a finite group, ab and ba have the same order.

4.6 *IMPORTANT RESULTS ON PERMUTATION GROUPS*

In **Example 1** of §4.3, we discussed the notion of a group of permutations on n symbols, and designated the group of all such permutations as the *symmetric group* S_n *of degree* n. While the basic set in that example was the set of the first n natural numbers, it should be emphasized that this was merely a convenient choice; for a permutation can be performed on the elements of *any* set. To introduce a point of history, group theory dealt at first only with groups of permutations, and abstract groups were introduced at a later date for a more complete understanding of permutations groups. The importance of permutation groups in the general theory, however, stems at least in part from the following theorem, due to Cayley.

Theorem 4.61 (Cayley). Every finite group of order n is isomorphic to a permutation group, a subgroup of the symmetric group of degree n.

Proof. Let G be a group of n elements which we may list as $a_1, a_2, a_3, \cdots, a_n$. If b is an arbitrary element of G, the products $a_i b$ ($i = 1, 2, 3, \cdots, n$) are all distinct (Why?), and so we can associate with b the mapping or permutation π_b such that $a_i \pi_b = a_i b$. This permutation is often referred to as the *right multiplication* of G by b and, in our earlier notation for permutations, can be designated by $\begin{pmatrix} a_1 & a_2 & a_3 & \cdots & a_n \\ a_1 b & a_2 b & a_3 b & \cdots & a_n b \end{pmatrix}$. Now let π_c be the permutation associated with $c \in G$, so that $a_i \pi_c = a_i c$, $i = 1, 2, 3, \cdots, n$. Then π_{bc} is the permutation associated with bc, and $a_i \pi_{bc} = a_i(bc) = (a_i b)c = (a_i \pi_b)\pi_c = a_i(\pi_b \pi_c)$, so that $\pi_{bc} = \pi_b \pi_c$. It follows that the mapping $b \rightarrow \pi_b$ is a homomorphism of G into the symmetric group S_n, and an application of **Theorem 4.45** allows us to assert that this homomorphic image is a subgroup of S_n. Moreover, two distinct elements of G give rise to distinct permutations in S_n: for if $a\pi_b = a\pi_{b'}$, for any $a \in G$, we have $ab = ab'$ and the Cancellation Law requires that $b = b'$. Hence the elements of the homomorphic image in S_n are in a one-to-one correspondence with the elements of G, and so the homomorphism is in fact an isomorphism. We have shown that G is isomorphic to a subgroup of S_n, as asserted in the theorem.

The isomorphism $b \rightarrow \pi_b$ is sometimes known as the *right regular realization* of G as a permutation group. By means of left multiplication it is possible, in a similar manner, to obtain a *left regular realization* of a finite group as a group of permutations. However, in this case, the mapping is not an isomorphism, but what is known as an "anti-isomorphism," a notion which we prefer not to discuss. Since a finite group—such as S_n—has only a finite number of subgroups, it follows from the Cayley theorem that there exists only a finite number of nonisomorphic groups of any given order.

Let us now consider some of the simple properties of permutations on a set of n symbols, which for *convenience* we shall designate as the natural numbers $\{1, 2, 3, \cdots, n\}$. It should be understood, however, that no special properties of the natural numbers are to be used in this discussion, for they are merely serving as convenient symbols. If $k\pi \neq k$, for a permutation π, the symbol k is said to be "moved" by π; otherwise k is left "invariant" by π. A permutation π, which permutes the elements of a subset $\{a_1, a_2, a_3, \cdots, a_r\}$ of the basic set such that $a_i\pi = a_{i+1}$ $(i = 1, 2, 3, \cdots, r-1)$, $a_r\pi = a_1$, and leaves invariant all other elements of $\{1, 2, 3, \cdots, n\}$, is known as a *cycle* of *length r*, and we write $\pi = (a_1a_2a_3\cdots a_r)$. Two cycles are *disjoint* if they move disjoint sets of elements, and it is clear that disjoint permutations commute with one another. A more convenient but equivalent **(Problem 5)** definition of a cycle is now given.

> **Definition.**   A permutation π is called *cyclic* or *a cycle* if, for any two symbols moved by π, each is carried into the other by some power of π.

A cycle of length 2 is a *transposition*. For example, the transposition $(5, 6)$ interchanges 5 and 6 but leaves all other elements of the set $\{1, 2, 3, \cdots, n\}$ invariant. Every cycle of length r can be written as a product of $r-1$ transpositions, for $(a_1a_2a_3\cdots a_r) = (a_1a_2)(a_1a_3)\cdots (a_1a_r)$, an equality which can be verified by actually comparing the images under each of these mappings of each element of the set $\{1, 2, 3, \cdots, n\}$. However, we have the following general result for any permutation.

Theorem 4.62   Every permutation π can be written as a product of disjoint cycles which is unique apart from the order of the factors.

Proof. Let a and b be arbitrary elements of the set $\{1, 2, 3, \cdots, n\}$. Then we define an equivalence relation in this set so that $a \sim b$ provided a is carried into b by some power of π. Since both positive and negative powers of π are defined, it can be easily checked that this relation is in fact an equivalence relation. The set $\{1, 2, 3, \cdots, n\}$ then splits up into disjoint classes, according to a familiar property of any equivalence relation. Each class consists of elements which can be carried into each other by some power of π, and so π is a cycle on the elements of each class. Since every element of $\{1, 2, 3, \cdots, n\}$ is in some one of these classes, and cycles on disjoint sets of elements have no connection with each other, it follows that the permutation π is a product—in any order—of the disjoint cycles associated with the equivalence classes.

It is easy on inspection to write a given permutation as a product of disjoint cycles. For example, consider the permutation

$$\pi = \begin{pmatrix} 1 & 2 & 3 & 4 & 5 & 6 & 7 \\ 4 & 3 & 2 & 5 & 1 & 7 & 6 \end{pmatrix}.$$

We notice that this permutation maps 1 onto 4, 4 onto 5, and 5 onto 1, thereby completing one of its component cycles. The effect of π on the elements $\{1, 4, 5\}$ is then the same as (145). In like manner we see that π on $\{2, 3\}$ is identical with (23), while on $\{6, 7\}$ it is the same as (67). It follows that $\pi = (145)(23)(67)$.

Problems 4–6

1. Express each of the following permutations as a product of disjoint cycles:

   (a) $\begin{pmatrix} 1 & 2 & 3 & 4 & 5 & 6 & 7 & 8 \\ 3 & 6 & 4 & 1 & 8 & 2 & 5 & 7 \end{pmatrix}$; (b) $\begin{pmatrix} 1 & 2 & 3 & 4 & 5 & 6 & 7 \\ 4 & 5 & 6 & 7 & 2 & 3 & 1 \end{pmatrix}$;

   (c) $(2345)\,(346)$; (d) $(1437)\,(2537)\,(1567)$.

2. Express each of the following cycles as a product of transpositions: (a) (134675); (b) (24631); (c) (364289).

3. Express each of the cycles in **Problem 2** as a product of transpositions with two additional factors.

4. If α, β, and γ are, respectively, the permutations given in (a), (b), and (c) of **Problem 1**, determine in simplest form the permutation (a) $\alpha\beta$; (b) $\alpha^2\beta$; (c) $\beta\gamma$.

*5. Prove that the formal definition which we gave for a cycle is equivalent to the earlier, more intuitive one.

6. Obtain the right regular realization of S_3 as a permutation group.

7. Use a Cayley square to write out the complete multiplication table of S_3.

**8. Determine the right regular realization of the additive group of integers modulo 4.

*9. Prove that any two permutations which move disjoint sets of symbols are commutative.

10. Prove that the order of any permutation is the least common multiple of the orders of its disjoint cycles.

11. Prove that the permutations of $\{1, 2, 3, 4\}$, which leave invariant the polynomial $x_1x_2 + x_3 + x_4$ is a subgroup of order 4 of S_4. Write down the multiplication table for this so-called *group of the polynomial*.

4.7 THE UNIQUENESS THEOREM

Since every permutation can be written as a product of disjoint cycles, and every cycle can be written as a product of transpositions, it follows that every permutation can be written as a product of transpositions. In fact, we have noted before that any cycle of length r can be written as a product of $r-1$ transpositions. Hence, if we can express a permutation on n symbols as a product of k disjoint cycles (including possibly some cycles of length 1), it is quite easy to see that we can write the permutation as a product of $n-k$ transpositions. To illustrate this argument, let us suppose that we have already written some permutation as $(123)(4)(567)(89)$. But $(123) = (12)(13)$ and $(567) = (56)(57)$, so that we can express the permutation in the form $(12)(13)(56)(57)(89)$. In this case $n = 9$, and $k = 4$, so that $n-k = 5$ and we note that there are 5 transpositions in our representation of the given permutation. The number of transpositions in the various representations of a permutation is, of course, not unique; for example, we could include $(25)(25)$ as a pair of additional factors which would not affect the permutation given in the illustration. However, while the number of these transpositions is not unique, it is always even or always odd. This is essentially the assertion of the following theorem, due to Cauchy (1789–1857).

Theorem 4.71 (Cauchy). If a permutation π on n symbols can be factored into k disjoint cycles, the number of transpositions in *any* representation of π as a product of transpositions is either always even or always odd, accordingly as $n-k$ is even or odd.

Proof. Since each cycle of length r can be written as a product of $r-1$ transpositions, it is possible to express π as a product of $n-k$ transpositions, as was shown above. We recall that, in obtaining $n-k$, we are allowing that some of the k cycles may have length 1, and so will contribute nothing to the set of transpositions. The number $n-k$ is an "invariant" of the permutation, since it depends only on the numbers n and k and not on any particular representation of the permutation, and it will be convenient to designate this number as $N(\pi)$. We shall show that if $N(\pi)$ is even (odd), then *any* factorization of π as a product of transpositions contains an even (odd) number of factors. The validity of the two following formulas can be readily checked for any permutation π_1.

1. If $\pi_1 = (ba_1 \cdots a_2 c a_3 \cdots a_4)$, then $\pi_1(bc) = (ba_1 \cdots a_2)(ca_3 \cdots a_4)$.
2. If $\pi_1 = (ba_1 \cdots a_2)(ca_3 \cdots a_4)$, then $\pi_1(bc) = (ba_1 \cdots a_2 c a_3 \cdots a_4)$.

In the case of **1**, the elements b and c lie in the same cycle of π_1, and multiplying π_1 by (bc) increases the number of cycles in the permutation by 1. In the case of **2**, the elements b and c lie in different cycles of π_1, and multiplying π_1 by (bc) decreases the number of cycles in the permutation by 1. Since k is the number of cycles in the original representation of π as a product of disjoint cycles, it follows that $N(\pi)$ is decreased or increased by 1 on the multiplication of π by a transposition, according as the elements of the transposition lie in the same or in different cycles of π. Now suppose that π is written as a product of m transpositions, say $\pi = (ab)(cd) \cdots (pq)$. Since any transposition is its own inverse, this implies that $\pi(pq) \cdots (cd)(ab) = 1$, where 1 is the identity permutation. Since $N(1) = 0$, we must have $0 = N(\pi) \pm 1 \pm 1 \cdots \pm 1$, where there are m terms of ± 1. It follows that m must be even or odd, according as $N(\pi)$ is even or odd, as asserted in the theorem.

A permutation π is called *even* or *odd* according as any factoriza-

tion of π as a product of transpositions contains an even or an odd
number of factors. This definition implies that the inverse of an
even permutation is even, and that the product of two even permutations is even. It is then an immediate consequence of **Theorem
4.51** that the set of all even permutations on n symbols is a subgroup
of the symmetric group S_n. This subgroup is known as the *alternating
group on n symbols*, and will be designated here as A_n.

Problems 4–7

*1. Give the complete proof that the set of even permutations on n
symbols forms a subgroup of S_n. Consider the set of odd permutations in a similar manner.

**2. Prove that the alternating group A_n has $n!/2$ elements.

3. Show that the mapping, that associates every even permutation of
S_n with 1 and every odd permutation of S_n with -1, is a homomorphism of S_n onto the group of **Example 4** in §4.2.

4. List the even permutations on 4 symbols.

5. Prove that a cycle of length r is even or odd according as r is odd
or even.

4.8 COSETS AND LAGRANGE'S THEOREM

We shall see in this section that any subgroup of a group gives
rise to a partition of the group into disjoint subsets known as
"cosets." If G is the group and H is the arbitrary subgroup, we shall
accomplish this by defining an equivalence relation in G as follows:
$a \sim b$, for $a, b \in G$, provided $a^{-1}b \in H$. It is a routine matter to
verify that this is an equivalence relation, but we include the details.
Since $a^{-1}a = 1 \in H$, the relation is reflexive; if $a^{-1}b \in H$, it follows
that $(a^{-1}b)^{-1} = b^{-1}a \in H$, and so the relation is symmetric; and
since $a^{-1}b \in H$ and $b^{-1}c \in H$ imply that $(a^{-1}b)(b^{-1}c) = a^{-1}c \in H$,
the relation is transitive. Hence the relation is an equivalence relation, and so it induces a partition of G into disjoint subsets (see
§1.4). We have seen earlier (in the proof of the result just referred
to) that a class of equivalent elements can be identified with the
class of elements that are equivalent to *any one* of its members. It
follows, in the present case, that if a is a member of an equivalence
class, the class consists of all elements b of the form $b = ah$, with h
an arbitrary element of H. If we consider aH to be the set of all

elements of the form ah, with $h \in H$, we have shown that each class of the partition has this form, for some $a \in G$. A set aH is known as a *left coset* of H in the group G. We note further that each left coset of H has the same number of elements as H. For, if $ah_1 = ah_2$, with h_1, $h_2 \in H$, the Cancellation Law for groups would require that $h_1 = h_2$. Hence there is a one-to-one correspondence between the elements of H and the elements of any left coset of H. This leads us to the following important theorem due to Lagrange (1736–1813).

Theorem 4.81 (Lagrange). The order of each subgroup of a finite group G is a divisor of the order of G.

Proof. Let m be the order of a subgroup H of a group G of order n. We have seen that G can be partitioned into disjoint left cosets of H, each of which has m elements. Since every element of G is in some coset, if there are r left cosets in the decomposition we must have $n = mr$. Hence $m \mid n$, as asserted.

It is clear that, if we define the equivalence relation to require that $ab^{-1} \in H$ instead of $a^{-1}b \in H$, we would encounter the notion of *right cosets* of the form Hb. This time we would obtain a partition of G into disjoint right cosets and, if s is the number of these cosets, the equation $n = ms$ would arise. It follows that $s = r$, and so the number of right cosets of a given subgroup is equal to the number of its left cosets, in any coset decomposition of a group. This common number is called the *index* of the subgroup in the group, according to the following definition.

Definition. The *index* of a subgroup H in a group G is the number of cosets in either (left or right) coset decomposition of G with respect to H.

While $H = 1H = H1$ is clearly a coset in either the left or right coset decomposition of G with respect to H, the other cosets in the two decompositions are usually distinct. Any element ah of the left coset aH has its inverse $(ah)^{-1} = h^{-1}a^{-1}$ in the right coset Ha^{-1}. It follows that the left and right cosets of H can be put in a one-to-one correspondence, in such a way that the elements of the cosets in one decomposition are the inverses of the elements of the corresponding coset in the other. In the case of abelian groups, of course, it is unnecessary to distinguish between left and right cosets. Let us now consider a few illustrations of coset decompositions.

1. If G is the additive group of integers, and H is the subgroup of integers divisible by 4, two integers a and b are in the same coset if $a - b$ is divisible by 4. There are then four cosets in the decomposition of G with respect to H: the coset H, and the three sets of integers which have the remainders 1, 2, 3, respectively, on division by 4. Since G is commutative, we do not distinguish between left and right cosets here.

2. If we decompose the symmetric group S_n with respect to its alternating subgroup A_n, there are two cosets: the coset A_n of even permutations, and the coset of odd permutations. For if a and b are two permutations in S_n, it is clear that ab^{-1} is even when a and b are both even or both odd. In this case, there is only one left or right coset in addition to A_n, and so again the left and right decompositions are identical—even though the group S_n is not commutative.

3. As an example of two distinct coset decompositions, let us consider the decomposition of S_3 with respect to the cyclic subgroup $H = [(12)]$, generated by (12). In this case, two permutations a and b are in the same left coset provided $a^{-1}b \in H$. It can be shown that there are three cosets in this left decomposition: the coset H, consisting of 1 and (12); the coset $(13)H$, consisting of (13) and (132); the coset $(23)H$ consisting of (23) and (123). On the other hand, two permutations a and b are in the same right coset provided $ab^{-1} \in H$, and in this case we discover the following three right cosets: the coset H; the coset $H(13)$, consisting of (13) and (123); the coset $H(23)$, consisting of (23) and (132). We note that the two decompositions are different, in this case.

4. For a final example, let us consider the decomposition of G, the additive group of all complex numbers, with respect to the subgroup H of all real numbers. In this case, two complex numbers are in the same coset provided their difference is real, i.e., their "pure imaginary" components are equal. If we think of the complex numbers as corresponding to the points of a plane, with the real numbers along the x-axis, the cosets are then the points

comprising the lines parallel to the x (or real) axis. We close this section with two elementary consequences of the theorem of Lagrange.

Theorem 4.82   Every group of prime order is cyclic.

Proof.   For each element a of a group generates a subgroup $[a]$ whose order must divide the order of the group. Since the order of the group is prime, *each* of its elements different from the identity must generate the whole group, and so the group is cyclic.

Theorem 4.83   If G is a finite group of order n, then $a^n = 1$ for each $a \in G$.

Proof.   For each element $a \in G$ generates a cyclic subgroup $[a]$ of some finite order m. Then $a^m = 1$, and $n = mr$ for some integer r, by Lagrange's theorem. Hence $a^n = a^{mr} = (a^m)^r = 1$, as asserted.

Problems 4–8

*1. Prove that the only left (right) coset of a subgroup H in a group G, which is also a subgroup of G, is H itself.

2. Let H be a subgroup of a finite group G. Then prove directly (i.e., without reference to the properties of an equivalence relation) that, if aH and bH have one element in common, they must be identical cosets.

3. Determine the coset decompositions of S_3 with respect to the subgroup $[(13)]$.

**4. Show that the permutations $\{(1), (123), (132)\}$ form a subgroup of S_3, and determine the coset decomposition of S_3 with respect to this subgroup.

5. Use Lagrange's theorem to prove the Fermat theorem: if a is an integer and p is a prime integer, then $a^p \equiv a \pmod{p}$. (Hint: The multiplicative group of nonzero integers modulo p has $p-1$ members.)

6. Use Lagrange's theorem to determine the multiplication table for the only noncyclic group of order 4. This group is known as the "four group." (Cf. **Problem 3** of **Problems 4-4.**)

7. Determine the coset decomposition of the group of symmetries of the square with respect to the subgroup $[I, D]$. (See **Example 8** of §4.2.)

8. Prove that any abelian group of order pq, p and q distinct prime integers, is necessarily cyclic.

4.9 NORMAL OR INVARIANT SUBGROUPS

Inasmuch as a subgroup of G induces a partition of G into cosets, it is natural to ask under what conditions such a partition is regular. For we recall the close connection between regular partitions and homomorphisms of a group. It will turn out that a partition induced by a subgroup is regular if and only if the subgroup is "normal" or "invariant," a notion explained in the following definition.

Definition. A subgroup H of a group G is *normal* (*invariant, self-conjugate*) in G if $aH = Ha$, for each $a \in G$.

In other words, a subgroup is normal if it permutes, *as a subset*, with each element of the group. However, it should be recognized that the actual elements of a normal subgroup do not necessarily commute with all elements of the group. It follows directly from the definition that if H is a normal subgroup of G, the left and right cosets of H in G are identical.

It is possible to arrive at the definition of a normal subgroup in a different way. Two elements a and b in G are said to be *conjugate in* G if there exists $g \in G$ such that $b = g^{-1}ag$ (or $a = g^{-1}bg$). It is not difficult to show **(Problem 3)** that the set of all conjugates of the elements of a subgroup H by a fixed $g \in G$ is also a subgroup of G. That is, $g^{-1}Hg$ is a subgroup of G. However, if H is normal in G, $Hg = gH$ for any $g \in G$, and so for this type of subgroup $g^{-1}Hg = H$. Hence if we designate $g^{-1}Hg$ as a *conjugate* subgroup of H, we see that a normal subgroup has the property that it is *equal to all of its conjugates* in G, or is *self-conjugate*.

In order to justify the use of the word "invariant" as a synonym for "normal," we first recall that any isomorphism of a system onto itself is known as an *automorphism*. It is evident that $a^{-1}Ga = G$, for any $a \in G$, so that the whole group G is self-conjugate. This means that there is a one-to-one correspondence between the elements of G and itself such that $g \in G$ corresponds to $a^{-1}ga \in G$. But then $g \to a^{-1}ga$ defines a mapping of G onto G, and it can be shown directly that this mapping is an automorphism of G **(Problem 6)**, a so-called *inner* automorphism. However, if H is a normal subgroup of G, we have just seen that $a^{-1}Ha = H$, for any $a \in G$, and so we can characterize a normal subgroup as one which is *invariant* under all inner automorphisms of G.

If A and B are subsets of a group G, we can define the product AB to be the set of all elements ab in G, where $a \in A$ and $b \in B$. This may be considered a generalization of the product aB of an element a and a subset B, a notion previously introduced. It is easy to verify that this multiplication of sets is associative, i.e., $(AB)C = A(BC)$, but in general not commutative. We emphasize, however, that if set multiplication *is* commutative so that $AB = BA$, this means that for any two elements $a \in A$ and $b \in B$, there exist elements $b', b'' \in B$ and $a', a'' \in A$, such that $ab = b'a'$ and $ba = a''b''$. We then say that the sets A and B *commute* or *are permutable*, but the *elements* of A need not permute individually with the elements of B. If A and B are subgroups of G, it is not necessarily the case that AB is a subgroup. However, to extend an earlier symbolism, the subgroup $[A, B]$ generated by A and B (i.e., the intersection of all subgroups containing A and B) is well defined. The following theorem, which we need at a later stage in the book, can now be established.

Theorem 4.91 If A and B are normal subgroups of a group G, the subgroup $[A, B]$, generated by A and B, coincides with the product AB.

Proof. Since $[A, B]$ contains all products ab, with $a \in A$ and $b \in B$, it is clear that $[A, B] \supseteq AB$. Conversely, let ab and $a'b'$ be any two elements of AB, where $a, a' \in A$ and $b, b' \in B$. Then $(ab)(a'b') = (aa')(a'^{-1}ba'b')$ and $(ab)^{-1} = b^{-1}a^{-1} = (b^{-1}ab)^{-1}b^{-1}$. But since A and B are normal in G, it follows that $a'^{-1}ba' \in B$ and $b^{-1}ab \in A$; and so AB is closed under the group operation, and contains the inverse of every element in AB. Hence AB is a subgroup of G, and $[A, B] \subseteq AB$. In view of the previous, reversed inequality, it follows that $[A, B] = AB$, as asserted in the theorem.

Problems 4–9

*1. If H is a nonempty subset of a finite group, prove that $HH = H$ only if H is a subgroup.

2. If a and b are elements of a finite group, show that ab and ba have the same order. (Hint: ab and ba are conjugates.)

*3. For a fixed element g and subgroup H of a group G, prove that the set $\{g^{-1}Hg\}$ comprises a subgroup of G.

4. Prove that the alternating group A_n is a normal subgroup of the symmetric group S_n.

**5. If G, H, and K are groups such that $G \supset H \supset K$, where K is normal in G, prove that K is also normal in H.

*6. If a is any fixed element of a group G, prove that the mapping $g \to a^{-1}ga$ is an automorphism of G, where $g \in G$.

7. If a and b are elements of a group G, the element $a^{-1}b^{-1}ab$ is called the *commutator* of a and b, since $ab = ba(a^{-1}b^{-1}ab)$. Prove that the subgroup generated by the commutators of all pairs of elements in G is normal in G. This normal subgroup is known as the *derived* group of G.

8. Prove that any subgroup of index 2 is normal in the group.

9. Prove that the center of a group is a normal subgroup. (See **Problem 4** of **Problems 4-5**.)

4.10 NORMAL SUBGROUPS AND HOMOMORPHISMS

We are now able to obtain the result, referred to at the beginning of the preceding section, which connects normal subgroups with regular partitions.

Theorem 4.101   The decomposition of a group G into cosets of a normal subgroup H is a regular partition of G. Conversely, if a regular partition of G is given, the class that contains the identity element is a normal subgroup H of G, and all other classes of the partition are cosets of H.

Proof.   Suppose two cosets of a normal subgroup H are given. If a and b are *arbitrary* elements of the respective cosets, these cosets can be designated as aH and bH. Then $(aH)(bH) = a(bH)H = abH$, and so the product of *any* two elements of the cosets is in the coset abH. This shows that the partition of G is regular. For the converse, let A be the class in a given regular partition which contains the identity element 1 of G. If a_1,

$a_2 \in A$, then a_1a_2 must be in the same class as $1 \cdot 1 = 1$ (by the definition of a regular partition), and so $a_1a_2 \in A$. For an arbitrary element $a \in A$, $aa^{-1} = 1$ must be in the same class as $1a^{-1} = a^{-1}$, and so $a^{-1} \in A$. Hence A is a subgroup of G. If b is an arbitrary element of G, and $a \in A$, then $b^{-1}ab$ must be in the same class as $b^{-1}1b = 1$. It follows that $b^{-1}ab \in A$, and so A is normal in G. Finally, let B be an arbitrary class of the given regular partition. If $a \in A$ and $b \in B$, the product ba must be in the same class as $b1 = b$, and so $bA \subseteq B$. If c is an arbitrary element of B, inasmuch as b and c lie in the same class, so do the products $b^{-1}c$ and $b^{-1}b = 1$. But then $b^{-1}c \in A$ and $c \in bA$, so that $B \subseteq bA$. In view of the reversed inequality obtained before, we have $B = bA$, and so every class of the partition is a coset, as asserted in the theorem.

As a result of this theorem, we see that there is a one-to-one correspondence between the regular partitions of a group and its normal subgroups. In each case, the normal subgroup appears as the class of the regular partition that contains the identity element of the group. Of course, it is a property of any regular partition that its members comprise a factor or quotient group. Hence the cosets of a normal subgroup H of a group G comprise a factor group, the multiplication table of which, we have seen before, is defined by: $(aH)(bH) = abH$, for $a, b \in G$. It is customary not to use the symbolism which we introduced in connection with partitions, but we designate the factor group induced by a normal subgroup H of G by G/H.

In order to connect the notion of a homomorphism with normal subgroups and factor groups, we need one further definition.

Definition.   The *kernel* of a homomorphism of a group G onto a group G' is the subset of G that is mapped onto the identity element of G'.

We have seen before that any homomorphism of G induces a regular partition (**Theorem 3.51**) and also maps the identity element onto the identity element of the image group G'. It follows from **Theorem 4.101** that the kernel of a homomorphism is a normal subgroup, since the kernel certainly contains the identity of G. On the other hand, any normal subgroup of G is the class that contains the identity element in some regular partition. But since this class is mapped onto the identity element of the image group G' by the induced natural homomorphism (see §3.5), we see that the given normal subgroup is the kernel of this homomorphism. This establishes the following important result.

Theorem 4.102   The normal subgroups, and only these, are the kernels of the homomorphisms of a group.

Problems 4–10

   *1. Make direct use of the definitions to prove that the kernel of any homomorphism of a group is a normal subgroup.

  **2. Prove that the subgroup $\{1, (12)\}$ is not normal in S_3.

   3. Let G be the multiplicative group of complex numbers with absolute value 1. Prove that the mapping $e^{i\theta} \to e^{ki\theta}$, where k is an integer, is a homomorphism of G and determine the kernel.

   4. Determine all the factor groups of the cyclic group of order 30.

   *5. Prove that the set of all automorphisms of a group is a group, and that the set of inner automorphisms is a normal subgroup of this group of all automorphisms.

4.11 A BRIEF SURVEY

In this final section we state a few results, omitting their proofs, and make several general comments on the present status of group theory.

Every group has at least two normal subgroups—the group itself, and the subgroup consisting of the identity element alone. If a group has no other normal subgroups, it is said to be *simple*. The other extreme from a simple group is one in which every subgroup is normal. Of course all abelian groups have this property, and so do certain other so-called *hamiltonian* groups. It can be shown that the alternating group A_n is simple for $n \geq 5$.

A normal subgroup H of a group G is said to be *maximal* in G if $G \supset H$, and there exists no normal subgroup K such that $G \supset K \supset H$. It can be shown that H is maximal in G if and only if the factor group G/H is simple.

A *subinvariant series* for a group G is a finite sequence of subgroups $G = G_0, G_1, G_2, \cdots, G_{r-1}, G_r = 1$, such that G_i is a normal subgroup of G_{i-1}, $i = 1, 2, 3, \cdots, r$. The factor groups $G/G_1, G_1/G_2, G_2/G_3, \cdots, G_{r-1}/G_r$ are known as the *factors* of the above series. If each G_i is maximal in G_{i-1}, the series is called a *composition* series. A group is said to be *solvable* if it possesses a composition series whose factors are all cyclic groups of prime order. Every group has at least one subinvariant series—whose members are the whole group and the subgroup consisting of only the identity element 1— but not every (infinite) group has a composition series. A solvable group belongs to a still more select class of groups. The following theorem, stated without proof, is one of the major theorems of elementary group theory.

Theorem 4.111 (Jordan-Hölder). The number of terms in any two composition series for a group is the same, and the factors of these composition series are isomorphic in some order.

One of the many beautiful applications of group theory is to the theory of equations. With every algebraic equation having real coefficients, there is associated a group of *automorphisms*—the so-called *galois group* of the equation. The mathematician Évariste Galois (1811–1832), before being vanquished in a duel over a love affair, was able to prove that an equation is solvable by radicals only if its galois group is solvable. The mathematics leading to this result is known as the *galois theory of equations*. It is possible to find equations of degree 5 or more whose galois groups are not solvable, and so we have the following important result: *polynomial equations of degree n are not solvable by radicals, in general, if $n > 5$.*

A group G is said to be a *direct product* of its subgroups H_i, and we write $G = \prod_i H_i$ if: (1) the elements of any one of the subgroups H_i are permutable with the elements of any other subgroup H_j, $j \neq i$; and (2) each element of G has a representation as a product of a finite number of elements from the subgroups H_i, this representation being unique except for the order of the factors. In case G is the direct product of n subgroups H_i, $i = 1, 2, 3, \cdots, n$, we write $G = H_1 \times H_2 \times H_3 \times \cdots \times H_n$. The structure theory of finite abelian groups is essentially completed with the following result, which we state without proof: *any finite abelian group can be represented as a direct product of cyclic subgroups.* The theory of infinite abelian groups is somewhat less complete, and a recent booklet by Kaplansky (see References) has been devoted entirely to this subject.

As for the theory of groups in general, the situation is much different from that for finite abelian groups. There are many problems which can be stated very simply, but which remain unsolved at the present time. For example, the following *Burnside* problem remains open, although considerable work has been done on it: *Is every finitely generated periodic group finite?* Another unanswered query is the following: *Do there exist infinite non-commutative groups whose proper subgroups are all finite?* We have only "scratched the surface" of group theory in the present chapter, but the interested student is invited to consult one of the many fine references which we list on this topic for his further study.

Suggested Assignment: Read the article by Emil Artin on "Theory of Braids" in the *American Scientist*, Vol. 38, p. 112, and write a brief condensation of it.

REFERENCES

BIRKHOFF, G., and MacLANE, S.: *A Survey of Modern Algebra*, Revised Edition, Chap. 6 (New York, Macmillan, 1953).

HALL, M.: *The Theory of Groups* (New York, Macmillan, 1959).

KAPLANSKY, I.: *Infinite Abelian Groups* (Ann Arbor, University of Michigan Press, 1954).

JACOBSON, N.: *Lectures in Abstract Algebra*, Vol. 1 (New York, Van Nostrand, 1951).

KUROSH, A.: *Theory of Groups*, Vols. 1, 2 (New York, Chelsea, 1955).

LEDERMANN, W.: *The Theory of Finite Groups* (New York, Interscience Publishers, 1953).

ZASSENHAUS, H.: *The Theory of Groups*, 2nd ed. (New York, Chelsea, 1956).

chapter 5

RINGS

5.1 DEFINITION AND EXAMPLES

In this chapter we study an important type of algebraic system with two binary compositions, which is known as a *ring*. Some of the examples which we have used previously in illustrations of simpler systems have actually been rings, but at that time we were interested in only one of their binary compositions. The foremost example of this usage is the system of integers, with the two operations of ordinary addition and multiplication. A consideration of some of the properties of this system, and of others like it, leads us to the following definition.

Definition. A *ring* A is an algebraic system, consisting of at least two elements and with two binary compositions known as addition and multiplication, such that:

1. A is an additive abelian group;
2. A is a multiplicative semi-group;
3. the following distributive laws hold for arbitrary elements $a, b, c \in A$: $a(b + c) = ab + ac$; $(b + c)a = ba + ca$.

We note in passing that our definition has excluded what some authors call the "zero ring," consisting of the zero element alone, but there are good reasons for omitting this trivial system from consideration as a ring. Our definition implies the existence in any ring A of the additive identity element 0, and an additive inverse $-a$ for each element $a \in A$. If a subset of A is closed under both compositions of A, and also satisfies conditions 1, 2, 3 as a subsystem, this subsystem is called a *subring* of A. This means that we are allowing the system consisting of 0 alone to be a subring of any ring, even though we have decided against it being classified as a ring.

We recall that $a - b$ is an equivalent notation for $a + (-b)$, and we have the following simple but important extension of **Theorem 4.51**.

Theorem 5.11 A subset B of a ring is a subring of A if and only if $a - b$ and ab are in B, for arbitrary elements a, b in B.

Proof. Since a subset of the additive group of a ring is a subgroup provided $a - b$ is in the subset, for arbitrary elements a, b in the subset, it follows that B is an additive subgroup of A. We are postulating that B is closed under the multiplicative operation in A, and since associativity of multiplication and the validity of the distributive laws are inherited from A, it follows from our definition that B is a subring.

Let us now develop some familiarity with the ring concept through the medium of a few examples.

1. We have previously referred to the most familiar example, that of the ring I of ordinary integers under addition and multiplication. The rational, real, and complex numbers, with the usual operations, are other familiar rings. Moreover, in this chapter, we shall often refer to these number systems as rings without further verification.

2. The set $I[\sqrt{2}]$ of real numbers of the form $a + b\sqrt{2}$, with a and b ordinary integers, is a ring with the usual operations of real numbers. Actually this system is a subring of R^*, as can be verified with the help of **Theorem 5.11.** For $(a + b\sqrt{2}) - (c + d\sqrt{2})$ $= (a - c) + (b - d)\sqrt{2}$ and $(a + b\sqrt{2})(c + d\sqrt{2}) = (ac + 2bd)$ $+ (bc + ad)\sqrt{2}$, for arbitrary integers a, b, c, d, and so the system is closed under subtraction and multiplication. The method used to show that the system in this example is a ring is an important one, and so we emphasize the point: in order to show that a subsystem of a ring is a ring or subring, all the postulates need not be checked. A simple application of **Theorem 5.11** is all that is sufficient. On the other hand, if the subsystem is *not* imbedded in what is known to be a ring, it will be necessary to check the complete set of postulates.

3. The set of all real-valued, continuous functions on R^* is a ring if we define addition as in **Problem 7** of **Problems 4-4,** and multiplication for arbitrary functions f and g of the set by $x(fg) = (xf)(xg)$. In this example we are continuing our practice of designating the value of a function f at a point x of its domain by xf rather than by $f(x)$. The 0 of this ring is the function whose value at each real number is 0, while $-f$ is the function defined so that $x(-f) = -(xf)$. While in a complete and detailed discussion it would be necessary to check all the postulates to verify that this system is a ring, this verification should cause no difficulty.

4. The set of ordinary integers forms a ring under the operations of ordinary addition and ordinary multiplication followed by reduction modulo m, for any positive integer m. As we saw in **Example 2** of **§4.3,** this algebraic system is merely the familiar system of integers with a different definition of equality. The verification that this is a ring is almost immediate.

5. If A is an arbitrary ring, we can define the ring A_n of all $n \times n$ (read "n by n") matrices with elements in A. The matrices or elements of A_n are the arrays $[a_{ij}]$ of the form:

$$[a_{ij}] = \begin{bmatrix} a_{11} & a_{12} & \cdots & a_{1n} \\ a_{21} & a_{22} & \cdots & a_{2n} \\ & \cdots\cdots\cdots & \\ a_{n1} & a_{n2} & \cdots & a_{nn} \end{bmatrix},$$

each of which consists of n (horizontal) *rows* and n (vertical) *columns* of elements a_{ij} from the ring A. The *order* of such a matrix is n. In this notation, a_{ij} is the element in the matrix $[a_{ij}]$ that lies at the intersection of the ith row and jth column. For example, a_{11} is at the intersection of the first row and first column, while a_{21} is at the intersection of the second row and first column, etc.

Two matrices in A_n are *equal* if corresponding elements in the matrices are equal elements of A. That is, $[a_{ij}] = [b_{ij}]$ if $a_{ij} = b_{ij}$, for all i and j from 1 to n. This is our customary usage of equality in the sense of identity.

We define the *addition* or *sum* of two matrices to be the matrix obtained by adding corresponding elements in the component matrices. This means that $[a_{ij}] + [b_{ij}] = [c_{ij}]$, where $c_{ij} = a_{ij} + b_{ij}$, for $i, j = 1, 2, 3, \cdots, n$. It is then easy to see that A_n is an abelian group under addition. Since we have defined addition for any two $n \times n$ matrices, the set A_n is closed under this operation; moreover, associativity of addition in A is carried over to A_n by the rule of composition. The additive identity, or zero matrix, is the matrix all of whose entries are 0; while the additive inverse of any matrix $[a_{ij}]$ is clearly the matrix whose entries are the respective negatives of the entries in $[a_{ij}]$. There is, of course, a different zero matrix associated with each n, but it is convenient to designate them all by 0 or, in case of confusion, by 0_n. We illustrate this symbolism in the 2×2 case below.

If $[a_{ij}] = \begin{bmatrix} a_{11} & a_{12} \\ a_{21} & a_{22} \end{bmatrix}$ and $[b_{ij}] = \begin{bmatrix} b_{11} & b_{12} \\ b_{21} & b_{22} \end{bmatrix}$, we have $[a_{ij}] +$

$[b_{ij}] = \begin{bmatrix} a_{11} + b_{11} & a_{12} + b_{12} \\ a_{21} + b_{21} & a_{22} + b_{22} \end{bmatrix}$, $-[a_{ij}] = \begin{bmatrix} -a_{11} & -a_{12} \\ -a_{21} & -a_{22} \end{bmatrix}$, and $0 =$

$0_2 = \begin{bmatrix} 0 & 0 \\ 0 & 0 \end{bmatrix}$.

The product $[p_{ij}]$ of two $n \times n$ matrices $[a_{ij}]$ and $[b_{ij}]$ is defined so that $p_{ij} = a_{i1}b_{1j} + a_{i2}b_{2j} + \cdots + a_{in}b_{nj}$ is the element in the $[i, j]$-position. This is sometimes referred to as the "row by column" rule of matrix multiplication, since the elements of the rows of $[a_{ij}]$ are multiplied, respectively, by the corresponding elements of the columns of $[b_{ij}]$, and these products are then added to obtain the elements of the matrix product $[a_{ij}][b_{ij}]$. For example, in the ring I_3 of 3×3 matrices with elements in the ring I of integers, the following matrix product is obtained by applying this rule:

$$\begin{bmatrix} 1 & 3 & -1 \\ 2 & 1 & 0 \\ 3 & -1 & 2 \end{bmatrix} \begin{bmatrix} 2 & 0 & 1 \\ 3 & -2 & 0 \\ 1 & 1 & 1 \end{bmatrix} = \begin{bmatrix} 10 & -7 & 0 \\ 7 & -2 & 2 \\ 5 & 4 & 5 \end{bmatrix}.$$

It is easy to see that multiplication is associative, for consider the product $[a_{ik}]([b_{kl}][c_{lj}])$ of matrices $[a_{ik}]$, $[b_{kl}]$, and $[c_{lj}]$, where it has been convenient to change the indexing symbols in the manner indicated. The rule for multiplication shows that the element of the product in the $[i, j]$-position is $\sum_{k,\,l=1}^{n} a_{ik}(b_{kl}c_{lj})$. The corresponding element of the product $([a_{ik}][b_{kl}])[c_{lj}]$ is $\sum_{k,\,l=1}^{n} (a_{ik}b_{kl})c_{lj}$, and because multiplication is associative in A, these two elements are the same. Hence $[a_{ik}]([b_{kl}][c_{lj}]) = ([a_{ik}][b_{kl}])[c_{lj}]$, so that the associative law holds for multiplication in A_n. (If the student finds the notation for the above summations a little condensed, he should let $n = 3$, say, and actually write out several such sums in detail. **Problem 1.**) The distributive laws in A_n can be verified in a similar manner. For, if we consider the matrices $[a_{ik}]([b_{kj}] + [c_{kj}])$ and $[a_{ik}][b_{kj}] + [a_{ik}][c_{kj}]$, it can be seen that the element in the $[i, j]$-position for the first matrix is $\sum_{k=1}^{n} a_{ik}(b_{kj} + c_{kj})$, while for the second matrix it is $\sum_{k=1}^{n} a_{ik}b_{kj} + \sum_{k=1}^{n} a_{ik}c_{kj}$. Since the distributive laws hold in A, these two elements are equal, and so $[a_{ik}]([b_{kj}] + [c_{kj}]) = [a_{ik}][b_{kj}] + [a_{ik}][c_{kj}]$, thus showing that this distributive law also holds in A_n. In a similar manner, it can be shown that $([b_{ik}] + [c_{ik}])[a_{kj}] = [b_{ik}] [a_{kj}] + [c_{ik}][a_{kj}]$, so that the other distributive law also remains in effect in A_n.

We have shown that A_n is an abelian group under addition and a semi-group under multiplication, with both distributive laws valid, so that A_n is a ring. Even if A is commutative, the ring A_n will not be commutative, however, except when $n = 1$. It is easy to check the "probable" truth of this remark with a random pair of matrices from I_3, for instance.

Problems 5–1

1. Write out each of the following sums completely:

   (a) $\displaystyle\sum_{k,l=1}^{3} (a_{ik}b_{kl})c_{lj}$; (b) $\displaystyle\sum_{k,l=1}^{3} a_{ik}(b_{kl}c_{lj})$.

2. List the nine individual postulates for a ring.
3. Verify that the system in **Example 3** is a ring.
4. Make addition and multiplication tables for the ring in **Example 4**, with $m = 4$.
5. Verify that the system containing two elements 0, 1, and having the following addition and multiplication tables, is a ring.

+	0	1
0	0	1
1	1	0

·	0	1
0	0	0
1	0	1

6. If we define multiplication in **Example 3** by $x(fg) = (xg)f$, is the resulting system a ring? (In the more customary notation for functions, this means that $(fg)(x) = f[g(x)]$.)

7. If $a = \begin{bmatrix} 2 & 3 & 0 \\ 1 & 1 & 3 \\ -2 & 2 & -1 \end{bmatrix}$ and $b = \begin{bmatrix} -2 & 3 & 1 \\ 4 & 0 & 6 \\ 1 & 1 & 5 \end{bmatrix}$,

determine both ab and ba.

8. If $c = \begin{bmatrix} 1 & 1 & 1 \\ -2 & 3 & 0 \\ 3 & 5 & 6 \end{bmatrix}$, use the matrices in **Problem 7** to verify that

$a(b + c) = ab + ac$, and also that $(b + c)a = ba + ca$.

**9. A *Gaussian integer* is a complex number $a + bi$, where a and b are ordinary integers. Show that the set of all Gaussian integers forms a ring under ordinary addition and multiplication of complex numbers.

*10. An element a of a ring is said to be *idempotent* if $a^2 = a$. Prove that a ring must be commutative if each of its elements is idempotent. (Hint: Consider $(a + a)^2$ and then $(a + b)^2$.)

11. If A and B are rings, prove that $A \times B$ is a ring if we define addition and multiplication in the product set as follows:
$(a_1, b_1) + (a_2, b_2) = (a_1 + a_2, b_1 + b_2)$, $(a_1, b_1)(a_2, b_2) = (a_1 a_2, b_1 b_2)$.

5.2 SOME ELEMENTARY PROPERTIES OF RINGS

Several of the elementary properties of rings are consequences of the fact that a ring is a group under the operation of addition, and a semi-group under the operation of multiplication. We have already noted that every ring contains the element 0, and the additive inverses or "negatives" of elements of the ring. In addition, it is a consequence of the additive group properties that $-(a + b) = -a - b$, and $-(a - b) = -a + b$. Also, since integral multiples of a ring are defined as for a group element in Chapter 4, it has been established that $n(a + b) = na + nb$, $(n + m)a = na + ma$, and $(nm)a = n(ma)$, for arbitrary ring elements a, b and arbitrary integers m, n. The following theorem lists some further simple properties of ring elements, properties which are familiar in the ring of integers.

Theorem 5.21 The equations $a0 = 0a = 0$, $(-a)b = a(-b) = -ab$, and $(-a)(-b) = ab$ are valid for arbitrary elements a, b of a ring.

Proof. If a is a ring element, the distributive laws imply that $a(0 + 0) = a0 + a0$, and also that $0a = (0 + 0)a = 0a + 0a$. Hence, $0a = a0 = 0$ (see **Problem 7** of **Problems 4-1**). If b is an arbitrary ring element, $[a + (-a)]b = 0 = ab + (-a)b$, so that $(-a)b = -ab$. In like manner we can show that $a(-b) = -ab$. A combination of these results then gives $(-a)(-b) = -a(-b) = -(-ab) = ab$.

The notions of *homomorphism, isomorphism, endomorphism,* and *automorphism,* as applied to a ring, are merely the application of these familiar ideas to its underlying additive group and multiplicative semi-group. Thus we say that a mapping of a ring A into a ring A' is a *homomorphism* if both operations are preserved by the mapping. In our usual symbolism, we can indicate this as follows.

$$
\begin{array}{ccc}
A & & A' \\
\hline
a & \longrightarrow & a' \\
b & \longrightarrow & b' \\
a + b & \longrightarrow & a' + b' \\
ab & \longrightarrow & a'b'
\end{array}
$$

If A and A' are the same algebraic system, a homomorphism is known as an *endomorphism.* In case a homomorphic mapping is bijective, the mapping is an *isomorphism* and the rings A and A' are *isomorphic;* if A and A' are identical systems, any isomorphic mapping of A onto A' (or A) is an *automorphism* of A.

Theorem 5.22 If a ring B is isomorphic to a subring B' of a ring A', then B can be imbedded in a ring A which is isomorphic to A', provided $A' \cap B = \phi$.

Proof. For let S be the subset of those elements in A' which are not in B', and designate by A the set consisting of the set-theoretic union of B and S, i.e., $A = B \cup S$. In any equations $a' + b' = c'$ or $a'b' = c'$ in A', we replace the elements a', b', c' which are in B' by their correspondents in B, and leave the other elements of A' (i.e., the elements of S) unaltered. This defines the operations of addition and multiplication in A, and it is clear that A is isomorphic to A'.

Problems 5-2

*1. Use some previous results and show that a homomorphic image of a ring is a ring or consists of 0 alone.

2. If n is an integer and a is an element of a ring, why must na *not* be considered the ring product of n and a unless a is an integer?

**3. Show that $(a + b)(c + d) = ac + ad + bc + bd$, where a, b, c, d are arbitrary elements of a ring.

*4. If a, b, c are arbitrary elements of a ring, prove that $a(b - c) = ab - ac$.

*5. If a and b are arbitrary ring elements and n is an integer, prove that $n(ab) = (na)b = a(nb)$.

6. Prove that the postulate that the additive group of a ring is abelian can be replaced by the condition that there exists an element c in the system, such that $ca = cb$ implies that $a = b$ for arbitrary elements a, b of the ring. That is, show that the existence of an element that can be left-cancelled will imply that the additive group of the ring is abelian.

7. Make a complete multiplication table for the ring of integers modulo 5.

8. Let $A \times B$ be the ring described in **Problem 11** of **Problems 5-1**. Then prove that the mappings ϕ and ψ of this ring, defined by $(a, b)\phi = (a, 0)$ and $(a, b)\psi = (0, b)$, are homomorphisms.

9. If A is an arbitrary ring, prove that the mapping $\begin{pmatrix} a & c \\ d & b \end{pmatrix} \to a$ of A_2 onto A is not a ring homomorphism, but is a homomorphism of the underlying additive group of A_2.

10. Prove that the only endomorphism of the ring I of integers are the identity mapping and the mapping that sends each integer into 0. (Hint: Recall that $n = 1 + 1 + 1 + \cdots + 1$ (n summands), for any positive integer n.)

5.3 TYPES OF RINGS

We obtain rings of different types if we impose various conditions on the multiplicative semi-group of a ring. Thus a ring is *commutative* if its multiplicative semi-group is commutative. It is said to *have an identity* if its multiplicative semi-group has an identity element. Since every ring has an additive identity, this usage of the word "identity" will always refer to the multiplicative system. In the event of any possible confusion, however, the words "additive" or "multiplicative" should be included. The ring I of integers, as well as most of the rings previously mentioned, is a commutative ring with an identity. The set of even integers, with the usual operations, is a simple example of a ring without an identity element. The ring I_n

of all $n \times n$ square matrices with elements in I is an especially important example of a noncommutative ring, as we have already noted. This ring does have an identity element, however, and this

can be seen to be the matrix 1_n defined by $1_n = \begin{bmatrix} 1 & 0 & 0 & \cdots & 0 \\ 0 & 1 & 0 & \cdots & 0 \\ 0 & 0 & 1 & \cdots & 0 \\ \cdots\cdots\cdots\cdots \\ 0 & 0 & 0 & \cdots & 1 \end{bmatrix}$, a

matrix in which the diagonal element 1 occurs n times, while all other elements are 0. If there is no danger of confusion, it will often be convenient to use the familiar 1 instead of 1_n. We note in passing that if $1 = 0$, for any ring A, then $a = a1 = a0 = 0$, for an arbitrary element $a \in A$, and so A consists of only the element 0. Since we have excluded this "zero ring," it follows that $1 \neq 0$ for any ring that we shall consider.

An element $a \neq 0$ in a ring A is said to be a *divisor of zero* if there exists an element $b \neq 0$, such that either $ab = 0$ or $ba = 0$. A ring without any divisors of zero is called an *integral domain*. An integral domain can also be described as a ring whose nonzero elements form a multiplicative semi-group; for in such a ring, if $a \neq 0$ and $b \neq 0$, it will follow that $ab \neq 0$. It may be observed that the ring I of integers is an integral domain, and this system may be regarded as the model from which the general system derives its name. It should be noted, however, that I is a commutative ring with an identity, while our definition of an integral domain has not required these properties. On the other hand, if other books on this topic are consulted, it will be found that some authors do define an integral domain to be a commutative ring with an identity as well as having no divisors of zero. This is one algebraic system on whose definition there appears to be no unanimity of opinion.

The ring A_n of matrices is not an integral domain except when $n = 1$ and A has no divisors of zero. For example, in the ring I_2, we

have $\begin{bmatrix} 0 & 1 \\ 0 & 1 \end{bmatrix} \begin{bmatrix} 2 & 3 \\ 0 & 0 \end{bmatrix} = \begin{bmatrix} 0 & 0 \\ 0 & 0 \end{bmatrix}$, so that the product of two nonzero matrices can be the zero matrix. As another example of a ring which is not an integral domain, consider the ring of real-valued functions described in **Example 3** of §5.1. For consider the functions f and g defined on R^* as follows:

$$xf \text{ [or } f(x)] = 0, \text{ for } x \leq \tfrac{1}{4},$$
$$= x^2 - \tfrac{1}{16}, \text{ for } \tfrac{1}{4} < x;$$

$$xg \text{ [or } g(x)] = -x^2 + \tfrac{1}{16}, \text{ for } x \leq \tfrac{1}{4},$$
$$= 0, \text{ for } \tfrac{1}{4} < x.$$

Then $f \neq 0$ (the constant function 0) and $g \neq 0$, but $fg = 0$.

Theorem 5.31 A ring A is an integral domain if and only if the following cancellation law holds: each of $ab = ac$ and $ba = ca$ implies that $b = c$, if $a \neq 0$, for otherwise arbitrary elements a, b, $c \in A$.

Proof. Let a, b, c be elements of an integral domain A, such that $ab = ac$, where $a \neq 0$. Then, $a(b - c) = 0$, and the defining property of an integral domain requires that $b - c = 0$ so that $b = c$, as desired. The "right" cancellation law is proved similarly. Conversely, if the "left" cancellation law holds and $ab = 0$, with $a \neq 0$, we have $ab = a0$ and so $b = 0$. Similarly, if the "right" cancellation law holds and $ba = 0$, where $a \neq 0$, it follows that $b = 0$. Hence the presence of either cancellation law in A requires the system to be an integral domain.

A ring is called a *division ring, skew field,* or *sfield* if its nonzero members comprise a subgroup of the multiplicative semi-group of the ring. Thus a division ring contains an identity element and also the multiplicative inverse a^{-1} of each element $a \neq 0$ of the ring. The rings of rational numbers, real numbers, and complex numbers are familiar examples of division rings. However, these important number rings are also commutative under multiplication, and as *commutative division rings* they are generally known as *fields*. It is somewhat more difficult to find an example of a division ring that is not also a field. They do exist, however, and we include a brief discussion of one in the following section.

1. Verify that the ring of integers modulo 3 is a field.

2. Discover a divisor of zero to verify that the ring of integers modulo 6 is not an integral domain, and so is also not a field.

3. Prove that if $e \neq 0$ is an idempotent element of an integral domain, then e is the identity of the system. (See **Problem 10 of Problems 5-1, and cf. **Problem 7 of Problems 4-1**.)

4. An element z of a ring is said to be *nilpotent* if $z^n = 0$, for some positive integer n. Prove that $z = 0$ is the only nilpotent element of an integral domain.

5. Let A be a ring with identity in which the operations are designated as usual in the additive and multiplicative symbolism. Then, if we define two new operations in the set A by $a \oplus b = a + b - 1$ and $a \odot b = a + b - ab$, show that the elements of A also comprise a ring with respect to these operations.

6. Prove that the ring $I[\sqrt{2}]$, discussed in **Example 2 of §5.1**, is an integral domain. Show that the system remains an integral domain if 2 is replaced by any integer m without square factors.

7. Prove that the set of all Gaussian integers forms a ring. Is this a division ring? (See **Problem 9 of Problems 5-1**.)

8. Prove that the ring of ordinary integers is a subring of the ring of Gaussian integers. (See **Problem 7**.)

9. Prove that an integral domain with a finite number of elements is a division ring. (Hint: Assume that an element $a \neq 0$ does not have a multiplicative inverse, and consider the set of products aa_i for all a_i in the integral domain.)

5.4 TWO IMPORTANT RINGS

In this section we are first going to present the example, promised in the preceding section, of a division ring which is not a field. In order to introduce this ring, let us use C to designate the set of complex numbers—which we shall consider here as a ring. The ring C_2 is then the ring of all 2×2 matrices of complex numbers, and we recall that the identity element of any such matrix ring is $\begin{bmatrix} 1 & 0 \\ 0 & 1 \end{bmatrix}$. It follows that the multiplicative inverse a^{-1} of any matrix $a \in C_2$, if it exists, must be such that $aa^{-1} = a^{-1}a = \begin{bmatrix} 1 & 0 \\ 0 & 1 \end{bmatrix}$.

If we consider the subset of C_2 of all matrices of the form

$$\begin{bmatrix} a + bi & c + di \\ -c + di & a - bi \end{bmatrix}$$, where a, b, c, d are arbitrary real numbers, it

can be verified directly that this subset is closed under both subtraction and multiplication. An application of **Theorem 5.11** then shows that this subset, which we may call Q, is a subring of C_2. It is clear, of course, that the zero matrix occurs as the member of Q in which $a = b = c = d = 0$, and only for these values is a matrix of Q equal to 0. Since $\Delta \equiv a^2 + b^2 + c^2 + d^2 = 0$ is a necessary and sufficient condition that $a = b = c = d = 0$, it follows that the condition $\Delta \neq 0$ is equivalent to asserting that the corresponding matrix in Q is not the zero matrix. It can be verified by direct multiplication that each matrix of Q, such that $\Delta \neq 0$, has an inverse in the form

$$\begin{bmatrix} \dfrac{a - bi}{\Delta} & -\dfrac{c + di}{\Delta} \\ \dfrac{c - di}{\Delta} & \dfrac{a + bi}{\Delta} \end{bmatrix}$$, and that the product of two nonzero ma-

trices of Q is a nonzero matrix of Q. Hence the nonzero members of Q form a multiplicative subgroup. Since we have shown previously that Q is a subring, the proof that Q is a division ring is complete. A simple product will verify the assertion that Q is not commutative, and so we have produced a division ring which is not a field. This ring is known as the *ring of Hamilton's quaternions*, named after the Irish mathematician W. R. Hamilton (1805–1865), and the elements of this ring are known as *quaternions*. It should be remarked that quaternions are frequently defined without any reference to matrices, but nevertheless comprise a system which is isomorphic to our ring of matrix quaternions.

The other important ring to be discussed briefly in this section is the so-called *ring of polynomials* with coefficients in a subring A. This ring can be introduced by considering A to be a subring of a ring B, and examining the subring of B generated by A and one additional element $u \in B$. This ring, usually designated $A[u]$, is the ring containing A and u which is "smallest" in the sense of set inclusion, a terminology which was introduced in our study of groups in Chapter 4. While the more general situation can be studied, in the interest of simplicity we shall assume the following in our brief study: **(1)** B has an identity element 1; **(2)** $1 \in A$; **(3)** $ua = au$, for every element $a \in A$. The properties of a ring imply that $A[u]$ certainly contains every element of B of the form $a_0 + a_1u + a_2u^2 + \cdots + a_nu^n$, for arbitrary elements $a_0, a_1, a_2, \cdots, a_n \in A$. An element such as this is called a *polynomial in u* with *coefficients* a_i in A. Inasmuch as these polynomials are elements of B, the addition and multiplication of polynomials of this kind is already prescribed by the rules for these operations in B. As a matter of fact, without going into details, we are able to state that the rules of operation for these polynomials turn out to be precisely the rules learned for polynomials in college algebra. The set of all polynomials in u with coefficients in A is a subset of B, and it is clear from the preceding remark that this subset is closed under both subtraction and multiplication. An application of **Theorem 5.11** then shows that this subset is a ring, and so $A[u]$ is merely this subset of polynomials in u with coefficients in A.

A general study of polynomial rings falls into two categories, according to the nature of the element u. If u is a solution of a polynomial equation with coefficients in A, so that $d_0 + d_1u + d_2u^2 + \cdots + d_mu^m = 0$ for certain elements $d_0, d_1, d_2, \cdots, d_m \in A$, the element u is said to be *algebraic* over A. If u is not algebraic, it is said to be *transcendental* over A. The *degree* of a polynomial in u, or of the polynomial equation resulting from equating the polynomial to 0, is the largest exponent of u in the polynomial whose coefficient is not 0. For example, the degree of u in $a + bu + cu^2$ or of $a + bu + cu^2 = 0$ is 2, provided $c \neq 0$. It is easy to see that, if u is algebraic and is a solution of an equation of degree m, any polynomial in $A[u]$ can be reduced to one of degree $m-1$ or less. On the other hand, if u is transcendental over A, polynomials of every finite degree will occur in $A[u]$, and no reduction in degree can take place.

The polynomials which are met in college algebra are, for the most part, elements of $I[x]$, where x is an element which is transcendental over the ring I. In this environment, we usually discard the "super" ring B and consider x to be merely a symbol. We now *define* the polynomials in x and the operations on these polynomials to be the same as if x were a transcendental element of B over A. Many of the characteristics of I are carried over to $I[x]$. For example, our method of multiplication in $I[x]$ shows that this ring can have no divisors of zero **(Problem 1)**, so that $I[x]$ is an integral domain. The ring $R[x]$ resembles I even more closely, for in this ring it is possible to derive a division algorithm similar to that of **Theorem 2.41.** By means of this algorithm any polynomial in $R[x]$ can be divided by any nonzero polynomial to produce a quotient, and a remainder whose degree is less than that of the divisor. For example, if $a = 2x^3 + x^2 - x + 1$ and $b = x^2 - 1$, there exist polynomials q and r such that $a = bq + r$, where the degree of r is less than 2. In fact, the "long division" process of college algebra exhibits $q = 2x + 1$ and $r = x + 2$ for this example. The proof of the *existence* of such a division algorithm is not difficult, but it parallels the proof of **Theorem 2.41.** A *monic* polynomial is one whose "leading" coefficient (i.e., the coefficient of the highest power of x) is 1. If we define the g.c.d. of two polynomials a and b to be the monic polynomial which divides both a and b and is divisible by all other common divisors of a and b, the result of **Theorem 2.42** can be extended to $R[x]$. Finally, in *either* $I[x]$ or $R[x]$ there is a valid extension of **Theorem 2.43,** which asserts that any polynomial can be expressed as a product of "prime" polynomials which is unique except for the order of the factors. In this connection a *prime* element of $I[x]$ (or $R[x]$) can be regarded as an element of I (or R) or a monic *irreducible* polynomial—i.e., one which cannot be expressed as a product of polynomials of lower degree. We now leave the discussion of polynomial rings, though we shall refer to them again.

Problems 5–4

   *1. If x is transcendental over I, prove that $I[x]$ has no divisors of zero.
   *2. Prove that the system of quaternions is closed under both the operations of addition and multiplication in C_2.
   *3. Verify that the inverse of a quaternion, as given in this section, does satisfy the requirements of a multiplicative inverse.
   4. The number $\triangle$, used in defining the multiplicative inverse of a quarternion, is called the *norm* of the quaternion. Prove that the norm of the product of two quaternions—in either order—is equal to the product of the individual norms.
   5. Refer to another book, if necessary, to establish the existence of a division algorithm in $R[x]$.

**6. If u is an algebraic element over I, and is a solution of the equation $3 - 2x + 4x^2 + x^3 = 0$, express the product $(2u^2 + 1)(3u^2 - 2u - 1)$ as a polynomial of degree 2. What is the product if u is transcendental over I?

7. Repeat **Problem 6** if u is a solution of $2 - 3x + x^2 - x^3 = 0$.

8. If u is a solution of the equation $3 - 5x + x^2 - 2x^3 - x^4 = 0$, express the product $(x^3 - x^2 + 1)(3x^2 + 1)$ as a polynomial of degree 3. What is this product if u is transcendental over I?

5.5 THE QUOTIENT FIELD OF A COMMUTATIVE INTEGRAL DOMAIN

The purpose of the present section is to establish the following important result.

Theorem 5.51   Any commutative integral domain can be imbedded isomorphically in a field.

Our most familiar example of a commutative integral domain is the system of ordinary integers, and the manner in which these integers are imbedded in the field of rational numbers, as discussed briefly in §2.5, serves as a guide for a similar imbedding of an arbitrary commutative integral domain. The field of rational numbers is "minimal" in the sense that any other field which contains the integers also contains the rational numbers. The field which we shall construct will also be minimal—up to an isomorphism—in the set of fields which contain the given integral domain.

We have defined a field as a commutative division ring, and so an algebraic system F is a field if it satisfies the following equivalent requirements:

1. F is an additive abelian group.
2. The nonzero elements of F comprise a multiplicative abelian group.
3. The left and right distributive laws hold.

Since **3** is automatically satisfied in any subsystem of F, it is an immediate consequence of these three conditions and **Theorem 4.51** that any subsystem K of F, with at least two elements, is a subfield if the following conditions are met:

1'. If $a, b \in K$, then $a - b \in K$.

2'. If $a, b(\neq 0) \in K$, then $ab^{-1} \in K$.

It is now easy to obtain the "field" version of **Theorem 4.52**.

Theorem 5.52 The intersection of any collection of subfields of a field is also a field.

Proof. If a and b are arbitrary elements of the intersection, condition 1' implies that $a - b$ is in each subfield of the collection, and so is in the intersection. The same argument shows that ab^{-1} is in the intersection provided a and $b \neq 0$ are elements of the intersection. It then follows from 1' and 2' that this intersection is a field, as asserted.

It may be of help in understanding the construction of the field in which the integral domain of **Theorem 5.51** is imbedded, if we first consider the integral domain to be *already imbedded* in a field. Thus let F be a field which contains the commutative integral domain A. By analogy with similar "generated" systems in earlier chapters, we define the field *generated* by A to be the intersection of all subfields of F which contain A. This intersection is a field, as a result of **Theorem 5.52**. It is now possible to give the following important characterization of this field: *The subfield H generated by the integral domain A is the set $\{xy^{-1}\}$ of all elements of the form xy^{-1}, where $x, y(\neq 0) \in A$.*

In order to prove this assertion, we note first that inverses of nonzero elements of A must be in H, and H is closed under multiplication. Hence $H \supseteq \{xy^{-1}\}$. We make use of **Theorem 5.52** to prove the reversed inclusion. Thus, if ab^{-1} and cd^{-1} are arbitrary elements of $\{xy^{-1}\}$, we have $ab^{-1} - cd^{-1} = add^{-1}b^{-1} - cbb^{-1}d^{-1} = (ad - cb)(bd)^{-1}$, which is clearly an element of $\{xy^{-1}\}$. Moreover, $(ab^{-1})(cd^{-1})^{-1} = (ab^{-1})(dc^{-1}) = (ad)(bc)^{-1} \in \{xy^{-1}\}$, and an application of 1' and 2' shows that $\{xy^{-1}\}$ is a subfield of F. Since each $a \in A$ can be expressed in the form $(ab)b^{-1}$, for any $b(\neq 0) \in A$, we must have $A \subseteq \{xy^{-1}\}$. But H is the intersection of all subfields of F which contain A, so that $H \subseteq \{xy^{-1}\}$. It follows from the two inclusions that $H = \{xy^{-1}\}$, as asserted. In the special case where $A = I$ is the ring of integers, and F is the field of real numbers, the field H generated by I is the field of rational numbers. Each element in this field has the form xy^{-1} or x/y, where x and $y(\neq 0)$ are integers.

We are now ready to return to the proof of the theorem enunciated at the beginning of this section.

Proof of Theorem 5.51.   As we are no longer assuming that the integral domain is contained in a field, it is now necessary for us actually to *construct* the elements of the imbedding field. However, it was the purpose of the preceding discussion to indicate that the elements of a minimal field containing a commutative integral domain A will probably be derived from pairs (a, b), with $a, b(\neq 0) \in A$. Accordingly, we let S be the set of all such pairs, where *intuitively* we may identify the pair (a, b) with ab^{-1} or a/b. We first define an equivalence relation in S by stating that $(a, b) \sim (c, d)$ if $ad = bc$. It can be easily verified that this does define an equivalence relation, and so S is partitioned into disjoint classes of equivalent or "equal" elements **(Theorem 1.41)**. We now think of each equivalence class as defining a unique, number, *which for convenience may be identified with the class itself,* and use the analogy of the field in the preceding discussion to define addition and multiplication in this set F of equivalence classes. Thus, if $\overline{(a, b)}$ is the equivalence class which contains (a, b) and $\overline{(c, d)}$ is the equivalence class which contains (c, d), we make the following definitions:

1. $\overline{(a, b)} + \overline{(c, d)} = \overline{(ad + bc, bd)}.$

2. $\overline{(a, b)}\overline{(c, d)} = \overline{(ac, bd)}.$

We note that since $b \neq 0$ and $d \neq 0$, also $bd \neq 0$, so that the pairs defined as sums and products by these definitions are actually in F. Moreover, if $(a', b') \sim (a, b)$ and $(c', d') \sim (c, d)$, it is easy to verify that $(a'd' + b'c', b'd') \sim (ad + bc, bd)$ and $(a'c', b'd') \sim (ac, bd)$, and this shows that the operations have been well defined by 1 and 2. It is now a straightforward matter to check the postulates and so verify that F is a field.

Finally, we assert that the mapping $a \rightarrow \overline{(ab, b)}$, where b is any nonzero element of A, is an isomorphism of A onto F. The

verification of this is illustrated schematically below with a,
$c \in A$.

$$
\begin{array}{ccl}
\underline{\quad A \quad} & & \underline{\quad F \quad} \\
a & \longrightarrow & \overline{(ab,\ b)} \\
c & \longrightarrow & \overline{(cb,\ b)} \\
a + c & \longrightarrow & \overline{((a+c)b,\ b)} = \overline{(ab,\ b)} + \overline{(cb,\ b)} \\
ac & \longrightarrow & \overline{(acb,b)} = \overline{(ab,b)}\ \overline{(cb,b)}
\end{array}
$$

This completes the proof of the theorem, for we have imbedded
an isomorphic image of A in a field F.

The field F, in which the integral domain A has been imbedded, is known as the *quotient field* of A. It can be shown—
though we omit the proof—that this quotient field is unique in
the sense that any field which contains an isomorphic image of A
also contains a minimal subfield which is isomorphic to F. It
might be conjectured that it would be possible to imbed an
arbitrary (noncommutative) integral domain in a division ring,
just as we have done in the commutative case. However, it can
be shown that this is not the case.

Problems 5–5

**1. Prove that the "equivalence" relation defined in the set S of the
proof of **Theorem 5.51** is an equivalence relation.

*2. Prove that addition has been well defined in the set F of equiv-
alence classes in the proof of **Theorem 5.51**.

*3. As in **Problem 2**, prove that multiplication has been well defined.

*4. Verify that the system F in the proof of **Theorem 5.51** is an additive abelian group.

*5. Verify that the nonzero elements of F in **Problem 4** comprise a
multiplicative group.

6. Prove that any commutative semi-group, in which the cancellation
law holds, can be imbedded in a group.

5.6 IDEALS IN A RING

In Chapter 4 we saw how certain "normal" or "invariant" subgroups play an important role in the theory of groups. These subgroups are the kernels of the various homomorphisms of the groups

in which they are contained, and the cosets of any subgroup constitute the elements of the associated quotient or factor group. In the theory of rings certain algebraic subsystems known as "ideals" play a part quite similar to that played by normal subgroups in group theory.

> **Definition.** An *ideal E* in a ring A is an additive subgroup of A such that $xa \in E$ and $ax \in E$, for arbitrary elements $a \in A$ and $x \in E$.

We may think intuitively of an ideal in a ring as an additive subgroup, with the somewhat unusual property of being able to "absorb" or "capture" the product of any element of the ring by any element of the subgroup. It is clear that the whole ring, and the "zero ideal" consisting of the single element 0, are included in the set of ideals in any ring. Any *other* ideal in the ring is said to be *proper*. It is not necessary for a ring to have any proper ideals, and a ring which has none is called *simple*. A field is then a simple ring **(Problem 6).**

The most general setting for a study of the theory of ideals is a ring that is not required to be commutative or to have an identity element. In such a ring we would need to distinguish between such ring products as ab and ba and, in the symbolism of the above definition, it is quite possible that one of xa and ax is in E while the other is not. This would lead us to a consideration of what are known as "left ideals" and "right ideals"—according as the ring elements are multiplied *on the left* or *on the right* of the elements of the subsystem. In order to avoid such complications here, however, we shall always assume that our basic ring is commutative so that left ideals are also right ideals. This will simplify our definition of an ideal to read as follows.

> **Definition.** An *ideal E* in a commutative ring A is an additive subgroup of A such that $xa \in E$ for arbitrary elements $a \in A$ and $x \in E$.

We can discover simple examples of an ideal in the ring I of ordinary integers, and also in the ring $I[x]$ of polynomials in a transcendental element x with coefficients in I. For example, the system of all even integers is an ideal in I: for this system is clearly an additive abelian subgroup, while the product of an arbitrary integer by an even integer is an even integer. As a matter of fact, it is easy to see that the set of integral multiples of any integer m is also an ideal in I, and we shall see later that every ideal in I is of this kind. In the ring $I[x]$, consider the set of all polynomials of the form pq, where q is some fixed polynomial and p is an arbitrary polynomial in the ring. For example, suppose $q = x^2 + 1$. If p_1 and p_2 are arbitrary polynomials in $I[x]$, it is true that $p_1q - p_2q = (p_1 - p_2)q$ and this is a polynomial of the form pq. An application of **Theorem 4.51** then shows that the set of "polynomial multiples" of $x^2 + 1$ comprises an additive abelian group. Furthermore, if $p_1q = p_1(x^2 + 1)$ is an arbitrary polynomial multiple of $x^2 + 1$, while p is any polynomial in $I[x]$, it is clear that $p(p_1q) = pp_1(x^2 + 1)$ is also a polynomial multiple of $x^2 + 1$. It follows that the collection of polynomial multiples of $x^2 + 1$ comprises an ideal in $I[x]$. It is clear that the particular polynomial $x^2 + 1$, which we used in this illustration, played no essential role except to make the discussion more explicit. Hence we can see that the set of all polynomial multiples of *any* polynomial in $I[x]$ constitutes an ideal in this ring. This is an illustration of the close parallelism which exists between the properties of the rings I and $I[x]$.

In order to lead into the next idea, we need the following extension of **Theorem 4.52** to ideals.

Theorem 5.61   The intersection of any collection of ideals in a ring is also an ideal in the ring.

Proof.   Since an ideal is an additive, abelian group, it follows from **Theorem 4.52** that this intersection is an additive, abelian subgroup. Moreover, for any element x in the intersection and an arbitrary element a in the ring, the product xa is in each of the individual ideals of the collection and so is in the intersection. Hence the intersection is an ideal as asserted.

We have noted previously that the set of all integral multiples of any integer m is an ideal in I, and the set of all polynomial multiples of any polynomial $q \in I[x]$ is an ideal in $I[x]$. Ideals of this kind are called "principal" and are included in the more general category of ideals which we now define.

Definition. In a ring A, the intersection of all ideals which contain a set of elements $\{a_1,\ a_2,\ a_3,\ \cdots,\ a_n\}$, where each $a_i \in A$, is known as the *ideal generated by* these elements. If E is this ideal, the set of generators is said to form a *basis* for E, and we write $E = (a_1,\ a_2,\ a_3,\ \cdots,\ a_n)$. The ideal (a) with only one generator or basis element is called a *principal* ideal.

For the commutative rings under discussion here, it is clear that any ideal which contains an element b also contains every element ab, where a is an arbitrary element of the imbedding ring A. Moreover, it is easy to see that the set $\{ab | a \in A\}$ is an ideal in A. **(Problem 1).** If A *has an identity element*, the ideal $\{ab | a \in A\}$ contains b and is contained in every ideal containing b, and so it must be the ideal generated by b. That is, $(b) = \{ab | a \in A\}$ or, as we sometimes write, $(b) = Ab = bA$. If $A = I$, the element b is an integer, and so (b) is the set of all integral multiples of b. Similarly, if $A = I[x]$, the element b is a polynomial, and so (b) in this case is the ideal consisting of all polynomial multiples of the polynomial b.

If $E = (a_1, a_2)$ is an ideal, with a basis of two elements a_1, a_2, in a ring A, the additive group properties of E imply that every element of the form $xa_1 + ya_2$, with $x, y \in A$, is in E. In fact, it is easy to show, by an argument similar to the principal ideal case, that E is exactly this collection of elements. We leave the proof of this, as well the extension to the case of any finite number of generators, to the student **(Problem 4).** For example, the ideal $(6, 9)$ in I is the collection of all integers of the form $6x + 9y$, where x, y are arbitrary integers in I. Likewise, in $I[x]$, the ideal (q_1, q_2) where $q_1 = x + 1$ and $q_2 = x^2 - 2$, is the collection of all polynomials of the form $p(x + 1) + q(x^2 - 2)$, where p and q are arbitrary polynomials in $I[x]$. We shall see in the following section that both of these ideals are actually principal, in spite of the presence of two generators in each case.

Problems 5–6

*1. If b is an arbitrary element of a commutative ring A, prove that the set of all ring multiples ab of b, for $a \in A$, is an ideal in A.

2. Explain why any ideal in a ring is a subring.

*3. Let n be an arbitrary but fixed integer. If A is a ring, prove that the set of all elements na, for $a \in A$, comprises an ideal in A.

*4. If a_1, a_2 are elements of a commutative ring A, with identity, prove that the ideal (a_1, a_2) is the set of all elements of A of the form $xa_1 + ya_2$, where $x, y \in A$. Can your proof be generalized to include ideals with an arbitrary number n of generators?

5. Decide whether the system of integers forms an ideal in the ring of rational numbers. Give a reason for your answer.

**6. Prove that a field, considered as a ring, can contain no proper ideals.

7. Go through the steps of the proof that the set of all polynomial multiples of $x^2 + x - 1$ is an ideal in $I[x]$.

8. List five elements of each of the following ideals in I:
   (a) (3); (b) $(2, 3)$; (c) $(5, 6, 10)$; (d) (1).

9. List five elements of each of the following ideals in $I[x]$:
   (a) $(x - 1)$; (b) $(x, 2x + 1)$; (c) $(x, 3x, 2x - 1)$;
   (d) $(2, x, x + 1, 2x + 1)$.

10. If A is a ring, prove that the set of all elements $x \in A$ such that $xa = 0$, for all $a \in A$, is an ideal in A.

5.7 QUOTIENT OR DIFFERENCE RINGS

In our introduction to group theory we were able to construct the factor or quotient group G/H for any normal subgroup H of a group G. The elements of any quotient group are the cosets of some subgroup H and, in the usual symbolism for multiplicative groups, these cosets are designated as aH (or Ha), where $a \,\epsilon\, G$. In the case of rings the underlying group is additive, and so additive notation is in order. Moreover, since the additive group of any ring is abelian, all additive subgroups are normal, and so it is not necessary to distinguish normal subgroups in this case. Hence if H is *any* subgroup of the additive group of a ring A, the factor group A/H is the set of all cosets $a + H$, with $a \in A$. If $x + H$ and $y + H$ are two arbitrary cosets of A/H, with $x, y \in A$, our earlier rule of composition for cosets—which we now identify with addition— requires that $(x + H) + (y + H) = x + y + H$. We now suppose that $H = E$ is an ideal in A, and define the multiplication of cosets by the rule that $(x + E)(y + E) = xy + E$.

It follows from the corresponding discussion in Chapter 4 that addition of cosets has been well defined by the above rule, but we must check this for multiplication. Thus, if x' and y' are other representatives for the cosets $x + E$ and $y + E$, respectively, we must check that $x'y' + E = xy + E$. In order to see this we note that $x' = x + e_1$ and $y' = y + e_2$, with $e_1, e_2 \in E$, so that $x'y' + E = (x + e_1)(y + e_2) + E = xy + ye_1 + xe_2 + e_1e_2 + E = xy + E$. The last equality follows from the fact that E is an ideal. Hence $x'y'$ and xy are representatives of the same coset, and so multiplication has been well defined.

Theorem 5.71   Let E be an arbitrary ideal in a ring A, with $x + E$ the collection of cosets of E, where $x \in A$. Then if we define addition and multiplication of cosets as above, the resulting system of cosets is a ring known as the *quotient* or *factor ring* of A relative to E. The same designation A/E is used for this quotient ring as for the underlying quotient group.

Proof.   Since E is a (normal) subgroup of the additive group of A, we already know that A/E is an additive group with the above rule of composition for addition. We have defined the operation of multiplication in the collection of cosets, so that closure under this operation is automatic. Hence, in order to prove that this system of cosets is a ring, it is merely necessary to establish the validity of the Associative and Distributive Laws. To this end, let $x + E$, $y + E$, $z + E$ be any three cosets in A/E, with $x, y, z \in A$. Then $[(x + E)(y + E)] \, (z + E) = (xy + E)(z + E) = (xy)z + E$; and $(x + E) \, [(y + E)(z + E)] = (x + E)(yz + E) = x(yz) + E$. Since $(xy)z = x(yz)$, the Associative Law is seen to hold in the quotient ring. Similarly, $(x + E) \, [(y + E) + (z + E)] = (x + E)(y + z + E) = x(y + z) + E$; and $(x + E)(y + E) + (x + E)(z + E) = xy + E + xz + E = xy + xz + E$. The validity of the Distributive Law in A assures us that $x(y + z) = xy + xz$, so that we have shown that the Distributive Law also holds in A/E. It follows that A/E is a ring, as asserted in the theorem.

Some of the elementary properties of a ring are carried over to its quotient rings. For example, if A is commutative, so is A/E for any ideal E in A **(Problem 4)**. If A has an identity, the coset $1 + E$ is clearly the identity element for any quotient ring A/E. However, some of the properties of a ring, such as the existence or nonexistence of divisors of zero, are not necessarily inherited by all of its quotient rings. Thus, it is possible for a ring to be an integral domain, while one of its quotient rings is not this kind of system.

We conclude this section with some further results which are parallel to similar results in the theory of groups.

Theorem 5.72 If η is a homomorphism of a ring A into a ring A', the image system of A is a subring of A'.

Proof. Since η is a homomorphism of the additive group of A, we have already seen that the image system is an additive subgroup of A' **(Theorem 4.45)**. If $a\eta$ and $b\eta$ are arbitrary elements of the image system, with $a, b \in A$, the definition of a ring homomorphism requires that $(a\eta)(b\eta) = (ab)\eta$. Since an additive group is closed under subtraction, we can now apply **Theorem 5.11** to assert that the image system is in fact a subring of A'.

A ring does not necessarily have an identity element, and so the following definition would seem to be appropriate.

Definition. The *kernel* of a homomorphism of a ring is the set of ring elements that are mapped onto the element 0 of the image system.

Theorem 5.73 The kernel of any homomorphism η of a ring A is an ideal in A.

Proof. We have already noted that a ring homomorphism is also a homomorphism of its additive group, so that **Theorem 4.102** assures us that the kernel K of η is an additive subgroup. Now let $b \in K$, with a an arbitrary element of A. Then $(ab)\eta = (a\eta)(b\eta) = (a\eta)(0) = 0$. In case A is not commutative, it is necessary to note also that $(ba)\eta = 0$, so that K is an ideal of A.

If E is any ideal in a ring A, it is easy to verify that the mapping $a \to a + E$ is a homomorphism of A onto A/E **(Problem 1)**, with kernel *E* **(Problem 2).** Thus every ideal is the kernel of some homomorphism and the kernel of every homomorphism is an ideal. We complete the analogy between normal subgroups and ideals with the following theorem which should be compared with **Theorem 4.102.**

Theorem 5.74 Every homomorphic image of a ring A is isomorphic to a quotient ring, in fact to A/K where K is the kernel of the homomorphism.

We leave the proof of this theorem to the student **(Problem 3).**

Problems 5-7

* **1.** If E is an ideal in a ring A, prove that the mapping $a \to a + E$ is a homomorphism of A onto A/E.
* *2.** Prove that E is the kernel of the homomorphism defined in **Problem 1.**
* *3.** Refer to the proof of **Theorem 4.102** to prove **Theorem 5.74.**
* 4. Explain why the quotient ring A/E is commutative if A is commutative.
* 5. Show that the mapping $a + bi \to a - bi$ is an automorphism of the ring of complex numbers.
* 6. Determine the ideals and hence all homomorphic images of the subring of I_2 of matrices of the form

$$\begin{bmatrix} a & b \\ 0 & c \end{bmatrix},$$

with $a, b, c \in I$.

5.8 PRIME IDEALS IN A COMMUTATIVE RING

In §5.6 we defined a principal ideal as an ideal with one basis or generating element. For example, the set of all integral multiples of 3 comprise the principal ideal (3) in the ring I. If every ideal in a commutative ring is principal, the ring is said to be a *principal ideal domain*. The following theorem verifies that the ring I is of this kind.

Theorem 5.81 The ring I is a principal ideal domain.

Proof. The zero ideal is of course the ideal (0), while the whole ring I can be regarded as (1), both of which are principal ideals. Now let E be any proper ideal in I, with e ($\neq 0, 1$) $\in E$. Since

$(-1)e = -e \in E$, the ideal contains at least one positive integer **(Problem 1)**, and let m be the least positive integer in E. If x is an arbitrary element of E, the division algorithm for integers **(Theorem 2.41)** assures us that there exist integers q and r such that $x = qm + r$, with $0 \leq r < m$. But $qm \in E$, so that $x - qm = r \in E$. Since $r < m$ and m was selected as the smallest positive integer in E, it follows that $r = 0$ and $x = qm$. Hence $E \subset (m) \subset E$, from which we conclude that $E = (m)$, as asserted.

As an illustration of this result let us take another look at the ideal $(6, 9)$ which we considered in §5.6. We shall show that this ideal is actually the principal ideal (3). For, since $6 = 2 \cdot 3$ and $9 = 3 \cdot 3$, it follows that $6 \in (3)$ and $9 \in (3)$, whence $(6, 9) \subset (3)$. But $3 = 1 \cdot 9 + (-1) \cdot 6$, in accordance with the result of **Theorem 2.42,** so that $3 \in (6, 9)$ and $(3) \subset (6, 9)$. It follows that $(6, 9) = (3)$. The student should refer to **Problem 2** for a generalization of this result.

If we assume the existence of a division algorithm in the ring $R[x]$, as was discussed briefly in §5.4, it is also quite easy to prove that this ring is a principal ideal ring. The only noticeable variation in this proof, from that of **Theorem 5.81,** is that the notion of "smallest" integer is replaced by the idea of "least degree" in a polynomial. We leave the proof of this result to the student **(Problem 7).**

In any commutative ring—such as the ring of integers—there arises the question of the divisibility of one element by another. Thus, if a, b, c are elements of a ring such that $a = bc$, we say that a is *divisible by* b and c or that b and c *divide* a. Two nonzero elements of a ring are *associates* if each divides the other. Hence if a and b are associates, $a = bc$ and $b = ad$ for certain ring elements c, d, so that $a = (ad)c = a(dc)$. If the ring is an integral domain with an identity element, it then follows that $dc = 1$. (Why?) It is customary to refer to a ring element that has an inverse as an *invertible element* or a *unit.* In view of the preceding remarks we now can make the following assertion: *two elements of a commutative integral domain with an identity element are associates if, and only if, each is the product of the other by a unit of the ring.* In the ring I of integers the only units are

1 and -1, and so the only associate of an integer m is the integer $-m$. In the case of a field, however, every nonzero element is a unit, and so any two nonzero elements are associates.

An element of an integral domain is said to be *prime* if it is not 0 or a unit, and its only divisors are units and associates. This is in agreement with our definition in Chapter 2 that an integer p is prime if it is neither 0, 1, nor -1 and is divisible by no integers except $\pm p$ and ± 1. In the lemma to **Theorem 2.43** we also showed that a prime integer p also has the following property: *if p divides the product of two integers a and b, then p must divide either a or b.* This idea is carried over to the theory of ideals to define a "prime" ideal.

> **Definition.**   Let E be an ideal in a commutative ring A, with x, y arbitrary elements of A. Then, if $xy \in E$ implies that either $x \in E$ or $y \in E$, the ideal E is said to be *prime*.

We have seen previously that every ideal in the ring I is principal, and it is not difficult to show that a proper ideal (m) in I is prime if, and only if, m is a prime integer. First, let (m) be a prime ideal, but suppose that m is not a prime integer. Then $m = ab$, where a and b are integers different from 0, 1, -1, so that $|a| < |m|$ and $|b| < |m|$. But since (m) is prime, $ab \in (m)$ implies that either $a \in (m)$ or $b \in (m)$, and from this we see that $|m|$ can not be the smallest positive integer in (m). Since this is in violation of the structure of a principal ideal, we must conclude that m is prime. Conversely, if $m = p$ is a prime integer and the ideal (p) contains ab, where a, $b \in I$, it follows that $ab = cp$, for some integer c. Hence p divides ab and so divides either a or b, whence (p) contains either a or b. It follows from our definition that (p)—i.e., (m)—is a prime ideal.

As a result of the preceding discussion, we see, for example, that the ideals (3) and (7) are prime ideals in I, while (4) and (12) are not. It can be shown without difficulty that the prime ideals in $R[x]$ are those which are generated by irreducible, monic polynomials. Hence, in this ring, the ideals $(2x + 1)$ and $(x^2 + x - 1)$ are examples of a prime ideal, while $(x^2 + x - 6)$ is not prime. We leave the verification of this general result to the student **(Problem 11)**.

Problems 5–8

1. Why does every proper ideal in I contain at least one positive integer?

*2. If a and b are integers, prove that $(a, b) = (d)$, where (d) is the g.c.d. of a and b.

3. Use the result of **Problem 2** to represent each of the following as principal ideals in I: **(a)** $(5, 15)$; **(b)** $(2, 6)$; **(c)** $(5, 7)$; **(d)** $(3, 9, 12)$.

4. In the ring of Gaussian integers (see **Problem 9** of **Problems 5-1**) decide whether the ideals (5) and $(1 + i)$ are prime.

5. Refer to **Problem 6** of **Problems 5-3** and show that $a + b\sqrt{m}$ is a unit in $I[\sqrt{m}]$ whenever $a + b\sqrt{m}$ is a unit. Then show that $a + b\sqrt{m}$ is a unit if and only if $a^2 - b^2m$ divides 1, and determine all units of $I[\sqrt{5}]$.

6. Prove that the ring of Gaussian integers (see reference in **Problem** 4) is a principal ideal domain.

*7. Assume a division algorithm in $R[x]$ and prove that this ring is a principal ideal domain.

8. An ideal E is said to be a *radical ideal* if $a^n \in E$ if and only if $a \in E$. Prove that every prime ideal is a radical ideal.

**9. Prove that the set of units in a commutative ring with identity is a multiplicative subgroup—called the *subgroup of units*.

10. The number of positive integers less than, and prime to, an integer m is known as the *totient* or "Euler ϕ-function" of m, usually written $\phi(m)$. Prove that the order of the subgroup of units of $I/(m)$ is $\phi(m)$. (See **Problem 9**.)

*11. Use the result of **Problem 7** and prove that every prime ideal in $R[x]$ is generated by an irreducible, monic polynomial.

5.9 FURTHER RESULTS ON QUOTIENT RINGS

In this section we derive two very important results on quotient rings, the first of which we now state.

Theorem 5.91   If P is an ideal in a commutative ring A, the quotient ring A/P is an integral domain if and only if P is a prime ideal.

Proof.   By definition, the ring A/P is an integral domain if and only if it has no divisors of zero. The elements of A/P are cosets of P, and it should be recalled that the zero coset in the quotient ring is P. Let us designate two arbitrary cosets $a + P$ and $b + P$ in A/P by $\bar{a}$ and $\bar{b}$, respectively. Then A/P is an integral domain if and only if $\bar{a} \cdot \bar{b} = 0 = P$ implies that either $\bar{a} = 0 = P$ or $\bar{b} = 0 = P$. Now a coset $\bar{x}$ in A/P is equal to P if and only if $x \in P$, and the definition of multiplication in the quotient ring requires that $\bar{a} \cdot \bar{b} = \overline{ab}$. Hence we have asserted that A/P is an integral domain if and only if $ab \in P$ implies that either $a \in P$ or $b \in P$. Since this latter condition is precisely the defining requirement that P be a prime ideal, our proof is complete.

Since the prime ideals in I are the principal ideals (p), where p is a prime integer, it follows that the quotient rings $I/(p)$ are integral domains. For example, the rings $I/(5)$, $I/(7)$, $I/(17)$, etc. are integral domains, while a ring such as $I/(6)$ will have divisors of zero. In the ring $I/(6)$, for example, we see that $\bar{2} \cdot \bar{3} = \bar{6} = 0$, while $\bar{2} \neq 0$ and $\bar{3} \neq 0$, so that $\bar{2}$ and $\bar{3}$ are divisors of zero. In the same way, if we use the result of **Problem 11** of **Problems 5-8,** the quotient ring $R[x]/(x+1)$ can be seen to be an integral domain, while $R[x]/(x^2 + 2x)$ is not.

Definition.   An ideal M in a commutative ring A is *maximal* if $0 \subset M \subset A$, and there does not exist an ideal E such that $M \subset E \subset A$.

In the ring I, every nonzero prime ideal is evidently maximal. For suppose (p) is a prime ideal, with (n) another ideal in I such that $(p) \subset (n) \subset I$. Since $(p) \subset (n)$, we must have $p = qn$, for some integer q. But p is a prime, a fact that we proved in §5.8, so that $q = \pm 1$. It follows that $n = \pm p$, whence $(n) = (p)$, contrary to assumption. Hence no such ideal as (n) can exist, and (p) is maximal.

For maximal ideals we are able to obtain a stronger result than we could for prime ideals. This is the content of the following theorem.

Theorem 5.92   If M is an ideal in a commutative ring with an identity element, the quotient ring A/M is a field if and only if M is maximal.

Proof.   For suppose M is a maximal ideal in A, with a an element in A but not in M. It can be seen that the set of all elements

of the form $m + xa$, with $m \in M$ and $x \in A$, is an ideal in A
(Problem 1). Since this ideal contains an element a, which is
not in the maximal ideal M, it follows that this constructed
ideal is the whole ring A. In particular, the identity element 1
is in this ideal, so that $1 = m_1 + ba$, where $m_1 \in M$ and $b \in A$.
In the quotient ring A/M, this means that $(b + M)(a + M) =$
$1 + M$ or, in the usual symbolism for cosets, $\bar{b} \cdot \bar{a} = \bar{1}$. Since a
was an arbitrary element of A that was not in M, we may regard
$\bar{a}$ as an arbitrary nonzero element of A/M, and we have shown
that $\bar{a}$ has a multiplicative inverse. Hence **(Problem 2)** A/M
is a field.

Conversely, let us suppose that A/M is a field. If M is not
maximal, there must exist an ideal E in A such that $M \subset E \subset A$.
Let a be an arbitrary element of A, with b an arbitrary element
of E which is not in M. In the quotient ring A/M, we let $a + M$
and $b + M$ be $\bar{a}$ and $\bar{b}$, respectively, and since A/M is a field we
know that there exists an element $\bar{c} \in A/M$ such that $\bar{b} \cdot \bar{c} = \bar{a}$
(Problem 3). But this equation can be written as $(b + M)(c +$
$M) = a + M$, from which we see that $bc - a \in M$. Since $M \subset E$
we must have $bc - a \in E$ and, since $b \in E$, this implies that
$a \in E$. We have shown that an arbitrary element of A is in E,
and so $E = A$. Hence M is a maximal ideal.

An application of **Theorem 5.92** to **Theorem 5.91** gives us the
following result.

Corollary. Any maximal ideal in a commutative ring with an
identity is prime.

It should be pointed out that a prime ideal in a commutative ring is
not necessarily maximal. We have already shown, however, that
every prime ideal in the ring I is maximal and so, for this ring, the
concepts of prime and maximal coincide. Hence the quotient rings,
such as $I/(5)$, $I/(7)$, $I/(17)$, etc., which we claimed were integral
domains at the close of **Theorem 5.91,** are in reality fields. In fact,
if (p) is a prime ideal in I, with $\bar{a}$ any nonzero element of $I/(p)$,

Theorem 2.42 asserts the existence of integers s and t such that $1 = sa + tp$. Hence $\bar{1} = \bar{s} \cdot \bar{a}$, so that $\bar{s}$ is the multiplicative inverse of $\bar{a}$ in $I/(p)$. In particular, if $p = 7$ and $a = 3$, we know that $1 = (-2) \cdot 3 + (1) \cdot 7$. Hence the multiplicative inverse of $\bar{3}$ is $\overline{-2}$ or, in the more usual equivalent form, $\bar{5}$.

The similarity between I and $R[x]$ continues with respect to prime and maximal ideals, for these notions again coincide for the ring $R[x]$ **(Problem 4)**. It then follows that an integral domain, such as $R[x]/(x + 1)$, is in fact a field; and the procedure for determining the inverse of an element in such a field is in every way similar to the procedure outlined above, with a suitable adaptation of the g.c.d. process to $R[x]$. We leave the details of this to the investigation of the student in other books.

Problems 5-9

*1. With reference to the proof of **Theorem 5.92**, why is the set of elements of the form $m + xa$ an ideal in A?

*2. The proof of the first part of **Theorem 5.92** consisted in proving that inverses exist. Why is this sufficient to verify that A/M is a field?

*3. In the converse portion of the proof of **Theorem 5.92**, how do we know that the element $\bar{a}$ exists?

4. Prove that any prime ideal in $R[x]$ is maximal.

5. Determine the multiplicative inverse of each of the following elements of $I/(7)$: **(a) $\bar{2}$; **(b)** $\bar{4}$; **(c)** $\bar{5}$.

6. Determine the multiplicative inverse of each of the following elements of $R[x]/(x + 1)$: **(a)** $\overline{3x}$; **(b)** $\overline{x^2}$; **(c)** $\overline{2x^2 - 1}$.

5.10 GAUSSIAN AND EUCLIDEAN DOMAINS

On many occasions we have referred to the ring I of ordinary integers, for this ring has provided us with illustrations of many of the ideas introduced in this chapter. Another ring, to which several references have been made, is the ring $R[x]$ of polynomials of finite degree with coefficients in the field R of rational numbers. We have already noted that these two rings have many characteristics in common. In the present section we shall exploit two of these characteristics and obtain two important general classifications of rings.

It is a familiar fact that any integer can be decomposed into a product of primes which is *essentially* unique—i.e., except for the order of the factors and the presence of units. The units of I are, of course, 1 and -1. In the ring $R[x]$, a similar situation prevails. In this case the units are the elements of R, while the primes are those monic polynomials which are *irreducible*—i.e., which cannot be decomposed into a product of polynomials of lower degree. It is well known from college algebra that any polynomial can be expressed as a power product of irreducible polynomials, and this representation is essentially unique. This notion of "essentially unique" factorization leads us to the first classification of rings in this section.

> **Definition.** A commutative integral domain with an identity is said to be *Gaussian*, if each nonunit has a factorization as a product of primes which is essentially unique.

We have already pointed out that both I and $R[x]$ are Gaussian domains. In §5.8 it was shown that every ideal in I is principal, and it was indicated that a similar argument could be used to show that $R[x]$ is also a principal ideal domain. That the Gaussian characteristic is common to all principal ideal domains is the content of the following theorem.

Theorem 5.101 Every principal ideal domain is Gaussian.

The proof of this theorem, though not difficult, is somewhat involved and so we omit it. The interested student is invited to consult one of the references listed at the end of the chapter for the proof.

An example of a ring which is not a Gaussian domain is the ring $I[\sqrt{-5}]$ of polynomials in $\sqrt{-5}$ with integral coefficients. The elements of this ring are simply numbers of the form $x + y\sqrt{-5}$, where x and y are integers; and it can be readily checked, for example, that $21 = 3 \cdot 7 = (1 + 2\sqrt{-5})(1 - 2\sqrt{-5}) = (4 + \sqrt{-5})(4 - \sqrt{-5})$. It can be shown that these factors are all prime **(Problem 3),** and so $I[\sqrt{-5}]$ can not be Gaussian.

The other basic notion, which we wish to generalize in this section, is the familiar division algorithm of the ring I. We have also referred, at various earlier points, to the existence of a similar division algorithm in $R[x]$. An attempt to generalize this idea leads us to the other ring classification of this section.

Definition. A commutative integral domain A with an identity is said to be *Euclidean*, if there exists an integral-valued function δ, defined on A such that:

1. $a\delta \geq 0$, and $a\delta = 0$ if and only if $a = 0$, for $a \in A$;
2. $(ab)\delta \geq a\delta$, for arbitrary nonzero elements $a, b \in A$;
3. For an arbitrary element $a \in A$, and any non-zero element $b \in A$, there exist elements $q, r \in A$ such that $a = bq + r$, where $0 \leq r\delta < b\delta$.

It is clear that the integral domain I is Euclidean, with the function δ defined so that $a\delta = |a|$, for each integer a. It can also be shown that $R[x]$ is Euclidean, with $a\delta$ defined to be the degree of the polynomial $a \in R[x]$. We have already noted that both of these rings are principal ideal domains, and the following theorem shows that this is a common characteristic of all Euclidean domains.

Theorem 5.102   Every ideal in a Euclidean domain is principal.

Proof.   Suppose E is an ideal in a Euclidean domain A. If E is the zero ideal, we know that $E = (0)$ and so E is principal. Hence let E be a nonzero ideal in A, so that E contains at least one element for which the functional value of δ is positive. As any set of positive functional values of δ is a set of positive integers, the Well-ordering Principle (See §2.2) assures us of the existence of at least one element $b \in E$, such that $0 < b\delta \leq x\delta$, for every nonzero element $x \in E$. But an arbitrary x in E can be expressed in the form $x = bq + r$, where $q \in A$ and $r\delta < b\delta$. Since E is an ideal, this shows that $r = x - bq$ is in E; but since $b\delta$ is the minimum positive function value for elements of E, this means that $r = 0$. Hence $x = bq \in (b)$, and $E = (b)$, completing the proof.

Inasmuch as every principal ideal domain is Gaussian **(Theorem 5.101)**, the following corollary is immediate.

Corollary.   Every Euclidean domain is Gaussian.

The ring $I[i]$ of Gaussian integers (See **Problem 9 of Problems 5-1**) provides us with another example of a Euclidean domain. We define the function δ so that $(x + iy)\delta = x^2 + y^2$, for each $(x + iy) \in I[i]$, and a little elementary algebra shows that $(ab)\delta = (a\delta)(b\delta)$, for arbitrary Gaussian integers a, b (**Problem 4**). It is immediate that δ satisfies requirements 1 and 2 in our definition of a Euclidean domain, and so all that remains is to prove that a division algorithm exists. It turns out that ordinary complex number division is satisfactory. For let a and $b(\neq 0)$ be elements of $I[i]$, and consider the complex quotient $a/b = \mu + \nu i$, where μ and ν are rational numbers. There certainly exist integers u and v such that $|u - \mu| \leq \frac{1}{2}$ and $|v - \nu| \leq \frac{1}{2}$. Hence, if $\mu - u = \eta_1$, and $\nu - v = \eta_2$, we are asserting that $|\eta_1| \leq \frac{1}{2}$ and $|\eta_2| \leq \frac{1}{2}$. Then $a/b = (u + \eta_1) + (v + \eta_2)i$ and we have shown that $a = bq + r$ where $q = u + vi \in I[i]$, and $r = b(\eta_1 + \eta_2 i)$. But we know that $r = a - bq$, so that $r \in I[i]$, and $r\delta = [b(\eta_1 + \eta_2 i)]\delta = (b\delta)[(\eta_1 + \eta_2 i)\delta] \leq (\frac{1}{4} + \frac{1}{4})(b\delta) < b\delta$. Hence 3 is satisfied, and $I[i]$ is Euclidean.

Problems 5-10

1. Why are the units of $R[x]$ merely the elements of R?

2. Prove that the ring $I[\sqrt{3}]$, consisting of all real numbers of the form $m + n\sqrt{3}$ where m and n are integers, is Euclidean.

3. Prove that $1 + 2\sqrt{-5}$ and $1 - 2\sqrt{-5}$ are prime elements of $I[\sqrt{-5}]$.

4. Use the δ-function defined in this section for Gaussian integers, and prove that $(ab)\delta = (a\delta)(b\delta)$, for any two Gaussian integers a and b.

**5. Prove that if an element a of a Euclidean domain is a unit, then $(ab)\delta = b\delta$ for any b, and $a\delta = 1\delta$.

6. Prove that any unit of a principal ideal domain generates the whole ring.

7. Imitate the g.c.d. process outlined after **Theorem 2.42** to determine the g.c.d. of the following polynomials in $R[x]$:
   (a) $x^3 + x^2 + x + 2$, $x^2 + 2x + 2$;
   (b) $x^4 - 2x^3 + x^2 - 1$, $x^5 - 3x^3 + 2x^2 - 1$.

8. Prove that $I[x]$ is not a principal ideal domain.

5.11 NOETHERIAN RINGS

Most types of algebraic systems include some special varieties with which it is easy to work, and whose structure can be completely described. For example, the structure theory of finite abelian groups is quite simple, and this was briefly outlined in §4.11. In the theory of rings, a quite similar situation prevails in connection with what we shall later define as "Noetherian" rings. The abstract development of the structure theory of these rings was initiated by Emmy Noether (1882–1935), which explains the origin of the name "Noetherian."

A ring A is said to satisfy the *acsending chain condition* (a.c.c.) for ideals if every sequence of ideals E_1, E_2, E_3, $\cdots$ in A, such that $E_1 \subset E_2 \subset E_3 \cdots$, has only a finite number of terms. In other words, there can exist no *infinite, properly ascending chain* of ideals in this kind of ring. Since a field has no proper ideals (**Problem 6 of Problems 5-6**), this condition is certainly satisfied in any field. In the ring I, since $(n) \subset (m)$ implies that m divides n, but n can have only a finite number of distinct divisors, it is immediate that the a.c.c. is also satisfied here. It can also be shown that the ring $R[x]$ of polynomials in a single symbol x satisfies the a.c.c., but consider the collection of all polynomials in infinitely many symbols x_1, x_2, x_3, $\cdots$, with coefficients in R. If we add and multiply these polynomials according to an evident extension of the familiar rules of college algebra, as applied to the case of two or three symbols, it can be seen without difficulty that the resulting algebraic system is a ring. In this ring we can construct the following chain of ideals: $(x_1) \subset (x_1, x_2) \subset (x_1, x_2, x_3) \subset \cdots$. Inasmuch as this chain clearly has no end, the ascending chain condition is not satisfied.

Theorem 5.111 In any commutative ring A, the following conditions are equivalent and define A as a *Noetherian* ring.

  i. A satisfies the ascending chain condition.
  ii. Every ideal in A has a finite basis, i.e., a finite number of basis elements.
  iii. Every nonempty set of ideals in A contains at least one which is not contained in any other of the set. Such an ideal may be said to be *maximal* in the set.

Proof. We shall show that **i** implies **ii**, **ii** implies **iii**, and **iii** implies **i** in this order. First, let E be an ideal in A, which we assume now to satisfy the a.c.c., and pick an element $e_1 \in E$. If $(e_1) = E$, the ideal E has a basis of one element and there is nothing to prove. Otherwise, pick another element $e_2 \in E$ so that $e_2 \not\subset (e_1)$, and it is clear that $(e_1) \subset (e_1, e_2) \subseteq E$. If $(e_1, e_2) = E$, the ideal E has a basis of two elements and again there is nothing to prove. Otherwise, we can select another element $e_3 \in E$ and repeat the above reasoning. In view of the a.c.c., the chain of ideals $(e_1) \subset (e_1, e_2) \subset (e_1, e_2, e_3) \subset \cdots$ must terminate, and so for some integer k, $(e_1, e_2, e_3, \cdots, e_k) = E$, thus establishing **ii**.

In order to prove **iii** from **ii**, we assume that every ideal in A has a finite basis, and let us consider any set S of ideals in A. Any particular ideal E_1 in S is either maximal or is properly contained in some other ideal $E_2 \in S$. Likewise, either E_2 is maximal or is properly contained in some other ideal $E_3 \in S$. A continuation of this reasoning leads either to a maximal ideal $E_k,$, after k selections, or to an infinite ascending chain of ideals: $E_1 \subset E_2 \subset E_3 \subset \cdots$. It can be seen **(Problem 1)** that the set-theoretic union of all ideals in this chain is an ideal in A, and so has a basis by our assumption in **ii**. Hence $E = (e_1, e_2, e_3, \cdots, e_r)$, for some integer r, and each element e_i is an element of some ideal E_{k_i} of the chain. If k is chosen as the largest of the k_i occurring, it follows that $E \subseteq E_k$. But $E_k \subseteq E$, and so $E = E_k$, which requires that each E_i lies in E_k. Hence no infinite, properly ascending chain of ideals is possible, and S must contain a maximal ideal, as required in **iii**.

In order to prove that **iii** implies **i**, let $E_1, E_2, E_3, \cdots$ be a collection of ideals such that $E_1 \subseteq E_2 \subseteq E_3 \subseteq \cdots$. By our assumption of **iii**, this collection contains a maximal ideal—say E_m—so that $E_m = E_{m+1} = \cdots$, and so the ascending chain must have finite length m. This is the statement of **i**, and completes the proof of the theorem.

If E_1 and E_2 are two ideals in a commutative ring, the *product* $E_1 E_2$ is the ideal generated by the set of all products $e_1 e_2$, with

$e_1 \in E_1$ and $e_2 \in E_2$. It is not difficult to see that this ideal is the set of all finite sums of such products e_1e_2 **(Problem 2)**. In the case of two ideals in the ring I, their product has a more simple description. For example, if $E_1 = (3)$ and $E_2 = (5)$, it is clear that $E_1E_2 = (3)(5) = (15)$, since I is a principal ideal domain. More generally, if $m = pq$ is a factorization of the integer m as a product of integers p, q, it is easy to see **(Problem 3)** that $(m) = (p)(q)$. If p and q are prime integers, the ideals (p) and (q) are prime and the decomposition of (m) as a product of prime ideals is unique except for order. An evident extension of this leads us to the fundamental factorization theorem in the ring of integers.

Theorem 5.112 Every ideal in I can be expressed in one and only one way (except for order) as a product of prime ideals.

The above factorization theorem holds in many other domains, including some which are not Gaussian. For example, the ring $I[\sqrt{-5}]$ is not Gaussian, but it can be shown that the theorem is still valid here—though we omit the proof of this. However, for Noetherian rings in general, we must be content with a weaker result. If $m = pq$ is the prime decomposition of an integer m, it is easy to show that $(m) = (p) \cap (q)$ **(Problem 4)**; or, more generally, $(p_1^{e_1}p_2^{e_2}\cdots p_r^{e_r}) = (p_1^{e_1}) \cap (p_2^{e_2}) \cap \cdots \cap (p_r^{e_r})$, where $p_1, p_2, \cdots, p_r$ are the distinct prime factors of m. It is this type of decomposition that is valid in any Noetherian ring but, before we give an exact statement of the theorem, we need some definitions.

Definition. An ideal Q in a commutative ring is said to be *primary*, if $ab \notin Q$, where $a \notin Q$, implies that $b^n \in Q$, for some positive integer n.

Definition. If E is an ideal in a commutative ring A, the set Z of all elements $a \in A$ such that $a^n \in E$, for some positive integer n, is known as the *radical* of E. If E is the zero ideal, its radical is often called the *radical of the ring*.

It is easy to prove that Z is an ideal **(Problem 5)**, and the definition of a primary ideal can then be rephrased as follows:

Definition. An ideal Q in a commutative ring is said to be *primary* if $ab \in Q$, where $a \notin Q$, implies that b is in the radical of Q.

It can be shown directly that the radical of a primary ideal is a prime ideal **(Problem 6)**. A representation of an ideal E as an intersection $E_1 \cap E_2 \cap \cdots \cap E_r$ of ideals E_1, E_2, $\cdots$, E_r is said to be *irredundant* if no one of the ideals can be omitted from the representation without it resulting in a set different from E. We are now able to state the fundamental decomposition theorem for ideals in Noetherian rings.

Theorem 5.113 Any ideal in a Noetherian ring can be represented as the irredundant intersection of a finite number of primary ideals with distinct radicals. The *number* of primary ideals in this representation, and the *set* of their radicals is unique, while the primary ideals themselves can vary from one representation to another.

We omit the proof of this theorem, a result which brings us in the theory of Noetherian rings to a point somewhat comparable to where we left abelian groups at the end of Chapter 4. Unfortunately, this result is a little less satisfactory than the earlier result for abelian groups.

Problems 5–11

1. If $E_1 \subset E_2 \subset E_3 \subset \cdots$ is an infinite, ascending chain of ideals in a commutative ring, prove that the set-theoretic union of all ideals in the chain is an ideal.
2. Use the definition given for the product of two ideals E_1 and E_2 in a commutative ring to prove that $E_1 E_2$ consists of the set of all finite sums of products $e_1 e_2$, with $e_1 \in E_1$ and $e_2 \in E_2$.
3. If $m = pq$ is a factorization of the integer m as a product of integers p and q, prove that $(m) = (p)(q)$.
4. If p and q are prime integers in **Problem 3**, show that $(m) = (p) \cap (q)$.
**5. Prove that the radical of an ideal in a commutative ring is an ideal in the ring.
6. Prove that the radical of a primary ideal in a Noetherian ring is a prime ideal in the ring.
7. Prove that any prime ideal in a Noetherian ring is primary.

8. Extend the definition of the product of two ideals in a commutative ring to include arbitrary products and powers of ideals. In particular, if E is an ideal, what would be a reasonable definition for E^n, for a positive integer n?

9. An ideal in a Noetherian ring is *nilpotent* if some positive integral power of the ideal is the zero ideal. (See **Problem 8**). If Z is the radical of an ideal E in a Noetherian ring, show that Z/E is nilpotent.

REFERENCES

Albert, A.: *Fundamental Concepts of Higher Algebra*, Chap. 2 (Chicago, University of Chicago Press, 1956).

Birkhoff, G., and MacLane, S.: *A Survey of Modern Algebra*, Revised Edition, Chap. 13 (New York, Macmillan, 1953).

Jacobson, N.: *Lectures in Abstract Algebra*, Vol. 1, Chaps. 2, 3, 6 (Princeton, N.J., Van Nostrand, 1951).

McCoy, N.: *Rings and Ideals* (Carus Mathematical Monograph No. 8, Buffalo, N. Y., The Mathematical Association of America, 1948).

Miller, K.: *Elements of Modern Abstract Algebra*, Chap. 2 (New York, Harper & Brothers, 1958).

Van Der Waerden, B.: *Modern Algebra*, Vol. 1, Chap. 3; Vol. 2, Chaps. 12–13 (New York, Ungar, 1949 and 1950).

chapter 6

VECTOR SPACES

6.1 INTRODUCTION

In this chapter we shall consider an abstract generalization of the familiar concept of a vector, as the latter occurs in elementary physics. We recall that a vector quantity is one which possesses both a magnitude and a direction and is usually represented by a *directed line segment* known as a *vector*. In this representation, the length of the segment measures the magnitude of the quantity, while its direction corresponds to the actual direction of the vector quantity. Familiar examples of vector quantities are forces, displacements, velocities, and accelerations.

There is a simple arithmetic of plane vectors which we now review very briefly. Two vectors are *equal* if they have the same length and direction. The *sum* $\mathbf{A} + \mathbf{B}$ of two vectors $\mathbf{A}$ and $\mathbf{B}$ is obtained with the use of the *parallelogram* or *triangle* law, as indicated in the figure below.

Thus, to obtain the sum of the vectors **A** and **B,** we place the tail of **B** on the head of **A**, and draw the directed segment from the tail of **A** to the head of **B**. This vector, a diagonal of the associated parallelogram, is the sum of **A** and **B** in both magnitude and direction, and we note that this direction is ordinarily different from that of either **A** or **B**.

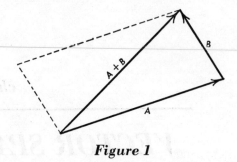

Figure 1

Another arithmetic operation of elementary vector analysis is usually known as *scalar multiplication* or *multiplication by a scalar.* We indicate this type of multiplication by writing a real number (i.e., a *scalar*) in juxtaposition with a vector. The result of this multiplication is a vector in the same direction as the original, but with a magnitude that is ordinarily different. For example, if **A** is a vector, the vectors 2**A**, 3**A**, and $\sqrt{3}$ **A** are vectors in the same direction as **A**, but whose magnitudes are, respectively, twice, three times, and the square root of three times as great as that of **A**. These vectors are shown in the diagram below. The product of a scalar and a vector is sometimes referred to as a "scalar product," but this usage is to be discouraged in deference to another "product" of two vectors which is a scalar. This latter product is referred to later as an "inner product," but the designation "scalar product" is also used in this connection.

We have recalled that the representation of a vector quantity as a directed line segment depends only on its magnitude and direction, so that the actual location of the segment is quite arbitrary. This suggests that it should be permissible to consider that all plane vectors emanate from the origin of a Cartesian coordinate system. But then each vector is completely determined by the coordinate pair of its end point, and so it is permissable to consider this coordinate pair as the algebraic equivalent of the vector. If, in fact, we agree to identify in this way any vector with its associated coordinate pair, it can be seen that the relation of equality

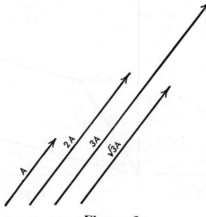

Figure 2

and the operations of addition and scalar multiplication in the set of plane vectors are equivalent to the equality relation and operations defined in the set of ordered pairs of real numbers as follows:

$$(a_1, b_1) = (a_2, b_2) \text{ if and only if } a_1 = a_2 \text{ and } b_1 = b_2;$$
$$(a_1, b_1) + (a_2, b_2) = (a_1 + a_2, b_1 + b_2);$$
$$c(a, b) = (ca, cb).$$

The definition of equality states, in effect, that two vectors are equal if their end points have the same coordinates. The rule for addition requires that the coordinates of the end point of the sum of two vectors be the respective sums of the coordinates of the end points of the vectors; this is in accordance with the parallelogram law. Finally, the rule for multiplication of a vector by a scalar states that this multiplication effects a multiplication of each of the coordinates of the end point of the vector by this scalar; and so this results in a stretching or compression of the vector, without any change in direction. In Figures 3 and 4 we have illustrated the two vector operations, with vectors considered as coordinate pairs.

If we consider $-\mathbf{A}$ to be the vector with the same magnitude as $\mathbf{A}$ but oriented in the opposite direction, it is clear that $\mathbf{A}$ and $-\mathbf{A}$ will annihilate each other on addition. Hence, if we designate the vector with zero magnitude by $\mathbf{0}$, we have $\mathbf{A} + (-\mathbf{A}) = \mathbf{0}$. More-

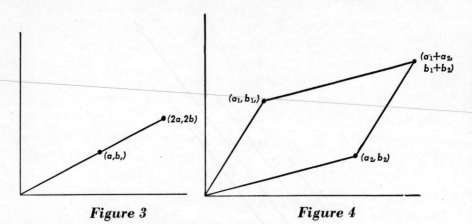

Figure 3   **Figure 4**

over, if $\mathbf{A} = (a_1, b_1)$ then $-\mathbf{A} = (-a_1, -b_1)$. If follows easily from either the physical concept or the arithmetic of vectors as coordinate pairs that $\mathbf{A} + (\mathbf{B} + \mathbf{C}) = (\mathbf{A} + \mathbf{B}) + \mathbf{C}$, and $\mathbf{A} + \mathbf{B} = \mathbf{B} + \mathbf{A}$, for arbitrary plane vectors $\mathbf{A}, \mathbf{B}, \mathbf{C}$. Hence we have the following result:

(1)   The set of all plane vectors comprises an
                 abelian group under vector addition.

The properties of scalar multiplication which are listed in (2) below can be verified either with reference to the meaning of the physical concept or directly from the arithmetic of coordinate pairs:

$$a(\mathbf{A} + \mathbf{B}) = a\mathbf{A} + a\mathbf{B}$$
(2) $$(a + b)\mathbf{A} = a\mathbf{A} + b\mathbf{A}$$
$$(ab)\mathbf{A} = a(b\mathbf{A})$$
$$1\mathbf{A} = \mathbf{A}.$$

In the above equations, $\mathbf{A}$ and $\mathbf{B}$ are arbitrary plane vectors, while a and b are arbitrary real numbers. We have used 1, as usual, to mean the multiplicative identity of the real number system.

Along with vector addition and scalar multiplication, most studies of elementary vector analysis include another operation on any two vectors known as their *inner product*. This is a metric concept, and it happens that a large part of the theory of analytic geometry depends only on the other two operations. In particular, the theory of linear dependence and linear transformations—which is to be the principal topic of this chapter—does not involve any metric notions. Thus we shall not be concerned with inner products.

The basic example we have given of a vector, as either a plane directed line segment or as an ordered pair of real numbers, is an illustration of an element of a *two-dimensional vector space over the field of real numbers*. The vector space is said to be "over the field of real numbers" because the scalars are real numbers. The idea of dimension will be made precise later, but for our example we may say tentatively that the *dimension* is two because it requires an ordered *pair* of real numbers to determine each vector.

Problems 6–1

**1. Use the arithmetic of ordered pairs to prove that the additive set of two-dimensional plane vectors is abelian and associative.

2. Use a diagram to illustrate the distributive law, $a(A + B) = aA + aB$, for vectors A, B and a real number a.

3. Show that every plane vector—considered as a directed line segment—can be represented as the sum of two vectors, one parallel to each of the coordinate axes of the Cartesian plane.

4. If $(1, 1)$ and $(3, 2)$ represent the vectors A and B, respectively, give the ordered pair representation of **(a)** $-A$; **(b)** $-B$; **(c)** $A + B$; **(d)** $A + 2B$.

5. With A and B as in **Problem 4**, and C represented by $(2, -3)$, determine the ordered pair representation of **(a)** $A - B + C$; **(b)** $2A - 3B + 4C$; **(c)** $(2A + 3B) + (4A - 6C) + 5B$.

6. Use a diagram to show that the sum of three vectors, considered as directed line segments, can be accomplished by "stringing" them together in a broken line with the head of one on the tail of the next and then joining the tail of the first with the head of the third. Generalize this to obtain the sum of any number of plane vectors.

6.2 GENERALIZATIONS

The basic example of the vector space of ordered pairs of real numbers can be readily generalized in two ways. In the first place, the "dimension"—which was two in the example—can be made arbitrary. That is, instead of ordered *pairs* of real numbers we can consider ordered sets or *n-tuples* $(a_1, a_2, \cdots, a_n)$ of n real numbers $a_1, a_2, \cdots, a_n$, where these numbers are called the *components* of the *n*-tuple. The definition of equality and the rules for addition and scalar multiplication for *n*-tuples will be strictly analogous to those in the case of ordered pairs. It is commonplace in physics to use *space* vectors for displacements, velocities, and accelerations, with components in three, mutually perpendicular directions. In a study of relativity the fourth dimension of time is included so that, in the four-dimensional world of relativity, each vector has four components. Even in Newtonian physics a force acting on a rigid body is often considered to have six components, three of a translational and three of a rotational nature. So there are many occasions when a physicist uses vectors with more than two components. To the mathematician it is more satisfying to make the number of components or the "dimension" of a vector quite arbitrary and to work with the vectors as *n*-tuples.

The other way in which the vectors of the introductory example can be generalized is in the choice of the number system from which the components are selected. In most physical applications the components of a vector are real numbers, though vectors with complex components are used regularly in the theory of electric circuits. It would appear to be a reasonable generalization to allow the field of real numbers to be replaced by an arbitrary field F, and we shall do this in our subsequent discussions. It is possible to go a step further and define vector spaces over division rings, but then the idea of "left" and "right" space arises—a matter which we do not wish to discuss at this time.

To recapitulate, we have generalized the primitive example of the preceding section to the vector space of *n*-tuples, with components in an arbitrary field F. We shall regularly use $\mathcal{V}_n(F)$ to designate this vector space. As indicated earlier, the definitions of equality and the two operations of vector addition and scalar multiplication are as follows:

$(a_1, a_2, \cdots, a_n) = (b_1, b_2, \cdots, b_n)$ if and only if $a_i = b_i$, $i = 1, 2, \cdots, n$;

$(a_1, a_2, \cdots, a_n) + (b_1, b_2, \cdots, b_n) = (a_1 + b_1, a_2 + b_2, \cdots, a_n + b_n)$;

$c(a_1, a_2, \cdots, a_n) = (ca_1, ca_2, \cdots, ca_n)$, for arbitrary $c \in F$.

It is a simple matter to check that properties **(1)** and **(2)** of our primitive vector space of §**6.1** remain in effect for $\mathcal{U}_n(F)$. (See **Problem 1.**)

We now direct our attention away from the *elements* of the vector spaces which we have considered, and use properties **(1)** and **(2)** to give a characterization of an *abstract vector space*.

> **Definition.** Let $\mathcal{U} = \{\xi, \eta, \cdots\}$ be a set of elements in which is defined an additive binary composition. Moreover, let us define a multiplication of the elements of $\mathcal{U}$ by the elements $\{a, b, \cdots\}$ of a field F, so that $a\xi \in \mathcal{U}$, for arbitrary $a \in F$ and arbitrary $\xi \in \mathcal{U}$. Then $\mathcal{U}$ is an *abstract vector space over* F, with the elements of $\mathcal{U}$ called *vectors* and the elements of F called *scalars*, provided the following conditions are satisfied, for arbitrary $\xi, \eta \in \mathcal{U}$ and arbitrary $a, b \in F$:
> 1. $\mathcal{U}$ is an additive abelian group;
> 2. $a(\xi + \eta) = a\xi + a\eta; (a + b)\xi = a\xi + b\xi; (ab)\xi = a(b\xi); 1\xi = \xi.$

The operations are called *vector addition* and *scalar multiplication*. We draw attention to the fact that properties **1** and **2** are the same as properties **1** and **2** of our basic example of §**6.1**. In addition it probably should be emphasized that the elements of $\mathcal{U}$ are no longer necessarily n-tuples, but are merely elements of a set in which our two operations have been appropriately defined.

It is easy to think of examples of the vector space concept. Of course the space $\mathcal{U}_n(F)$ of n-tuples is fundamental, and will, at a later date, prove to be of even more importance than is now evident. The field of complex numbers is a vector space over the field of real numbers. In this case, the "vectors" are the complex numbers, and the real numbers play the role of scalars, while the vector space operations are identified with the familiar operations in the complex number system. It is immediate that conditions **1** and **2** are satisfied. Another elementary example is provided by the ring $R[x]$ of polynomials in a symbol x, with coefficients in the field R of rational numbers. In this example, the "vectors" are the polynomials, while the scalars are the elements of R. The ordinary operations of polynomial addition and multiplication by field elements are the operations of the vector space, and it is elementary to check that conditions 1 and 2 are satisfied **(Problem 2)**. The preceding example can be modified to include only polynomials of, at most, some finite degree—say polynomials of degree three or less. Our illustration with $\mathcal{V}_n(F)$ can also be modified so that the "vectors" are infinite sequences $(a_1, a_2, a_3, \cdots)$, with operations analogous to those of $\mathcal{V}_n(F)$; or we can consider the "vectors" to be infinite sequences, each with a finite number of nonzero components. In either of these cases, the validity of properties 1 and 2 can be easily established.

As a final, and not quite so simple, example of a vector space, consider the set of all continuous real-valued functions on R^*. The functions are the "vectors," and two functions f and g are *equal* if $xf = xg$, for each $x \in R^*$. We define vector addition in the familiar way: $x(f + g) = xf + xg$, for any $x \in R^*$. The scalars are the real numbers, and scalar multiplication is defined as follows: $x(cf) = c(xf)$, for each $x \in R^*$ and arbitrary scalar $c \in R^*$. It is easy to verify that conditions 1 and 2 are satisfied, so that the set of functions under consideration forms a vector space over R^*. If we wish, we may regard any function f of the space as having a "component" xf at each point $x \in R^*$. The number of components of each vector is then infinite.

Problems 6–2

*1. Verify that the "space" of 3-tuples of real numbers does satisfy requirements 1 and 2 of a vector space.

*2. Verify that the "space" of polynomials in x with real coefficients does satisfy requirements 1 and 2 of a vector space.

*3. Verify that the "space" of functions described above does satisfy requirements 1 and 2 of a vector space.

**4. Let $\xi = (1, -2, 3)$, $\eta = (-3, -2, 5)$, and $\zeta = (2, -5, 6)$.
   (a) Determine $\xi + 2\eta - 3\zeta$.
   (b) Solve the equation $4\xi + 2x - 3\zeta = 0$ for x.

5. Let $\xi = (0, i, -2)$, $\eta = (1 + i, -i, 4)$, and $\zeta = (1 - i, -3, 1)$.
   (a) Determine $4\xi - 2\eta + \zeta$.
   (b) Solve the equation $3y - 6\xi = 2\eta$ for y.

6. Prove that the set of all ordered triples (a_1, a_2, a_3) of real numbers such that $2a_1 + 3a_2 - 5a_3 = 0$ is a vector space over the field R^*.

7. Decide whether the set of all real-valued functions on R^* such that

$xf = (x + 1)f$ for each function f of the set is a vector space over R^*.

8. Consider the set of all polynomials in a symbol x with real coefficients and zero constant term, and decide whether it constitutes a vector space over the field R^*, with the usual polynomial operations.

9. Show that the polynomials of the set $\{0, 1, 2, x + 1, x + 2, 2x + 1, 2x + 2, x, 2x\}$ constitute the elements of a vector space over the field $I/(3)$, with the usual operations for polynomials.

6.3 SIMPLE PROPERTIES OF A VECTOR SPACE

Before we proceed with any further development of the theory of vector spaces, it might be well to consider the matter of how vector spaces fit into the general category of algebraic systems. For, while vector addition is quite normal, the operation of scalar multiplication has some unusual features. Our familiar concept of an operation in a set S is a mapping of $S \times S$ into S, but in the case of scalar multiplication the scalars or "operators" are elements of a set which is ordinarily quite different from the set of vectors. If F is the field of scalars, scalar multiplication of the members of a vector space $\mathcal{U}$ is a mapping of $F \times \mathcal{U}$ into $\mathcal{U}$. The actual effect of a scalar multiplier is that of an operator which induces an endomorphism in $\mathcal{U}$, where $\mathcal{U}$ is regarded as an additive abelian group. For if $a \in F$ and $\xi, \eta \in \mathcal{U}$, we have $a(\xi + \eta) = a\xi + a\eta$, which is the characteristic property of an endomorphism—except for the minor detail that in the past we have usually written a mapping symbol on the right of the element mapped. A vector space is then an example of the more general type of algebraic system, which is described in the following definition.

Definition.   A *group with operators* is an algebraic system which consists of a group G and a set M (known as the *operators*), with the property that the mapping $x \to mx$, where $x \in G$ and $m \in M$, is an endomorphism of G.

Of course it is apparent that our definition of a vector space requires that it possess certain additional properties, but it is nonetheless a group with operators. The manner in which the product

mx is determined varies from system to system, but it is important to understand that in any case mx is in the original system G. For vector spaces, the operators are the scalars and scalar multiplication has been defined to obey the rules designated in previous sections as (2). An ideal in a ring is another example of a group with operators. In this case the additive group of the ideal is the basic group of the system, and the set of operators comprises the whole ring wherein scalar multiplication is identified with ordinary ring multiplication. There is an elaborate theory of groups with operators, which includes much of the theories of vector spaces and ideals as special cases. However, now that we have established the position of vector spaces within the framework of algebraic systems, we shall leave the more general study of groups with operators and continue our study of vector spaces.

Our definition of a vector space implies the existence of a vector $-\xi$, associated with each vector ξ, such that $\xi + (-\xi) = 0$. The symbol 0 in this equation designates the zero vector—i.e., the additive identity of the group of the vector space—but in other contexts the same symbol will designate the zero element of the coefficient field. (By this time the student should be used to the multiple usage of the symbols 0 and 1!) A few of the elementary properties of a vector space are described in the following theorem.

Theorem 6.31   Let $\mathcal{V}$ be a vector space over the field F. Then, for any $a \in F$ and $\xi \in \mathcal{V}$, the following are true:

1. $a0 = 0$;
2. $0\xi = 0$;
3. $a(-\xi) = (-a)\xi = -a\xi$;
4. if $a\xi = 0$, then either $a = 0$ or $\xi = 0$.

Proof.   Since $a\xi = a(\xi + 0) = a\xi + a0$, it follows that $a0 = 0$, which is **1**. To prove **2**, we note that $0\xi = (0 + 0)\xi = 0\xi + 0\xi$, so that $0\xi = 0$. Since $a\xi + a(-\xi) = a(\xi - \xi) = a0 = 0$, it follows that $a(-\xi)$ is the additive inverse of $a\xi$, and so $a(-\xi) = -a\xi$. Also, $a\xi + (-a)\xi = (a - a)\xi = 0\xi = 0$, so that $(-a)\xi = -a\xi$, completing the proof of **3**. Finally, if $a \neq 0$, then a^{-1} exists. Hence if $a\xi = 0$, $0 = a^{-1}(a\xi) = (a^{-1}a)\xi = 1\xi = \xi$, so that $\xi = 0$ and **4** is proven.

Whenever an algebraic system is discussed, the notion of a subsystem arises. In the case of a vector space $\mathcal{V}$, the subsystem is usually referred to as a *subspace* and is merely a subset of $\mathcal{V}$, which is itself a vector space with respect to the operations of $\mathcal{V}$. The proof of the following important result is almost immediate.

Theorem 6.32 A nonempty subset S of a vector space is a subspace if S is closed under the operations of addition and scalar multiplication of the vector space.

Proof. Since $-x = (-1)x$, for any vector $x \in S$, it follows that $-x \in S$. Hence the supposition on closure requires that $y - x = y + (-x) \in S$, for arbitrary $x, y \in S$; whence an application of **Theorem 4.51** shows that S is an additive abelian subgroup. The other requirements for a subspace are evidently satisfied by S **(Problem 2)**.

As an illustration of the preceding theorem, consider the elements of $\mathcal{V}_3(F)$ of the form $(x_1, 0, x_3)$, where $x_1, x_3 \in F$. It is clear that the sum of two elements of this form is another element of the same form, and an almost immediate application of **Theorem 6.32** shows that these elements form a subspace **(Problem 3)**. Similarly, it can be shown that the set of all polynomials in a symbol x, with real coefficients and degree at most 5, is a subspace of the vector space $R[x]$. In like manner we can show that the set of all continuous real-valued functions on R^* comprises a subspace of the vector space of all functions on R^*, with the usual operations for functions.

By a "linear combination" of vectors $\xi_1, \xi_2, \cdots, \xi_n$ from a vector space over a field F we mean an element of the form $c_1\xi_1 + c_2\xi_2 + \cdots + c_n\xi_n$, where $c_1, c_2, \cdots, c_n \in F$. For a particularly interesting application of **Theorem 6.32** let us consider the set of all such linear combinations of the given vectors and derive the following important result.

Theorem 6.33 The set S of all linear combinations of an arbitrary set of vectors from a vector space $\mathcal{V}$ is a subspace of $\mathcal{V}$.

Proof. In the symbolism of the paragraph preceding the theorem, let us suppose that $c_1\xi_1 + c_2\xi_2 + \cdots + c_n\xi_n = \xi \in S$ and also $c_1'\xi_1 + c_2'\xi_2 + \cdots + c_n'\xi_n = \xi' \in S$. Then $\xi + \xi' = (c_1 + c_1')\xi_1 + (c_2 + c_2')\xi_2 + \cdots + (c_n + c_n')\xi_n \in S$; and likewise, $c\xi = c(c_1\xi_1) + c(c_2\xi_2) + \cdots + c(c_n\xi_n) = (cc_1)\xi_1 + (cc_2)\xi_2 \cdots + (cc_n)\xi_n \in S$, for arbitrary $c \in F$. Hence, by **Theorem 6.32** S is a subspace of $\mathcal{V}$.

The subspace S of **Theorem 6.33** is evidently the smallest subspace that contains the given set of vectors, and so it may be called the subspace *generated* or *spanned* by them. These vectors may be called *generators* of the subspace, a word with a similar meaning in both the theory of groups and the theory of rings.

Problems 6–3

1. List the properties of a vector space that are not required in the definition of a group with operators.
*2. Complete the proof of **Theorem 6.32**.
3. Prove that the system of vectors $(x_1, 0, x_3)$, with $x_1, x_3 \in F$, is a subspace of $\mathcal{V}_3(F)$.
*4. Prove that the set-theoretic intersection of any two subspaces of a vector space $\mathcal{V}$ is a subspace of $\mathcal{V}$.
*5. If S and T are subspaces of a vector space $\mathcal{V}$, we can define $S + T$ to be the set of all sums $\xi + \eta$, with $\xi \in S$ and $\eta \in T$. Prove that $S + T$ is a subspace of $\mathcal{V}$.
*6. Prove the following "cancellation" laws for elements ξ, η of any vector space over a field F.
   (a) If $\xi \neq 0$, then $a\xi = b\xi$ implies that $a = b$, where $a, b \in F$.
   (b) If ξ and η are nonzero elements of $\mathcal{V}$, prove that $a\xi = a\eta$ implies that $\xi = \eta$, where $a(\neq 0) \in F$.
**7. Which of the following subsets of $\mathcal{V}_4(R^*)$ constitute subspaces where $X = (x_1, x_2, x_3, x_4)$?
   (a) All X where x_1, x_2, x_3, x_4 are integers.
   (b) All X where $x_2 = 2x_1$ and $x_3 = x_1 + x_2$.
   (c) All X where $x_2 = x_3 = 0$.
   (d) All X where $3x_1 - 2x_2 = 0$.
8. Determime all subspaces of $\mathcal{V}_2(I/(3))$.
9. Which of the following subsets of real-valued functions on R^* are subspaces of the vector space of all such functions?
   (a) All polynomial functions of degree 5.
   (b) All functions f such that $xf = (x - 1)f$ [or $f(x) = f(x - 1)$].
   (c) All polynomial functions of degree 5 or less—including the zero function.
   (d) All functions f such that $3(0f) = 2(1f)$ [or $3f(0) = 2f(1)$].

10. The additive group of $\mathcal{U}_2(I/(2))$ has four elements. List them and decide whether the group is isomorphic to $I/(4)$.
11. The additive group of $\mathcal{U}_2(I/(3))$ has nine elements. List them and decide whether the group is isomorphic to $I/(9)$.
12. In $\mathcal{U}_3(R)$ let S be the subspace spanned by $(1, 2, -1)$, $(1, 0, 2)$, and $(-1, 4, -8)$, while T is the subspace spanned by all vectors of the form $(x_1, 0, x_3)$. Refer to **Problems 4** and **5** and describe the intersection of S and T and also the space $S + T$.
13. Show that every vector in $\mathcal{U}_3(R)$ can be expressed as a linear combination of $(1, 1, 1)$, $(1, 0, 1)$, and $(1, -1, -1)$.

6.4 LINEAR DEPENDENCE

The notion of *dimension* of a vector space of n-tuples was introduced intuitively in the early sections of this chapter, but up to this point we have not defined it precisely for an abstract vector space. In this section we define the concept of *linear dependence*, an idea which plays a central role in the theory of vector spaces and in particular in connection with any definition of dimension.

> **Definition.** A set of vectors $\{\xi_1, \xi_2, \cdots, \xi_n\}$ is said to be *linearly dependent* over the field F of scalars, if and only if there exist scalars $c_1, c_2, \cdots, c_n$, *not all zero*, such that $c_1\xi_1 + c_2\xi_2 + \cdots + c_n\xi_n = 0$. Otherwise, the vectors $\xi_1, \xi_2, \cdots, \xi_n$ are *linearly independent*. That is, the vectors $\xi_1, \xi_2, \cdots, \xi_n$ are linearly independent if $c_1 = c_2 = \cdots = c_n = 0$ whenever $c_1\xi_1 + c_2\xi_2 + \cdots + c_n\xi_n = 0$.

For example, in $\mathcal{U}_3(R)$ the vectors $(1, 0, 1)$, $(0, 1, 1)$, $(1, 3/2, 5/2)$ are linearly dependent over the field R of rational numbers, for it is easy to check that $2(1, 0, 1) + 3(0, 1, 1) - 2(1, 3/2, 5/2) = (0, 0, 0) = 0$. On the other hand it is clear that the vectors $(1, 0, 0)$, $(0, 1, 0)$, $(0, 0, 1)$ constitute a linearly independent set over the rational numbers. For if $c_1(1, 0, 0) + c_2(0, 1, 0) + c_3(0, 0, 1) = (c_1, c_2, c_3) = (0, 0, 0)$, it follows that $c_1 = c_2 = c_3 = 0$. In any study of a vector space of n-tuples, questions of the solvability of systems of equations are tied up with questions of linear independence of vectors. For an example, if we wish to determine whether the vectors $(1, 1, 1)$, $(2, 0, 1)$, $(1, 2, -1)$ are linearly independent over R, we must ask whether there exist rational numbers c_1, c_2, c_3, not all zero, such that $c_1(1, 1, 1) + c_2(2, 0, 1) + c_3(1, 2, -1) = (0, 0, 0)$. The question now is whether the equations below have any nontrivial (i.e., not all zero) solutions:

$$c_1 + 2c_2 + c_3 = 0$$
$$c_1 + 0c_2 + 2c_3 = 0$$
$$c_1 + c_2 - c_3 = 0.$$

The theory of equations tells us that such a homogeneous system of equations has a nontrivial solution if and only if the determinant of the coefficients is 0. On expansion of this determinant, we find that

$\begin{vmatrix} 1 & 2 & 1 \\ 1 & 0 & 2 \\ 1 & 1 & -1 \end{vmatrix} = 5 \neq 0$. Hence the only possible solution of the sys-

tem is the trivial one, and the given vectors are linearly independent.

The following theorem expresses the essential property of linear dependence as applied to a set of vectors.

Theorem 6.41   The set $\{\xi_1, \xi_2, \cdots, \xi_n\}$ of nonzero vectors from a vector space $\mathcal{V}$ over F comprise a linearly dependent set if and only if some member of the set can be expressed as a linear combination of the preceding members.

Proof.   If ξ_k is a linear combination of ξ_1, ξ_2, $\cdots$, ξ_{k-1}, then $\xi_k = c_1\xi_1 + c_2\xi_2 + \cdots + c_{k-1}\xi_{k-1}$, for scalars c_1, c_2, $\cdots$, c_{k-1}, and this equation can be written in the form:

$$c_1\xi_1 + c_2\xi_2 + \cdots + c_{k-1}\xi_{k-1} + (-1)\xi_k + 0\xi_{k+1} + \cdots + 0\xi_n = 0.$$

Inasmuch as not all the coefficients in this equation are zero, our definition implies that the set $\{\xi_1, \xi_2, \cdots, \xi_n\}$ is linearly dependent. Conversely, suppose that $\{\xi_1, \xi_2, \cdots, \xi_n\}$ is a linearly dependent set of vectors, so that some linear combination of ξ_1, ξ_2, $\cdots$, ξ_n is equal to zero, while not all the coefficients are zero. If we select the vector with the largest subscript whose coefficient is not zero, say ξ_k, we can solve for ξ_k as a linear combination of ξ_1, ξ_2, $\cdots$, ξ_{k-1}, unless $k = 1$. But it is not possible that $k = 1$, since $c_1\xi_1 = 0$, with $c_1 \neq 0$, would imply that $\xi_1 = 0$ **(Theorem 6.31)**, contrary to assumption. Hence the theorem is proven.

Corollary. Any finite set of vectors, not all zero, contains a linearly independent subset which generates or "spans" the same space.

Proof. In the first place, we may discard any zero vector of the set. Then, if $\{\xi_1, \xi_2, \cdots, \xi_n\}$ is the remaining set of nonzero vectors, we can examine each of these vectors in order from left to right and discard it if and only if it can be expressed as a linear combination of the preceding vectors. The remaining subset of vectors will generate the same space as the original set, and since no vector is a linear combination of those which precede it in the array, **Theorem 6.41** shows that the subset is linearly independent.

Problems 6–4

1. Why is it reasonable to require in the definition of linear dependence that not all the scalar coefficients be zero?
*2. If one vector of a set of vectors is zero, could the set be linearly independent?
*3. Show that a single vector ξ comprises a linearly independent set if $\xi \neq 0$.
*4. Prove that any nonempty subset of a linearly independent set of vectors is linearly independent.
5. Let $\xi_1, \xi_2, \cdots, \xi_m$ be a linearly independent set of vectors over the field F. Then prove that if $a_1\xi_1 + a_2\xi_2 + \cdots + a_m\xi_m = b_1\xi_1 + b_2\xi_2 + \cdots + b_m\xi_m$, with $a_1, a_2, \cdots, a_m, b_1, b_2, \cdots, b_m \in F$, it follows that $a_1 = b_1, a_2 = b_2, \cdots, a_m = b_m$.
6. Let us suppose that of the five vectors $\xi_1, \xi_2, \xi_3, \xi_4, \xi_5$, vectors ξ_4 and ξ_5 can be expressed as linear combinations of the vectors which respectively precede them. Then show that ξ_1, ξ_2, ξ_3 will generate the same space as the given set of five vectors.
**7. Prove that the vectors (a_1, b_1) and (a_2, b_2) are linearly dependent over any field containing a_1, b_1, a_2, b_2, if and only if $a_1b_2 - a_2b_1 = 0$.
8. Determine whether the following sets of vectors in $\mathcal{V}_3(R)$ are linearly dependent or independent over R:
  (a) $\{(0, 1, 2), (1, 1, 1), (1, -2, 1)\}$;
  (b) $\{(1, 0, 2), (2, 0, 1), (1, 1, 1)\}$;
  (c) $\{(2, 0, 1), (0, 1, 4), (2, 1, 5)\}$;
  (d) $\{(1, 1, 1), (0, 3, 2), (1, 0, 0), (2, 1, -1)\}$.
9. Prove that two vectors comprise a linearly dependent set if and only if one is a scalar multiple of the other.

10. Determine whether the following sets of vectors from $\mathcal{U}_3(I/(3))$ are linearly dependent or independent:
    (a) $\{(1, 2, 1), (0, 1, 1)\}$;
    (b) $\{(0, 1, 1), (0, 2, 2)\}$;
    (c) $\{(1, 0, 2), (1, 1, 1), (2, 2, 1)\}$.

11. If $c_1\xi_1 + c_2\xi_2 + c_3\xi_3 = 0$, where ξ_1, ξ_2, ξ_3 are vectors and c_1, c_2, c_3 are scalars such that $c_1 c_3 \neq 0$, show that ξ_1 and ξ_2 generate the same subspace as do ξ_2 and ξ_3.

12. In the space $R[x](R)$, decide whether the vectors $1 + 2x$, $\frac{1}{2} - x$, $2 + x - 3x^2$ comprise a linearly independent set.

13. Prove that three vectors with rational components are linearly independent in $\mathcal{U}_3(R^*)$, if and only if they are linearly independent in $\mathcal{U}_3(R)$.

14. For what values of x and y are vectors $(x, y, 3)$, $(2, x - y, 1)$ linearly independent in $\mathcal{U}_3(R^*)$?

15. Show that the vectors $(1, -1, 1)$, $(8, 4, 2)$, $(2, 2, 0)$, $(2, 6, -2)$ comprise a linearly dependent set of vectors in $\mathcal{U}_3(R^*)$ and determine a linearly independent subset which generates the same subspace of $\mathcal{U}_3(R^*)$.

16. Determine maximal subsets of linearly independent vectors of the following sets of vectors:
    (a) $\{(1, 0, 1), (2, 0, 1), (3, 0, 0), (3, 0, 1)\}$ in $\mathcal{U}_3(R^*)$;
    (b) $\{(6, 3, -9), (3, -2, 1), (2, 1, -3), (3, 1, -8), (5, 2, -11)\}$ in $\mathcal{U}_3(R)$;
    (c) $\{(2, 0, 1), (1, 2, 1), (0, 0, 2), (1, 2, 2)\}$ in $\mathcal{U}_3(I/(3))$;
    (d) $\{1, x, 2x^2 + 1, x^3 - 2x, x - 1\}$ in $R[x](R)$.

6.5 BASES FOR A VECTOR SPACE

A set of vectors $\{\xi_1, \xi_2, \cdots, \xi_n\}$ has been called a set of *generators* for a vector space $\mathcal{U}$ over F if each $\xi \in \mathcal{U}$ can be expressed in the form $\xi = c_1\xi_1 + c_2\xi_2 + \cdots + c_n\xi_n$, for suitable $c_1, c_2, \cdots, c_n \in F$. The notion of a "basis" is closely associated with that of a set of generators, and this association is made clear by the following definition.

Definition.   A *basis* for a vector space is a set of generators with the property that each vector of the space can be expressed in a *unique* way as a linear combination of the generating elements with scalar coefficients.

In the symbolism introduced above this means that the set $\{\xi_1, \xi_2, \cdots, \xi_n\}$ is a basis if $c_1, c_2, \cdots, c_n$ are *unique* elements of F, dependent only on the vector ξ.

Theorem 6.51. A set of vectors forms a basis for a vector space if and only if the vectors of the set are linearly independent and generate the space.

Proof. If $\{\xi_1, \xi_2, \cdots, \xi_n\}$ is a basis for a vector space $\mathcal{V}$, these vectors certainly generate $\mathcal{V}$. Moreover, if there exist scalars $c_1, c_2, \cdots, c_n$ such that $c_1\xi_1 + c_2\xi_2 + \cdots + c_n\xi_n = 0 = 0\xi_1 + 0\xi_2 + \cdots + 0\xi_n$, the uniqueness of representation of the vector 0 requires that $c_1 = c_2 = \cdots = c_n = 0$. Hence a basis is a linearly independent set of generators. Conversely, suppose that $\{\xi_1, \xi_2, \cdots, \xi_n\}$ is a linearly independent set of generators and that some vector ξ has two representations in terms of this basis as follows: $\xi = c_1\xi_1 + c_2\xi_2 + \cdots + c_n\xi_n = d_1\xi_1 + d_2\xi_2 + \cdots + d_n\xi_n$, for certain scalars $c_1, c_2, \cdots, c_n, d_1, d_2, \cdots, d_n$. But then $(c_1 - d_1)\xi_1 + (c_2 - d_2)\xi_2 + \cdots + (c_n - d_n)\xi_n = 0$, and the linear independence of the generators requires that $c_1 = d_1, c_2 = d_2, \cdots, c_n = d_n$. Hence each vector of $\mathcal{V}$ has a unique representation, and $\{\xi_1, \xi_2, \cdots, \xi_n\}$ is a basis.

As a prelude to **Theorem 6.52,** the proof of which is relatively difficult, let us consider a proof of the following simple proposition: *If a vector space $\mathcal{V}$ has a basis of two elements η_1, η_2, any three vectors ξ_1, ξ_2, ξ_3 of $\mathcal{V}$ are linearly dependent.* If one of ξ_1, ξ_2, ξ_3 is 0, the set is clearly dependent (**Problem 2 of Problems 6-4**), so let us assume that each of these vectors is nonzero. Then there exist scalars $c_{11}, c_{12}, c_{21}, c_{22}, c_{31}, c_{32}$, where no two with the same first subscript are 0, such that

$$\xi_1 = c_{11}\eta_1 + c_{12}\eta_2$$
$$\xi_2 = c_{21}\eta_1 + c_{22}\eta_2$$
$$\xi_3 = c_{31}\eta_1 + c_{32}\eta_2.$$

If perchance $c_{12} = c_{22} = c_{32} = 0$, the vectors ξ_1, ξ_2, ξ_3 are in the subspace $\mathcal{V}_0$ of scalar multiples of η_1. In this case $c_{21}\xi_1 + (-c_{11})\xi_2 + 0\xi_3 = 0$, where neither c_{21} nor c_{11} is 0, so that the set $\{\xi_1, \xi_2, \xi_3\}$ is linearly dependent as desired. If, on the other hand, at least one of ξ_1, ξ_2, ξ_3.

say ξ_3, is not in $\mathcal{V}_0$, so that $c_{32} \neq 0$, we can define two vectors ζ_1 and ζ_2 which *are* in $\mathcal{V}_0$ as follows:

$$\zeta_1 = \xi_1 - c_{12}(c_{32}^{-1})\xi_3; \ \zeta_2 = \xi_2 - c_{22}(c_{32}^{-1})\xi_3.$$

But since each vector in $\mathcal{V}_0$ is a scalar multiple of η_1, there exist scalars d_1, d_2 such that $\zeta_1 = d_1\eta_1$ and $\zeta_2 = d_2\eta_1$, so that $d_2\zeta_1 + (-d_1)\zeta_2$ $= d_1d_2\eta_1 - d_1d_2\eta_2 = 0$. If we replace ζ_1 and ζ_2 by their equivalent representations in terms of ξ_1, ξ_2, ξ_3, this equation becomes $d_2\zeta_1 + (-d_1)\zeta_2 = 0 = d_2\xi_1 + (-d_1)\xi_2 + (-c_{32}^{-1})(d_2c_{12} - d_1c_{22})\xi_3$, which shows, if d, and d_2 are not both zero, that $\{\xi_1, \xi_2, \xi_3\}$ is a linearly dependent set. If $d_1 = d_2 = 0$, then $\zeta_1 = \zeta_2$ and so $\xi_1 - \xi_2 + c_{32}^{-1}(c_{22} - c_{12})\xi_3 = 0$, and again $\{\xi_1, \xi_2, \xi_3\}$ is a linearly dependent set. Our simple proposition has thus been established.

The following result is the one from which the important property is derived.

Theorem 6.52 If a vector space $\mathcal{V}$ has a basis of n vectors, any $n + 1$ vectors from $\mathcal{V}$ are linearly dependent.

Proof. We shall prove this theorem by induction on n. First let us suppose that $n = 1$. Since a set of vectors is necessarily dependent if one of its vectors is the zero vector, we may assume that ξ_1 and ξ_2 are nonzero vectors of a vector space with one basis vector η. But then $\xi_1 = c_1\eta$ and $\xi_2 = c_2\eta$, for certain scalars c_1, c_2, and so $c_2\xi_1 + (-c_1)\xi_2 = c_1c_2\eta - c_1c_2\eta = 0$. Hence $\{\xi_1, \xi_2\}$ is a dependent set, and the theorem is proven for $n = 1$. Now let us assume that the theorem is true for $n = k$, i.e., if a vector space has a basis of k vectors, any $k + 1$ of its vectors are linearly dependent. We must show that, if a space has a basis of $k + 1$ vectors, any $k + 2$ of its vectors are linearly dependent. To this end let us consider a space with a basis $\{\eta_1, \eta_2, \cdots, \eta_{k+1}\}$. If $\xi_1, \xi_2, \cdots, \xi_{k+2}$ are $k + 2$ vectors of this space, they can be expressed in the form $\xi_i = c_{i1}\eta_1 + c_{i2}\eta_2 + \cdots + c_{i,k+1}\eta_{k+1}$, for $i = 1, 2, \cdots, k + 2$. If each ξ_i is in the subspace $\mathcal{V}_0$ generated by $\eta_1, \eta_2, \cdots, \eta_k$, our inductive assumption implies that any $k + 1$ of the vectors $\xi_1, \xi_2, \cdots, \xi_{k+2}$, are linearly dependent, and so $\{\xi_1, \xi_2, \cdots, \xi_{k+2}\}$ is a linearly dependent set. There remains the case where at least one of the vectors $\xi_1, \xi_2, \cdots, \xi_{k+2}$ is not in $\mathcal{V}_0$; let us relabel them if necessary so that $\xi_{k+2} \notin \mathcal{V}_0$, which in turn implies that $c_{k+2, k+1} \neq 0$.

But then the $k + 1$ elements $\zeta_i = \xi_i - c_{i, k+1}(c_{k+2, k+1})^{-1}\xi_{k+2}$ are in $\mathcal{U}_0$, for $i = 1, 2, \cdots, k + 1$; and by our inductive assumption there exist scalars $d_1, d_2, \cdots, d_{k+1}$, not all zero, such that $d_1\zeta_1 + d_2\zeta_2 + \cdots + d_{k+1}\zeta_{k+1} = d_1\xi_1 + d_2\xi_2 + \cdots + d_{k+1}\xi_{k+1} + (-c_{k+2, k+1})^{-1}[d_1c_{1, k+1} + \cdots + d_{k+1}c_{k+1, k+1}]\xi_{k+2} = 0$. Hence $\{\xi_1, \xi_2, \cdots, \xi_{k+2}\}$ is a linearly dependent set, and our theorem is established for $n = k + 1$. An application of the Principle of Mathematical Induction then completes the proof of the theorem for arbitrary n.

The important result in the next theorem now follows easily.

Theorem 6.53   The number of elements in a basis of a vector space $\mathcal{U}$ is unique. This number is known as the *dimension* of $\mathcal{U}$.

Proof.   For suppose $\mathcal{U}$ has two bases S_1 and S_2, with n_1 and n_2 elements, respectively. If $n_1 < n_2$ and we consider S_1 as a basis and S_2 as a set of elements, it follows from **Theorem 6.52** that S_2 is a linearly dependent set. But this is contrary to **Theorem 6.51**. A similar untenable conclusion is reached if we assume that $n_2 < n_1$, so we are forced to conclude that $n_1 = n_2$.

In the case of $\mathcal{U}_n(F)$ the vectors $\epsilon_1 = (1, 0, 0, \cdots, 0)$, $\epsilon_2 = (0, 1, 0, 0, \cdots, 0)$, $\cdots$, $\epsilon_n = (0, 0, 0, \cdots, 0, 1)$ certainly generate the space. For if $\xi = (a_1, a_2, \cdots, a_n)$ is an arbitrary element of $\mathcal{U}_n(F)$, $\xi = a_1\epsilon_1 + a_2\epsilon_2 + \cdots + a_n\epsilon_n$. Moreover, if there exist scalars $c_1, c_2, \cdots, c_n)$ such that $c_1\epsilon_1 + c_2\epsilon_2 + \cdots + c_n\epsilon_n = (c_1, c_2, \cdots c_n,) = (0, 0, \cdots, 0)$, it follows that $c_1 = c_2 = \cdots = c_n = 0$. Since any set of generators must contain a basis as a subset **(Problem 2)**, the set $\{\epsilon_1, \epsilon_2, \cdots, \epsilon_n\}$ must be a basis for $\mathcal{U}_n(F)$. This is sometimes referred to as the "ϵ-basis" of the space.

Problems 6–5

*1. If $\{\eta_1, \eta_2, \cdots, \eta_n\}$ is a basis and $\{\xi_1, \xi_2, \cdots, \xi_r\}$ is a linearly independent subset of vectors of a vector space $\mathcal{U}$, why is it clear that $\{\xi_1, \xi_3, \cdots, \xi_r, \eta_1, \eta_2, \cdots, \eta_n\}$ is a generating set?

*2. Explain why any set of generators of a vector space must contain a subset of basis elements.

**3. In the vector space of real-valued functions on R^* decide whether the following vectors are linearly independent:

     (a) 1, x, x^2; (b) 2, $\sin x$, $\cos x$; (c) 1, $\sin^2 x$, $\cos^2 x$;
     (d) x, $x + x^2$, $x^2 + 4x$, $3 - x^2$.

4. Explain why $(1, 1, 0)$ and $(0, 1, 1)$ could not comprise a basis for the space $\mathcal{U}_3(R^*)$. Generalize this result to $\mathcal{U}_n(F)$.

5. Show that the vector space of all real polynomial functions on R^* does not have a finite dimension.

6. Decide whether the following polynomial functions constitute a basis for the space of all such functions on R^* of degree 3 or less: $\{3, x^2 - x, 3x^3 + 2, x + 1\}$.

7. Prove that the set $\{a + bi, c + di\}$ is a basis for the vector space of complex numbers over the field of real numbers, if and only if $ad - bc \neq 0$.

6.6 AN IMPORTANT THEOREM

In this section we consider the problem of actually determining a basis for a vector space and conclude with an important theorem concerning any finite dimensional vector space.

For the basis-construction problem we note that any set of r linearly independent vectors of an n-dimensional vector space can be supplemented with $n - r$ other vectors to form a basis. For suppose $\{\xi_1, \xi_2, \cdots, \xi_r\}$ is a linearly independent set of vectors from a space with $\{\eta_1, \eta_2, \cdots, \eta_n\}$ as a basis. The set $\{\xi_1, \xi_2, \cdots, \xi_r, \eta_1, \eta_2, \cdots, \eta_n\}$ generates the space, as we saw in **Problem 1** of **Problems 6-5.** We now examine each of these elements in order, as in the proof of the corollary to **Theorem 6.41** and discard it if it is a linear combination of the preceding elements. Since the first r are linearly independent, none of these will be discarded, and the resulting basis of linearly independent vectors will include the original r vectors. In particular we note that *any maximal subset of linearly independent vectors is a basis for a vector space.* In other words any subset of linearly independent vectors with the property that the inclusion of any additional vector will make the set dependent is a basis set.

It is the characterization of a basis as a maximal linearly independent subset, along with the invariance of the number of elements in any basis **(Theorem 6.53)**, which allows us to determine a basis for a vector space from a given set of generators. All that is necessary is to be able to tell whether a set of vectors is linearly independent or dependent. In the case of elements of any $\mathcal{U}_n(F)$, the method discussed in §6.4 for $n = 3$ and $F = R$ could be easily generalized. For a vector space of real-valued functions on R^*, it is known* that a set of functions $f_1, f_2, \cdots, f_r$ is linearly independent if their Wronskian $W(f_1, f_2, \cdots, f_r)$ is not identically 0 on R^*, where $W(f_1, f_2, \cdots, f_r)$ is the determinant defined as follows:

$$W(f_1, f_2, \cdots, f_r) = \begin{vmatrix} f_1 & f_2 & \cdots & f_r \\ f_1' & f_2' & \cdots & f_r' \\ f_1'' & f_2'' & \cdots & f_r'' \\ \cdots & \cdots & \cdots & \cdots \\ f_1^{(r-1)} & f_2^{(r-1)} & \cdots & f_r^{(r-1)} \end{vmatrix}.$$

We do not give a method for determining the linear independence of vectors from an arbitrary vector space. For the most part, however, our examples will be drawn from the above two types of spaces.

The notion of "isomorphism," introduced in Chapter 3 for general algebraic systems, may be applied to vector spaces. We recall that an isomorphism is a bijective mapping which preserves the operations of the system to which it is applied. Hence, if $\mathcal{U}$ and $\mathcal{U}'$ are vector spaces over a field F, a bijective mapping $\xi \rightarrow \xi'$ of $\mathcal{U}$ onto $\mathcal{U}'$ is an isomorphism provided:

$$\xi_1 + \xi_2 \longrightarrow \xi_1' + \xi_2'$$
$$c\xi_1 \longrightarrow c\xi_1'$$

for arbitrary vectors $\xi_1, \xi_2 \in \mathcal{U}$, and arbitrary $c \in F$. Under these circumstances we also say that $\mathcal{U}$ is isomorphic to $\mathcal{U}'$.

The importance of spaces of n-tuples is made apparent by the following theorem.

Theorem 6.61 Any n-dimensional vector space $\mathcal{U}$ over a field F is isomorphic to the vector space $\mathcal{U}_n(F)$.

Proof. Let $\{\eta_1, \eta_2, \cdots, \eta_n\}$ be a basis for $\mathcal{U}$. We shall show that the mapping $\xi_1 = c_1\eta_1 + c_2\eta_2 + \cdots + c_n\eta_n \rightarrow (c_1, c_2, \cdots, c_n)$, where ξ_1 is an arbitrary element of $\mathcal{U}$, is the desired isomorphism. Since the representation of a vector in terms of a basis of the

---

*For example, see Earl D. Rainville, *Elementary Differential Equations*, 2nd ed., p. 100 (New York, Macmillan, 1958).

space is unique, it is clear that this mapping is bijective. Now let $\xi_2 = d_1\eta_1 + d_2\eta_2 + \cdots + d_n\eta_n$ be another arbitrary element of $\mathcal{V}$. But then $\xi_1 + \xi_2 = (c_1 + d_1)\eta_1 + (c_2 + d_2)\eta_2 + \cdots + (c_n + d_n)\eta_n$, so that $\xi_1 + \xi_2 \to (c_1 + d_1, c_2 + d_2, \cdots, c_n + d_n) = (c_1, c_2, \cdots, c_n) + (d_1, d_2, \cdots, d_n)$, thereby verifying that addition is preserved by the correspondence. Finally, if $c \in F$, $c\xi_1 = cc_1\eta_1 + cc_2\eta_2 + \cdots + cc_n\eta_n \to (cc_1, cc_2, \cdots, cc_n) = c(c_1, c_2, \cdots, c_n)$, so that scalar multiplication is also preserved by the correspondence. It follows that the mapping is an isomorphism, as desired.

The above theorem suggests that a study of finite dimensional vector spaces might well be restricted to spaces of n-tuples of field elements. While this is true, it is sometimes simpler not to do this but rather to work with vector spaces in their original definition. The theorem is an important one, however, for it gives a complete characterization of finite dimensional vector spaces. In view of the isomorphism between one of these spaces and a space of n-tuples, it is meaningful to talk about an ϵ-basis for an arbitrary n-dimensional vector space, as discussed in §6.5.

Problems 6–6

1. In the indicated vector space, determine a basis which includes the given vectors:
    (a) $(1, 1, 0)$, $(0, 1, 1)$ in $\mathcal{V}_3(R)$;
    (b) $(-3, 1, -2, 0)$, $(1, 1, 1, 0)$, $(0, 0, 1, 1)$ in $\mathcal{V}_4(R)$;
    (c) $3x$, $x^2 - 1$, $x^3 + x$ in the space of all polynomial functions on R^*, of degree 4 or less;
    (d) $2 + i$, in $C(R^*)$, where C is the space of complex numbers;
    (e) $(1, 0, 2, 1)$, $(1, 1, 0, 0)$ in $\mathcal{V}_4(I/(3))$.

2. Show that the set $\{(1, 2 + i, 3), (2 - i, i, 1), (i, 2 + 3i, 2)\}$ is a basis for $\mathcal{V}_3(C)$ and express each member of the ϵ-basis for $\mathcal{V}_3(C)$ in terms of these vectors.

**3. In $\mathcal{V}_3(R)$, determine a basis as a subset of $\{(-1, 2, 2), (2, 2, -1), (3, 0, -3), (2, -1, 2)\}$ and express the dependent member as a linear combination of these basis elements.

4. Determine a basis for the subspace of $\mathcal{V}_4(R)$ consisting of all vectors (a_1, a_2, a_3, a_4) for which $a_1 = a_2 - a_3$, and $a_3 = a_4$.

5. In $\mathcal{V}_4(R^*)$ let S be the subspace generated by $\{(1, -2, 1, -1), (2, 0, 0, 6), (-4, -4, 2, -14)\}$ and T be the subspace generated by $\{(0, 1, 1, 3), (3, -3, 0, 0), (9, -11, -2, -6)\}$. Determine the

dimensions of S, T, $S + T$, and $S \cap T$. (See **Problem 5** of **Problems 6-3**.)

6. Supplement the vectors $(1, -1, 2, 3)$, $(3, 0, 4, -2)$ to form a basis for $\mathcal{U}_4(R)$.

7. Prove that two vector spaces are isomorphic if and only if they have the same dimension.

8. Show that $\{1, 2^{1/3}, 2^{2/3}\}$ is a basis for the vector space of all polynomials, with rational coefficients, in the number $2^{1/3}$. If $\mathcal{U}_3(R)$ is mapped isomorphically onto this space so that $(1, 0, 1) \to 1$ and $(2, 3, -1) \to 2^{1/3}$, describe the possible choices for the inverse image of $2^{2/3}$.

9. Prove that an isomorphic mapping between two vector spaces is completely determined by the correspondence between their basis elements.

10. Show that the subspace of $\mathcal{U}_3(R)$, consisting of triples of rational numbers with first component 0, has dimension 2 and is isomorphic to $\mathcal{U}_2(R)$.

11. Prove that the vector space of polynomials of degree at most 3 in a symbol x, with coefficients in a field F, is isomorphic to $\mathcal{U}_4(F)$.

6.7 LINEAR TRANSFORMATIONS

The theory of matrices is closely associated with the study of vector spaces through what are known as *linear transformations* of these spaces. In fact, vector spaces may almost be considered the *raison d'être* of matrices! But first let us clarify the notion of a linear transformation.

If f and g are real-valued polynomial functions which are differentiable at the point x, and c is an arbitrary real number, it is well known from a study of differential calculus that:

$$[f(x) + g(x)]' = f'(x) + g'(x) \text{ and}$$
$$[c\, f(x)]' = c\, f'(x),$$

where we have used the customary symbolism of calculus. If we consider the mapping $f \to f'$ of a polynomial function onto its derived function (or derivative), this provides us with an example of a *linear transformation* of the vector space of all such polynomial functions onto itself. For the derivative of the sum of two functions is the sum of their derivatives, and the derivative of a scalar multiple of any function is the same scalar multiple of its derivative. To be precise we have the following definition.

Definition. A *linear transformation* $T: \mathcal{V}_1 \to \mathcal{V}_2$ of a vector space $\mathcal{V}_1$ into a vector space $\mathcal{V}_2$ over the same field F is a mapping of $\mathcal{V}_1$ into $\mathcal{V}_2$ such that:

$$(\xi_1 + \xi_2)T = \xi_1 T + \xi_2 T \text{ and}$$
$$(c\xi_1)T = c(\xi_1 T),$$

for arbitrary vectors $\xi_1, \xi_2 \in \mathcal{V}_1$ and an arbitrary scalar $c \in F$. In many instances the spaces $\mathcal{V}_1$ and $\mathcal{V}_2$ are the same space $\mathcal{V}$, and then we speak simply of a *linear transformation of* $\mathcal{V}$.

It may be readily verified that the mapping defined on the polynomial function space above is in fact a linear transformation according to this definition. As another example we might consider the mapping of $\mathcal{V}_3(F)$ onto F, defined by $(c_1, c_2, c_3) \to c_1\lambda + c_2\mu + c_3\nu$, where λ, μ, ν are arbitrary but fixed elements of F. The student should verify that this is a linear transformation **(Problem 1)**. This type of linear transformation is more frequently called a *linear function* on $\mathcal{V}_3(F)$, for it maps the elements of the vector space onto the field F of scalars. Of course, the field may be considered a vector space of dimension 1 over itself! For we can regard the additive group of the field as the basic group of the vector space, with all the field elements as scalars, and consider the identity 1 (or any nonzero field element) as a basis. Hence a linear function is a special kind of linear transformation.

There are many illustrations of a linear transformation in plane geometry. For plane geometry can be considered a study of the vector space $\mathcal{V}_2(R^*)$ of ordered pairs (x, y) of real numbers, just as solid geometry can be considered a study of $\mathcal{V}_3(R^*)$. As an illustration, let us suppose that the plane has been coordinatized with a rectangular coordinate system and that there has been effected a rotation R_θ of all points of the plane about the origin through an angle of $\theta°$. The situation "before and after" is shown in Figure 5 below. It is clear that, if ξ_1 and ξ_2 are the original vectors under observation, $(\xi_1 + \xi_2)R_\theta = \xi_1 R_\theta + \xi_2 R_\theta$; for the figure shows that the diagonal $\xi_1 + \xi_2$ of the original parallelogram is rotated onto the diagonal $\xi_1 R_\theta + \xi_2 R_\theta$ of the rotated parallelogram. Moreover, $(c\xi_1)R_\theta = c(\xi_1 R_\theta)$; for any scalar multiple of the vector ξ_1 is clearly rotated onto the same scalar multiple of $\xi_1 R_\theta$. The rotation R_θ is then a linear transformation of $\mathcal{U}_2(R^*)$ onto itself **(Problem 4)**. The following theorem is of great interest in this connection.

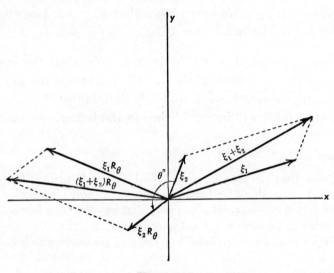

Figure 5

Theorem 6.71 Any transformation T of $\mathcal{U}_2(R^*)$ into itself defined by $(x, y) \rightarrow (x', y')$ is linear if and only if there exist real numbers a_1, a_2, b_1, b_2 such that $x' = a_1 x + a_2 y$ and $y' = b_1 x + b_2 y$.

Proof. First, let us suppose that the transformation T is defined as above so that $x' = a_1 x + a_2 y$, $y' = b_1 x + b_2 y$. It then follows that $[(x_1, y_1) + (x_2, y_2)]T = (x_1 + x_2, y_1 + y_2)T = (a_1(x_1 + x_2) + a_2(y_1 + y_2), b_1(x_1 + x_2) + b_2(y_1 + y_2)) = (a_1 x_1 + a_2 y_1 + a_1 x_2 + a_2 y_2, b_1 x_1 + b_2 y_1 + b_1 x_2 + b_2 y_2) = (a_1 x_1 + a_2 y_1, b_1 x_1 + b_2 y_1) + (a_1 x_2 + a_2 y_2, b_1 x_2 + b_2 y_2) = (x_1, y_1)T + (x_2, y_2)T$, so that T satisfies the first requirement of a linear transformation. Also, if c is an arbitrary real number, $[c(x, y)]T = (cx, cy)T = (a_1(cx) + a_2(cy), b_1(cx) + b_2(cy)) = (c(a_1 x + a_2 y), c(b_1 x + b_2 y)) = c(a_1 x + a_2 y, b_1 x + b_2 y) = c[(x, y)T]$, completing the proof that T is linear. Conversely, let T be an arbitrary linear transformation on $\mathcal{U}_2(R^*)$. Then, using the ϵ-basis for the space, with $\epsilon_1 = (1, 0)$ and $\epsilon_2 = (0, 1)$, let us suppose that $\epsilon_1 T = (a_1, b_1)$ and $\epsilon_2 T = (a_2, b_2)$, where

a_1, b_1, a_2, b_2 are certain real numbers. If (x, y) is an arbitrary vector in $\mathcal{U}_2(R^*)$, we can write $(x, y) = x\epsilon_1 + y\epsilon_2$, and the linearity condition on T implies that $(x, y)T = (x\epsilon_1 + y\epsilon_2)T = (x\epsilon_1)T + (y\epsilon_2)T = x(a_1, b_1) + y(a_2, b_2) = (xa_1 + ya_2, xb_1 + yb_2)$. Hence, if $(x, y)T = (x', y')$, we have shown that $x' = a_1x + a_2y$ and $y' = b_1x + b_2y$, as desired.

The converse portion of this theorem points out the important fact that, if the transforms of the "unit" vectors ϵ_1 and ϵ_2 are known, the linear transformation is completely determined. A more general form of this result will be established in the following section.

Problems 6–7

**1. Prove that the transformation $T: \mathcal{U}_3(F) \to F$, defined by $(c_1, c_2, c_3) \to c_1\lambda + c_2\mu + c_3\nu$ for fixed elements λ, μ, ν in F, is linear.

 2. Verify all the postulates to prove that any field can be considered a vector space of dimension 1 over itself.

 3. Prove that an "expansion" of the real plane, in which each point is moved radially out to a position k times as far from the origin as orginally, is a linear transformation of $\mathcal{U}_2(R^*)$.

 4. Why is a rotation of $\mathcal{U}_2(R^*)$ about the origin a mapping of the plane *onto* itself; i.e., why is it surjective?

 5. Show that a rotation of the Cartesian plane about the origin through an angle of θ radians is defined by $(x, y) \to (x', y')$, where $x' = x \cos \theta - y \sin \theta$ and $y' = x \sin \theta + y \cos \theta$. (Hint: Consider the transforms of ϵ_1 and ϵ_2.)

 6. Use the result of **Problem 5** to define a rotation of the Cartesian plane about the origin through an angle of 135°.

 7. A transformation T of $\mathcal{U}_2(R^*)$ into $\mathcal{U}_3(R^*)$ is defined by $(x, y) \to (x', y', z')$, where $x' = x - y$, $y' = x + y$, $z' = 2x + y$. Verify that the transformation is linear, and determine the transforms of ϵ_1 and ϵ_2 in $\mathcal{U}_2(R^*)$.

 8. Describe the geometric effect of each of the following linear transformations of $\mathcal{U}_2(R^*)$: $(x, y) \to (x', y')$.
   (a) $x' = 0$, $y' = x$; (b) $x' = cx$, $y' = cy$; (c) $x' = y$, $y' = x$;
   (d) $x' = -y$, $y' = -x$; (e) $x' = 3x$, $y' = y$.

 9. Generalize **Theorem 6.71** to apply to $\mathcal{U}_3(R^*)$.

10. Use the result of **Problem 9** to describe the transformation of $\mathcal{U}_3(R^*)$, defined by $x' = 3x$, $y' = 3y$, $z' = z$.

11. Use the result of **Problem 9** to describe the transformation of $\mathcal{U}_3(R^*)$, defined by $x' = y$, $y' = y$, $z' = x + y - 2z$.

12. Which of the following mappings of $\mathcal{U}_2(R^*)$ are linear transformations?
    - (a) $(x, y) \to (0, 0)$;
    - (b) $(x, y) \to (2x + y, x - y)$;
    - (c) $(x, y) \to (x + 1, y - x)$;
    - (d) $(x, y) \to (x, y)$.
13. A linear transformation T of $\mathcal{U}_3(R^*)$ is defined by the following: $\epsilon_1 T = \epsilon_1 + \epsilon_2$; $\epsilon_2 T = \epsilon_1 + \epsilon_3$; $\epsilon_3 T = \epsilon_2 + \epsilon_3$.
    - (a) Determine the transform of the vector $\epsilon_1 - \epsilon_2 + \epsilon_3$.
    - (b) Verify that the transforms of the ϵ-basis comprise another basis for $\mathcal{U}_3(R^*)$, and represent the vector in (a) in terms of this new basis.

6.8 THE ISOMORPHISM THEOREM

Before we establish the isomorphism theorem, which shows the important relationship between matrices and linear transformations of vector spaces, we shall derive the generalization referred to at the end of the preceding section. This result is that a linear transformation is completely determined once the transforms of any basis set are known.

Theorem 6.81 If $\{\eta_1, \eta_2, \cdots, \eta_n\}$ is a basis for a vector space $\mathcal{U}$, and $\{\xi_1, \xi_2, \cdots, \xi_n\}$ is an arbitrary set of vectors from a vector space $\mathcal{W}$, both spaces over the same field F, there is one and only one linear transformation $T : \mathcal{U} \to \mathcal{W}$, such that $\eta_1 T = \xi_1$, $\eta_2 T = \xi_2$, $\cdots$, $\eta_n T = \xi_n$. Moreover, this transformation is given by $\eta T = c_1\xi_1 + c_2\xi_2 + \cdots + c_n\xi_n$, for an arbitrary vector $\eta = c_1\eta_1 + c_2\eta_2 + \cdots + c_n\eta_n \in \mathcal{U}$.

Proof. Let us define T so that, if $\eta = \sum_{i=1}^{n} c_i\eta_i$ is an arbitrary element of $\mathcal{U}$, $\eta T = \sum_{i=1}^{n} c_i\xi_i$. If $c_i = 1$ and $c_j = 0$, for $j \neq i$, this definition requires that $\eta_i T = \xi_i$, so that T is consistent with the given mapping of the basis elements. To prove that T is linear, suppose that $\eta' = \sum_{i=1}^{n} d_i\eta_i$ is another element of $\mathcal{U}$, so that $\eta' T = \sum_{i=1}^{n} d_i\xi_i$. Then $(\eta + \eta')T = \left(\sum_{i=1}^{n} c_i\eta_i + \sum_{i=1}^{n} d_i\eta_i\right)T = \left[\sum_{i=1}^{n} (c_i + d_i)\eta_i\right]T$

$= \sum_{i=1}^{n} (c_i + d_i)\xi_i = \sum_{i=1}^{n} c_i\xi_i + \sum_{i=1}^{n} d_i\xi_i = \eta T + \eta' T$. Also, for an arbitrary $c \in F$, $(c\eta)T = \left[c\sum_{i=1}^{n} c_i \eta_i \right] T = \left[\sum_{i=1}^{n} (cc_i) \eta_i \right] T = \sum_{i=1}^{n} (cc_i) \xi_i$

$= c \left[\sum_{i=1}^{n} c_i \xi_i \right] = c(\eta T)$. Hence T is a linear transformation of $\mathcal{U}$.

Finally, T is unique with the assigned mappings, for suppose T' is another linear transformation of $\mathcal{U}$ such that $\eta_i T' = \xi_i$, $i = 1, 2, \cdots, n$. Then $\eta T' = \left(\sum_{i=1}^{n} c_i \eta_i \right) T' = \sum_{i=1}^{n} c_i (\eta_i T') = \sum_{i=1}^{n} c_i \xi_i = \eta T$.

Since η is an arbitrary element of $\mathcal{U}$, it follows that $T' = T$, as stated in the theorem.

As an illustration of this result, a linear transformation of the Cartesian plane can be completely defined by means of the following mappings:

$$\epsilon_1 = (1, 0) \longrightarrow (1, 0); \; \epsilon_2 = (0, 1) \longrightarrow (2, 1).$$

Theorem 6.81 then asserts that this transformation can be described in terms of an arbitrary vector $(x, y) \in \mathcal{U}_2(R^*)$ by

$$(x, y) = x\epsilon_1 + y\epsilon_2 \longrightarrow x(1, 0) + y(2, 1) = (x + 2y, y).$$

Expressed in this form, it is clear that this particular transformation is a horizontal "shear" in which each point is moved parallel to the x-axis a distance proportional to its ordinate. For example, under this transformation a rectangle whose sides are parallel to the coordinate axes is mapped into a parallelogram which is not a rectangle.

Let us now consider an arbitrary n-dimensional vector space $\mathcal{U}$ over a field F and which is mapped into itself by a linear transformation T_1. We have just seen that T_1 is completely determined by the images of the elements of any basis set. Thus, if $\{\eta_1, \eta_2, \eta_3, \cdots, \eta_n\}$ is a basis set for $\mathcal{U}$, let us suppose that these basis elements are mapped by T_1 as follows, where $a_{ij} \in F$, $i, j = 1, 2, \cdots, n$:

$$\eta_1 T_1 = a_{11}\eta_1 + a_{12}\eta_2 + \cdots + a_{1n}\eta_n$$
$$\eta_2 T_1 = a_{21}\eta_1 + a_{22}\eta_2 + \cdots + a_{2n}\eta_n$$
$$\cdots \cdots \cdots \cdots$$
$$\eta_n T_1 = a_{n1}\eta_1 + a_{n2}\eta_2 + \cdots + a_{nn}\eta_v.$$

Then the transformation T_1 is determined and completely described

by the matrix
$$\begin{bmatrix} a_{11} & a_{12} & \cdots & a_{1n} \\ a_{21} & a_{22} & \cdots & a_{2n} \\ \cdots\cdots\cdots\cdots \\ a_{n1} & a_{n2} & \cdots & a_{nn} \end{bmatrix}.$$

In fact, if we represent this matrix by $[a_{ij}]$ to indicate that it is the matrix with a_{ij} in its ith row and jth column, it is clear that the correspondence $T_1 \leftrightarrow [a_{ij}]$ is one-to-one between the set of linear transformations of $\mathcal{U}$ and the set of $n \times n$ matrices with elements in F. We recall that the sum and product of mappings of a set were defined in Chapter 1. Hence, since transformations of a vector space are mappings, the sum $T_1 + T_2$ and product $T_1 T_2$ of two linear transformations T_1 and T_2 have already been defined. To review, however, if ξ is an arbitrary element of the vector space $\mathcal{U}$, these operations are defined as follows:

$$\xi(T_1 + T_2) = \xi T_1 + \xi T_2; \; \xi(T_1 T_2) = (\xi T_1) T_2.$$

We are now in a position to state the important isomorphism theorem for linear transformations.

Theorem 6.82 The set of linear transformations of an n-dimensional vector space $\mathcal{U}$ over a field F forms a ring under the operations of addition and multiplication of mappings, and this ring is isomorphic to the ring of all $n \times n$ matrices with elements in F.

Proof. It is a simple matter of checking the postulates for a ring to verify that the set of all linear transformations of $\mathcal{U}$ is a ring with an identity element (**Problems 3** and **4**). We have then merely to show that the correspondence between transformations and matrices is an isomorphism. Inasmuch as we have noted already that this correspondence is one-to-one, there remains only the verification that the correspondence preserves the operations in the two rings.

In addition to $T_1 \leftrightarrow [a_{ij}]$, let $T_2 \leftrightarrow [b_{ij}]$ be the correspondence between another linear transformation T_2 of $\mathcal{U}$ and the matrix $[b_{ij}]$, where we are assuming the same basis $\{\eta_1, \eta_2, \cdots, \eta_n\}$ in both instances. Then, since $\eta_i T_1 = \sum_{j=1}^{n} a_{ij}\eta_j$ and $\eta_i T_2 = \sum_{j=1}^{n} b_{ij}\eta_j$.

$i = 1, 2, \cdots, n$, it follows that:

$$\eta_i(T_1 + T_2) = \eta_i T_1 + \eta_i T_2 = \sum_{j=1}^{n} a_{ij}\eta_j + \sum_{j=1}^{n} b_{ij}\eta_j = \sum_{j=1}^{n} (a_{ij} + b_{ij})\eta_j.$$

Hence $T_1 + T_2 \leftrightarrow [a_{ij} + b_{ij}] = [a_{ij}] + [b_{ij}]$, which verifies that addition is preserved by the correspondence. Now let us change an index symbol and write η_j instead of η_i in the formula for $\eta_i T_2$,

so that $\eta_j T_2 = \sum_{k=1}^{n} b_{jk}\eta_k, j = 1, 2, \cdots, n.$ Then $\eta_i(T_1 T_2) = (\eta_i T_1) T_2$

$$= \left(\sum_{j=1}^{n} a_{ij}\eta_j\right) T_2 = \sum_{j=1}^{n} a_{ij}\left(\sum_{k=1}^{n} b_{jk}\eta_k\right) \qquad \sum_{k=1}^{n}\left(\sum_{j=1}^{n} a_{ij}b_{jk}\right)\eta_k = \sum_{k=1}^{n} c_{ik}\eta_k,$$

where $c_{ik} = \sum_{j=1}^{n} a_{ij}b_{jk}.$ But if we recall the rule for matrix multiplication, we know that the matrix $[c_{ij}]$ is then precisely the product $[a_{ij}][b_{ij}]$ of the matrices $[a_{ij}]$ and $[b_{ij}]$. Hence $T_1 T_2 \leftrightarrow [a_{ij}][b_{ij}]$, so that the correspondence between transformations and matrices also preserves multiplication. This completes the proof of the theorem.

As a result of **Theorem 6.82** a study of linear transformations of finite dimensional vector spaces is equivalent to a study of matrices. That is, any theorem about matrices can be phrased as a theorem about linear transformations, and conversely. Sometimes a study of matrices is made in close relation to associated linear transformations; and at other times matrices are studied without any apparent connection with linear transformations, but as mere arrays of numbers. The approach to matrix theory depends on the viewpoint.

There is another point which we would like to emphasize in connection with **Theorem 6.82**. While this theorem has established an isomorphism between a ring of linear transformations and a ring of matrices, the actual correspondences depend on the basis that is chosen for the vector space. As different bases are chosen for the space, the matrix which corresponds to a *given* linear transformation T will change. One of the important problems in the theory of vector spaces is to choose a basis for a space so that the matrix of a given linear transformation is in some simple form. In matrix theory this is known as the process of reducing a matrix to its various "canonical" forms. We shall leave this problem for further investigation in courses on matrix theory.

Problems 6–8

*1. Why is the correspondence $T \leftrightarrow [a_{ij}]$ between a linear transformation and a matrix *unique* with respect to a given basis?

2. Prove the Associative and Distributive Laws for matrix multiplication by using the corresponding properties for linear transformations.

*3. Verify that the set of linear transformations of a vector space forms an abelian group under addition.

*4. Use the result of **Problem 3** and complete the proof that these linear transformations form a ring with identity, with the inclusion of the definition of multiplication of transformations.

5. Let $R^*{}_n[x]$ be the vector space of polynomials in a symbol x, with coefficients in R^* and of degree less than n. If D is the derivative operator, show that D is *nilpotent* in the sense that $D^n = 0$ (see **Problem 4** of **Problems 5-3**); and determine the matrix of D, regarded as a linear transformation, relative to the basis $\{1, x, x^2, \cdots, x^{n-1}\}$ of $R^*{}_n[x]$.

6. Let C be the vector space of complex numbers over the field R^* of real numbers. Show that the mapping $a + bi \rightarrow a - bi$ of each complex number onto its conjugate is a linear transformation and determine its associated matrix with respect to the basis $\{1, i\}$.

7. Write down the matrix of the linear transformation of $\mathcal{U}_2(R^*)$ defined by:
   (a) $(1, 0) \rightarrow (3, 0)$, $(0, 1) \rightarrow (-2, 1)$;
   (b) $(1, 0) \rightarrow (-3, 6)$, $(0, 1) \rightarrow (3, -2)$.

8. Verify that $\{(1, 1), (-2, 3)\}$ is a basis for $\mathcal{U}_2(R^*)$ and write down the matrices of the linear transformations given in **Problem 7**, with respect to this basis.

**9. A linear transformation T of $\mathcal{U}_2(R^*)$ takes $(0, 1)$ into $(0, 1)$, and $(-1, 1)$ into $(1, -2)$. What is the matrix of T with respect to the ϵ-basis of the space?

10. The matrix of a linear transformation T of $\mathcal{U}_3(R^*)$ is $[a_{ij}]$, where $a_{ij} = i^2 - ij$, $i, j = 1, 2, 3$.
   (a) Determine the transform of each element of the ϵ-basis.
   (b) Determine $(x, y, z)T$, where (x, y, z) is an arbitrary element of the space.

11. The matrix of a linear transformation of $\mathcal{U}_3(R^*)$ is $\begin{bmatrix} -1 & 0 & 3 \\ 1 & 1 & 1 \\ -2 & 0 & 1 \end{bmatrix}$

with respect to the ϵ-basis. Determine the images of each of the
following vectors under this transformation:
(a) $(-2, 3, 1)$; (b) $(1, 1, 1)$; (c) $(0, -3, 2)$.

6.9 SYSTEMS OF EQUATIONS

One of the interesting applications of both the theory of matrices
and the theory of vector spaces is in the solution of systems of linear
equations, with coefficients in an arbitrary field F. In the most
general case we have a system of the following form in which the
number n of unknowns is not necessarily the same as the number m
of equations:

(1)
$$
\begin{aligned}
a_{11}x_1 + a_{12}x_2 + \cdots + a_{1n}x_n &= b_1 \\
a_{21}x_1 + a_{22}x_2 + \cdots + a_{2n}x_n &= b_2 \\
&\cdots \\
a_{m1}x_1 + a_{m2}x_2 + \cdots + a_{mn}x_n &= b_m.
\end{aligned}
$$

The coefficients a_{ij} $(i = 1, 2, 3, \cdots, m; j = 1, 2, 3, \cdots, n)$ are, of
course, in the field F. If $b_i = 0$ for every i (i.e., all the right members
are 0), the system is said to be *homogeneous*; if at least one right
member is nonzero, the system is said to be *nonhomogeneous*. The
$m \times n$ matrix A, defined by

$$
A = \begin{bmatrix}
a_{11} & a_{12} & \cdots & a_{1n} \\
a_{21} & a_{22} & \cdots & a_{2n} \\
& \cdots & & \\
a_{m1} & a_{m2} & \cdots & a_{mn}
\end{bmatrix},
$$

is known as the *coefficient matrix* of the system (1). If we now define
the "column" matrices X and B so that $X = \begin{bmatrix} x_1 \\ x_2 \\ \cdot \\ \cdot \\ x_n \end{bmatrix}$, $B = \begin{bmatrix} b_1 \\ b_2 \\ \cdot \\ \cdot \\ b_m \end{bmatrix}$,

it follows from the definitions of matrix multiplication and the
equality of matrices that the system (1) of equations is equivalent
to the simple matrix equation $AX = B$. Any "column" matrix X_1
which satisfies the equation $AX = B$ in X is a *solution* of this
equation and provides a solution of (1).

It is clear that "column" matrices, such as X and B above, can be regarded as k-tuples (for suitable integers k) which we have chosen to write as vertical rather than horizontal arrays. Hence the set of all such column k-tuples of elements from F forms a vector space over F, when we define addition and scalar multiplication in a manner analogous to that for horizontal or row k-tuples. We note, incidently, that the addition of these k-tuple vectors of either the row or column variety is identical with what we obtain when we add them *as matrices*, and so a k-tuple may be regarded as *either* a matrix or a vector. In this and the following sections all k-tuples will be written as *column* vectors.

Before we attempt to solve the nonhomogeneous system $AX = B$, we consider the associated homogeneous equation $AX = 0$, and we have the following interesting result.

Theorem 6.91   Let $AX = 0$ be the matrix form of a system of linear equations in n unknowns, with coefficients in a field F. Then the set of all solution vectors of $AX = 0$ comprises a vector subspace of the space $\mathcal{U}_n(F)$.

> **Proof.** If X_1 and X_2 are solution vectors of $AX = 0$, we know that $AX_1 = 0$ and $AX_2 = 0$, so that $A(X_1 + X_2) = AX_1 + AX_2 = 0$ **(Problem 1)**. Moreover, $A(cX_1) = c(AX_1) = c0 = 0$, for arbitrary $c \in F$ **(Problem 2)**. Hence the set of solution vectors is closed under both addition and scalar multiplication and so, by **Theorem 6.32,** is a subspace of $\mathcal{U}_n(F)$.

Since the space $\mathcal{U}_n(F)$ has dimension n, the dimension of the subspace of solution vectors—or the *solution space*—is k where $k \leq n$. Hence, this solution space has a basis of k vectors which we can designate $X_1, X_2, \cdots, X_k$, and *every* solution of $AX = 0$ can be expressed in the form $c_1X_1 + c_2X_2 + \cdots + c_kX_k$, for suitable scalar elements $c_1, c_2, \cdots, c_k \in F$. Inasmuch as every solution of the equation has this form, we usually refer to this as the *complete solution* of $AX = 0$.

We now have the central theorem on the solutions of a system of linear equations.

Theorem 6.92   Let the complete solution of the matrix equation $AX = 0$ be $c_1X_1 + c_2X_2 + \cdots + c_kX_k$. Then if X_p is any particular solution of $AX = B$, every solution of this nonhomogeneous system can be expressed in the form $c_1X_1 + c_2X_2 + \cdots + c_kX_k + X_p$, for a suitable choice of the scalar elements $c_1, c_2, \cdots, c_k$.

Proof.   In order to prove this theorem, let $\tilde{X}$ be an arbitrary solution of $AX = B$. Then $A\tilde{X} = B$ and by assumption $AX_p = B$, so that $A\tilde{X} - AX_p = A(\tilde{X} - X_p) = 0$. Hence $\tilde{X} - X_p$ is a solution of the homogeneous system $AX = 0$ and so must have the form $c_1X_1 + c_2X_2 + \cdots + c_kX_k$, for suitable elements $c_1, c_2, \cdots, c_k \in F$. It follows that $\tilde{X} = c_1X_1 + c_2X_2 + \cdots + c_kX_k + X_p$ and, since $\tilde{X}$ is a completely arbitrary solution of $AX = 0$, the theorem is established.

We wish to point out at this time that we have not considered the question of whether a system of equations does have any solution at all. For it is quite possible for a system of nonhomogeneous equations to be "inconsistent" and to have no solution. It is clear, however, that any *homogeneous* system has the "trivial" solution in which every unknown is equal to 0, but this may or may not be the only solution. In case the system of homogeneous equations has only the trivial solution, the solution space of **Theorem 6.91** contains only the zero vector. In the following sections we shall consider the circumstances under which a system of equations can be solved.

Problems 6–9

*1. In the proof of **Theorem 6.91**, why are we justified in stating that $A(X_1 + X_2) = AX_1 + AX_2$? (Notice that this is *not* the ordinary distributive law for matrices.)

2. In the proof of **Theorem 6.91, explain why we may write $A(cX) = c(AX)$.

3. Write the following system of equations in the matrix form $AX = B$, and verify that $\begin{bmatrix} 2 \\ 3 \\ 7 \end{bmatrix}$ is a solution:

$$
\begin{aligned}
2x + y + z &= 14 \\
3x + 2y + 6z &= 54 \\
8x + y - z &- 12.
\end{aligned}
$$

4. Given the following system of equations:

$$x + y - 5z = 26$$
$$x + 2y + z = -4$$
$$x + 3y + 7z = -34$$

(a) Write the system in matrix form as $AX = B$.

(b) Verify that $\begin{bmatrix} 11 \\ -6 \\ 1 \end{bmatrix}$ is a solution of $AX = 0$, as is also any real multiple of this solution.

(c) Verify that $\begin{bmatrix} 56 \\ -30 \\ 0 \end{bmatrix}$ is a solution of $AX = B$, and that $k \begin{bmatrix} 11 \\ -6 \\ 1 \end{bmatrix}$ $+ \begin{bmatrix} 56 \\ -30 \\ 0 \end{bmatrix}$ is also a solution for any real number k. This will be an illustration of **Theorem 6.92.**

*5. Explain why the dimension of a subspace of a finite dimensional vector space must not exceed the dimension of the whole space.

*6. Explain why the solution vectors of $AX = B$ can never form a subspace as do those of the homogeneous system $AX = 0$, unless $B = 0$.

7. State the rules for the addition and scalar multiplication of column n-tuples, which are analogous to those for row n-tuples.

8. Let the left members of the equations of the system **(1)** be the respective values at a vector X of the m functions $f_1, f_2, \cdots, f_m$. Then prove that if the system of equations has a solution, the existence of scalars $c_1, c_2, \cdots, c_m$ such that $\sum_{i=1}^{m} c_i f_i = 0$ (the 0 function) implies that also $\sum_{i=1}^{m} c_i b_i = 0$. This is known as the *consistency condition* for a system of linear equations.

6.10 CRAMER'S RULE AND MATRIX INVERSION

In this and the final sections of this chapter we shall consider the problem of the actual determination of the solutions of the system of equations **(1)** of §6.9. We shall regularly designate this system by $AX = B$, where A, X, and B have the meanings assigned to them in the preceding section. There are three methods which we shall consider, not all of which are necessarily applicable to any given system of equations. For the purposes of this discussion, we shall assume that the reader is familiar with the elementary theory of determinants. Thus, if A is a *square* $n \times n$ matrix with elements in the field F, there is associated with A an *element of F* called its *determinant*, which is symbolized by det A or $|A|$. If the ith row and jth column of A are deleted, there remains an $n-1$ by $n-1$ submatrix, whose determinant is known as the *minor* M_{ij} of the element a_{ij} at the intersection of the ith row and jth column of A. The quantity $(-1)^{i+j}M_{ij}$, which we shall abbreviate by A_{ij}, is known as the *cofactor* of a_{ij}. The two following theorems will now be assumed without further proof (**Problems 2 and 3**).

Theorem 6.101 $\displaystyle\sum_{j=1}^{n}a_{ij}A_{ij} = \sum_{i=1}^{n}a_{ij}A_{ij} = \det A$, where the "unsummed" indices are fixed but arbitrary. That is, if the elements of *any* row (column) of A are respectively multiplied by their cofactors and the sum of these n products determined, the result is the determinant of A.

Theorem 6.102 $\displaystyle\sum_{i=1}^{n}a_{ji}A_{ki} = \sum_{i=1}^{n}a_{ij}A_{ik} = 0$, provided $j \neq k$.

That is, if the elements of any row (column) of A are respectively multiplied by the cofactors of the corresponding elements of a *different* row (column), and the sum of these n products is determined, the result is 0.

We now turn to a brief discussion of the first two methods which may be available for solving $AX = B$.

(a) *Cramer's Rule.* This method is essentially an "elimination" procedure, which is abbreviated by means of determinants. But first, in addition to the matrix A of coefficients, we need to define the following n matrices:

$$B_1 = \begin{bmatrix} b_1 & a_{12} & a_{13} & \cdots & a_{1n} \\ b_2 & a_{22} & a_{23} & \cdots & a_{2n} \\ \cdots\cdots\cdots\cdots \\ b_n & a_{n2} & a_{n3} & \cdots & a_{nn} \end{bmatrix}, \quad B_2 = \begin{bmatrix} a_{11} & b_1 & a_{13} & \cdots & a_{1n} \\ a_{21} & b_2 & a_{23} & \cdots & a_{2n} \\ \cdots\cdots\cdots\cdots \\ a_{n1} & b_n & a_{n3} & \cdots & a_{nn} \end{bmatrix},$$

$$\cdots B_n = \begin{bmatrix} a_{11} & a_{12} & \cdots & a_{1,n-1} & b_1 \\ a_{21} & a_{22} & \cdots & a_{2,n-1} & b_2 \\ \cdots\cdots\cdots\cdots \\ a_{n1} & a_{n2} & \cdots & a_{n,n-1} & b_n \end{bmatrix}$$

If we now multiply both members of the first equation by A_{11}, both members of the second equation by A_{21}, $\cdots$, and both members of the nth equation by A_{n1}, and then add the corresponding members of each new equation, the result is $(a_{11}A_{11} + a_{21}A_{21} + \cdots + a_{n1}A_{n1})$ $x_1 + (a_{12}A_{11} + a_{22}A_{21} + \cdots + a_{n2}A_{n1})x_2 + \cdots + (a_{1n}A_{11} + a_{2n}A_{21}$ $+ \cdots + a_{nn}A_{n1})x_n = b_1A_{11} + b_2A_{21} + \cdots + b_nA_{n1}$. It follows from **Theorem 6.102** that the coefficients of $x_2, x_3, \cdots, x_n$ are 0, while it is a consequence of **Theorem 6.101** that the coefficient of x_1 is $|A|$. Moreover, the right member of this equation is seen to be an evaluation of $|B_1|$ in terms of the first column of B_1. Hence $|A|x_1 = |B_1|$, and so $x_1 = |B_1|/|A|$, provided $|A| \neq 0$. In a similar manner **(Problem 4)** we can obtain $x_2 = |B_2|/|A|$, $x_3 = |B_3|/|A|$, $\cdots$, $x_n = |B_n|/|A|$. This result is known as Cramer's rule and may be used only if A is a square matrix with nonvanishing determinant.

(b) *Matrix Inversion.* We have seen earlier that the inverse A^{-1} of an $n \times n$ matrix, if it exists, is a unique $n \times n$ matrix such that $AA^{-1} = A^{-1}A = 1_n$, where 1_n is the identity matrix of order n. If each element a_{ij} of A is replaced by the cofactor A_{ji} of the element a_{ji} (i.e., each element is replaced by its own cofactor and the rows and columns of the resulting matrix are then interchanged in order), the new matrix is called the *adjoint* of A, and is designated adj A. It is now a matter of simple computation to verify that $\dfrac{\text{adj } A}{|A|} = A^{-1}$. For

$$\begin{bmatrix} a_{11} & a_{12} & \cdots & a_{1n} \\ a_{21} & a_{22} & \cdots & a_{2n} \\ & \cdots\cdots\cdots\cdots & \\ a_{n1} & a_{n2} & \cdots & a_{nn} \end{bmatrix} \begin{bmatrix} A_{11} & A_{21} & \cdots & A_{n1} \\ A_{12} & A_{22} & \cdots & A_{n2} \\ & \cdots\cdots\cdots\cdots & \\ A_{1n} & A_{2n} & \cdots & A_{nn} \end{bmatrix} =$$

$$\begin{bmatrix} |A| & 0 & \cdots & 0 \\ 0 & |A| & \cdots & 0 \\ & \cdots\cdots\cdots\cdots & \\ 0 & 0 & \cdots & |A| \end{bmatrix} = |A| \begin{bmatrix} 1 & 0 & \cdots & 0 \\ 0 & 1 & \cdots & 0 \\ & \cdots\cdots\cdots\cdots & \\ 0 & 0 & \cdots & 1 \end{bmatrix},$$

so that $A\dfrac{(\text{adj } A)}{|A|} = 1_n$, provided $|A| \neq 0$. In a like manner it can be verified that $\dfrac{(\text{adj } A)}{|A|}A = 1_n$, so that $A^{-1} = \dfrac{(\text{adj } A)}{|A|}$. We note that A^{-1} always exists if A is square and $|A| \neq 0$.

Subject to the condition on A just stated, we are now able to solve the matrix equation $AX = B$. If we multiply each member of this equation by A^{-1} on the left, the result is $A^{-1}(AX) = (A^{-1}A) X = 1_nX = X = A^{-1}B$. Thus, as soon as $A^{-1}B$ is computed, the solution X is known.

Problems 6-10

1. According to our definition, is a determinant a square array of elements or a single element of the underlying field? Answer the same question with respect to a minor.
2. Look up a proof of **Theorem 6.101.**
3. Look up a proof of **Theorem 6.102.**
4. Outline the steps in the proof of Cramer's rule for x_2.
5. Let $n = 3$ in the "matrix inversion" method, and carry out the computation to show that $A \dfrac{(\text{adj } A)}{|A|} = \dfrac{(\text{adj } A)}{|A|} A = 1_3$.

**6. Use both Cramer's rule and the "matrix inversion" method to solve the following system of equations:

$$2x - 3y + 8z = 19$$
$$3x - \ y + \ z = \ 6$$
$$2x + 4y - 3z = \ 7.$$

7. Use the "matrix inversion" method to solve the following system of equations:

$$2x - 3y + 4z = \ 8$$
$$3x + 4y - 5z = -4$$
$$4x - 5y + 6z = 12.$$

8. Use both Cramer's rule and the "matrix inversion" method to solve the following system of equations:

$$4x + 2y - 2z = -5$$
$$3x - 3y - 4z = \ \ 0$$
$$5x - 7y \qquad = 25.$$

9. Use the "matrix inversion" method to solve the following system of equations:

$$1/x + 3/y = -3/4$$
$$2/x - 5/y = -7/6.$$

6.11 SOLUTIONS BY GAUSS REDUCTION

The final method which we shall discuss is applicable to any system of equations and does not even require that the coefficient matrix be square. The method takes its name from Karl Friedrich Gauss (1777-1855) and is known as the "Gauss reduction" method.

In some instances it may be a more complicated method, but it has the distinct advantage that it may be used in many instances when the other two methods fail.

Two systems of equations are said to be *equivalent* if they have precisely the same solutions. To epitomize the method we are about to present, we can say that it replaces the original system of equations by an equivalent system whose solutions can be determined immediately. The transformations which can be performed on a system of equations to produce an equivalent system are called "elementary operations" and are of three types.

Type 1: The interchange of any two equations.

Type 2: The multiplication of both members of any equation of the system by a nonzero element of the field F of coefficients. Such a product by an element of F may be referred to as an "F-multiple."

Type 3: The addition of an F-multiple of both members of any equation of the system to the corresponding members of another equation of the system.

It is an elementary matter to verify that the result of each of these operations on a system of equations is an equivalent system **(Problem 1).** We are then free to perform any sequence of operations of these types, with the assurance that the resulting system will have the same solutions as the original. The general system under consideration will be the same system **(1)** of **§6.9,** a system which we shall continue to designate in matrix form as $AX = B$.

In the first place, it should be clear that we are to be essentially concerned with the coefficients of the equations rather than with the equations themselves. For example, the system of equations:

$$3x - y + 2z = 9$$
$$2x + y - z = 7$$
$$x + 2y - 3z = 4$$

may be replaced conveniently by the so-called *augmented* matrix

$$\begin{bmatrix} 3 & -1 & 2 & 9 \\ 2 & 1 & -1 & 7 \\ 1 & 2 & -3 & 4 \end{bmatrix},$$

if we keep in mind that the columns of this matrix are, respectively, the coefficients of x, y, and z, followed by the column of "constants." The elementary operations on the equations may now be replaced by their equivalent operations performed on the rows of the augmented matrix. For example, a Type 1 operation on the matrix will involve an interchange of any two rows of the matrix, and the other two types of operations will have their similar matrix counterparts. In the example above it is possible (we shall see how later) to perform a sequence of elementary row operations on the augmented matrix to

produce the matrix $\begin{bmatrix} 1 & 0 & 0 & 3 \\ 0 & 1 & 0 & 2 \\ 0 & 0 & 1 & 1 \end{bmatrix}$, where in this and in subsequent

discussions we are assuming that F is the field of rational numbers. If we recall now the significance of the various columns of this matrix, it is immediate that the solution of the corresponding system of equations *and of the original system* is: $x = 3$, $y = 2$, $z = 1$. Or, in

matrix notation, with $A = \begin{bmatrix} 3 & -1 & 2 \\ 2 & 1 & -1 \\ 1 & 2 & -3 \end{bmatrix}$ and $B = \begin{bmatrix} 9 \\ 7 \\ 4 \end{bmatrix}$, the solution

of the equation $AX = B$ is $X = \begin{bmatrix} 3 \\ 2 \\ 1 \end{bmatrix}$. The matrix, from which we

were able to obtain the solution so easily, was in "reduced echelon" form according to the following definition.

Definition. A matrix is in *reduced echelon* form if it satisfies the following three conditions.
1. The first nonzero, or "leading," entry of any row is 1.
2. The column containing the leading entry of any row has 0 for all of its other entries.
3. If the leading entry of the ith row appears in the t_ith column, then $t_1 < t_2 < t_3 < \cdots < t_r$, where r is the number of nonzero rows.

The following three matrices provide additional illustrations of matrices in reduced echelon form, with elements in the field R:

$$\begin{bmatrix} 1 & 0 & 0 \\ 0 & 1 & 0 \\ 0 & 0 & 1 \end{bmatrix}, \begin{bmatrix} 1 & 0 & 0 & \frac{2}{3} \\ 0 & 1 & 2 & 1 \\ 0 & 0 & 0 & 0 \end{bmatrix}, \begin{bmatrix} 1 & 1 & 0 & 0 & 1 \\ 0 & 0 & 1 & 2 & -\frac{1}{2} \\ 0 & 0 & 0 & 0 & 0 \\ 0 & 0 & 0 & 0 & 0 \\ 0 & 0 & 0 & 0 & 0 \end{bmatrix}.$$

Our earlier example was of a system with a single *unique* solution for each unknown. This is always the case when the determinant of the original coefficient matrix is nonzero, and the methods of §6.10 can be used to solve such a system. If the first matrix of the above three in echelon form is regarded as the augmented matrix of a system of equations in two unknowns x and y, however, it is evident that the third row indicates that $0 = 1$. Since this is an absurd result, the matrix must be associated with an *inconsistent* system of equations, i.e., a system possessing no solution. If we consider the central matrix above to be associated with a system of equations in x, y, z, it is clear that the matrix signifies that $x = \frac{2}{3}$, $y = 1 - 2z$ in its first two rows, while the final row signifies nothing. In other words, z is arbitrary so that we can put $z = c$, and then $x = \frac{2}{3}$, $y = 1 - 2c$.

Hence $x = \qquad \frac{2}{3}$
$ y = -2c + 1$
$ z = \qquad c \qquad$ or, in the notation of **Theorem 6.92,** the so-

lution $X = \begin{bmatrix} x \\ y \\ z \end{bmatrix} = c\begin{bmatrix} 0 \\ -2 \\ 1 \end{bmatrix} + \begin{bmatrix} \frac{2}{3} \\ 1 \\ 0 \end{bmatrix} = cX_1 + X_p$. If the final matrix

above is the augmented matrix of a system of equations in x_1, x_2, x_3, x_4, the form of the matrix shows that $x_1 = 1 - x_2$, $x_3 = -\frac{1}{2} - 2x_4$, while x_2 and x_4 are arbitrary. Hence if we put $x_2 = c_1$ and $x_4 = c_2$, the solutions can be expressed in the following form:

$$x_1 = \quad 1 \quad -c_1$$
$$x_2 = \qquad c_1$$
$$x_3 = -\tfrac{1}{2} \qquad -2c_2$$
$$x_4 = \qquad c_2.$$

In matrix form, this solution becomes:

$$X = \begin{bmatrix} x_1 \\ x_2 \\ x_3 \\ x_4 \end{bmatrix} = \begin{bmatrix} 1 \\ 0 \\ -\frac{1}{2} \\ 0 \end{bmatrix} + c_1 \begin{bmatrix} -1 \\ 1 \\ 0 \\ 0 \end{bmatrix} + c_2 \begin{bmatrix} 0 \\ 0 \\ -2 \\ 1 \end{bmatrix} = X_p + c_1 X_1 + c_2 X_2, \text{ in}$$

the notation of **Theorem 6.92.** It then appears that if the augmented matrix of a system of linear equations is in reduced echelon form, the solutions of the system can be written down immediately. The problem of putting a given matrix in reduced echelon form is now up for our consideration.

Let us now reproduce the augmented matrix of the original system **(1)** of §6.9 as follows:

$$\begin{bmatrix} a_{11} & a_{12} & a_{13} & \cdots & a_{1n} & b_1 \\ a_{21} & a_{22} & a_{23} & \cdots & a_{2n} & b_2 \\ a_{31} & a_{32} & a_{33} & \cdots & a_{3n} & b_3 \\ & & \cdots\cdots\cdots & & \\ a_{m1} & a_{m2} & a_{m3} & \cdots & a_{mn} & b_m \end{bmatrix}.$$

Either $a_{11} \neq 0$ or, as the result of an operation of Type 1, a_{11} can be replaced by a nonzero element. On multiplication of the elements of the first row by the inverse of a_{11} (or its replacement), the entry in the upper left hand corner of the matrix becomes 1. If we now subtract the correct multiple of the elements of the first row from the corresponding elements of each of the other rows (Type 3 operations), all other elements in the first column become 0. This completes the first step of the reduction process. If the remaining $n-1$ rows of the matrix now contain only zeros, the reduction is complete. But if not, we consider the first column after the first which *does* contain a nonzero entry in other than the first row. If this nonzero entry is not in the second row, a simple interchange (Type 1 operation) will make it so, while a multiplication of the elements of this row by the inverse of this element will reduce it to 1 (Type 2 operation). If we now apply the correct sequence of Type 3 operations, we can reduce all entries in this column to 0, except for 1 in the second row, and the second stage of the reduction process is completed. If the reduction is not now complete, it is continued in the same manner until the resulting matrix is in reduced echelon form. As we have seen, the solutions of the original system of equations can then be written down immediately.

We have considered several illustrations of possible solutions of a system of equations $AX = B$ and have expressed these solutions in the general form of the solutions guaranteed by **Theorem 6.92.** In one instance the solution space of the associated homogeneous system $AX = 0$ contained no vectors at all and so was the empty set; in one instance it contained only the vector 0; in another only one nonzero basis vector; and in the final illustration the solution space had a basis of two vectors. We note that the Gauss reduction method actually *produces* a basis for the associated solution space, if this space exists. The dimension of this solution space is closely related to what is known as the *rank* of A, where this rank is defined as the order of the largest submatrix of A with nonzero determinant. It is shown in courses in matrix theory that the elementary row operations do not alter the rank of a matrix, and since the rank of a matrix in reduced echelon form with r leading entries of 1 is certainly r, the following theorem follows immediately **(Problem 2).**

Theorem 6.111   If $AX = 0$ is the matrix form of a system of linear equations in n unknowns, the solution space of this matrix equation has dimension $n - r$ where r is the rank of A.

It may be well to caution at this point, of course, that the solution space of $AX = 0$ may have dimension r, whereas the nonhomogeneous system $AX = B$ can be inconsistent and have no solution at all. In this connection, the following theorem from matrix theory is of interest, but we omit its proof.

Theorem 6.112   A system of linear equations is consistent if and only if the coefficient matrix of the system has the same rank as its associated augmented matrix.

Problems 6–11

   *1. Outline a proof that the three elementary operations on a system of equations transform the system into an equivalent system.
   *2. If a matrix is in reduced echelon form, why is its rank equal to the number of leading row entries of 1?

Use the Gauss reduction method to solve the systems of equations in **Problems 3 to 6**, if consistent, and express each complete solution in the form suggested by **Theorem 6.92**.

**3. $x + y - 5z = 26$
$\quad x + 2y + z = -4$
$\quad x + 3y + 7z = -34$

4. $3x - y + 2z = 3$
$\quad 2x + 2y + z = 2$
$\quad x - 3y + z = 2$

5. $4x_1 + x_2 + x_3 - 2x_4 + x_5 = 5$
$\quad 11x_1 + x_2 - 3x_3 - 4x_4 + 2x_5 = 8$
$\quad 2x_1 + 2x_2 - x_3 + 2x_4 - x_5 = 1$
$\quad 3x_1 \qquad\qquad - 2x_4 + x_5 = 3$

6. $2x + 3y + 4z = 0$
$\quad 3x + 4y + 5z = 0$
$\quad 5x + 7y + 9z = 0$

7. Use the Gauss reduction method to solve the system of equations given in **Problem 6** of **Problems 6-10**.

REFERENCES

BIRKHOFF, G., and MACLANE, S.: *A Brief Survey of Modern Algebra*, Chaps. 7–8 (New York, Macmillan, 1953).

HOHN, F.: *Elementary Matrix Algebra* (New York, Macmillan, 1958).

JOHNSON, R.: *First Course in Abstract Algebra*, Chaps. 7–9 (Englewood Cliffs, N.J., Prentice-Hall, 1953).

McCoY, N.: *Introduction to Modern Algebra*, Chaps. 10–13 (Boston, Allyn and Bacon, 1960).

MOORE, J.: *Fundamental Principles of Mathematics*, Chap. 11 (New York, Holt, 1960).

chapter 7

LATTICES AND BOOLEAN ALGEBRA

7.1 INTRODUCTION

A portion of the study of any algebraic system is devoted to certain, distinguished subsystems of elements, rather than to the elements themselves. For example, in our earlier study of groups, we became interested in normal subgroups, while the topic of ideals was of importance in our treatment of rings. In the case of groups, the culmination of our study from the point of view of invariant or normal subgroups was the Jordan-Hölder theorem. The notion of a "lattice" arises in an attempt to obtain an abstract system which includes such systems as the subgroups of a group, the normal subgroups of a group, and the ideals of a ring as special cases. Historically, lattices were first studied as Boolean algebras by George Boole (1815–1864). This early study was actually a study of the calculus of propositions, and it was not until much later that this logical system was recognized to be equivalent to a certain type of ring.

Definition. A set S is said to be *partially ordered* by a relation $\geq$, if the following requirements are satisfied by arbitrary elements $a, b, c \in S$:
1. $a \geq b$ and $b \geq a$ if and only if $a = b$.
2. If $a \geq b$ and $b \geq c$, then $a \geq c$.

We note that the "antisymmetric" law, as stated in **1**, also implies the reflexive law; for if b is replaced by a, **1** asserts that $a \geq a$. The statement in **2** is, of course, just the transitive law. If a is not in the given relation to b, we can write $a \not\geq b$; if $a \geq b$ and $a \neq b$, it is customary to write $a > b$. The notations $b \leq a$ and $b < a$ may be considered alternative for $a \geq b$ and $a > b$, respectively.

It should be noted that for an arbitrary pair of elements a and b in S, it may be the case that neither $a \geq b$ nor $b \geq a$. In such an instance, the elements a and b are said to be *not comparable*. If, however, every pair of elements of the set are comparable, it is possible to order the whole set by the relation, and S is then said to be *linearly ordered* or a *chain*. An example of a partially ordered set which is a chain is the set of ordinary integers with the usual $\geq$ relation. If we define $a \geq b$ to mean that $a|b$, these integers form a partially ordered set which is not a chain. For it is clear that conditions **1** and **2** for a partially ordered set are satisfied, but it is not necessary for either of two arbitrary integers to divide the other. An example of a partially ordered set which is basic in a study of Boolean algebra is the set of all subsets of a set, with $A \geq B$ meaning that B is a subset of A. Another example of the same type would be the set of all subgroups of a group, with the relation defined in the same way as set-inclusion.

If a_1 and a_2 are elements of a partially ordered set, such that $a_1 > a_2$, but there exists no element a such that $a_1 > a > a_2$, the element a_1 is said to *cover* a_2. If the set is finite, we are then able to connect any two comparable elements by a chain in which each element of the chain covers the adjacent element. Thus, if $a > b$, we can find elements $a_1, a_2, \cdots, a_n$ in the set such that $a = a_1 >$

$a_2 > a_3 > \cdots > a_{n-1} > a_n = b$, where each a_i covers a_{i+1}. As a result of this, it is possible to represent any finite, partially ordered set by means of a diagram. In such a diagram we represent the elements by points, and if a_i is a cover for a_{i+1} we place a_i above a_{i+1}, and join them by a line segment. For any two elements a and b such that $a > b$, there is then a descending series of line segments from a to b. A few such diagrams are given in Figure 6.

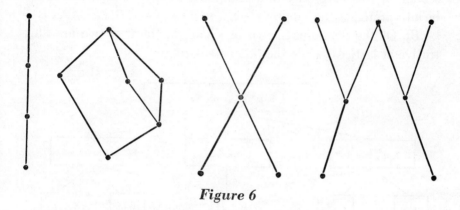

Figure 6

An *upper bound* for a subset A of a partially ordered set S is an element u such that $u \geq a$, for every $a \in A$. This upper bound u is a *least upper bound* (l.u.b.) if $u \leq v$, for any upper bound v of A. A similar definition applies to *lower bounds*, and a *greatest lower bound* (g.l.b.), and it is clear that if a g.l.b. or l.u.b. exists, this element is unique. We are now able to define a lattice.

Definition. A *lattice* is a partially ordered set in which any two elements have a l.u.b. and a g.l.b.

It is customary to denote the l.u.b. of a and b by $a \cup b$, and the g.l.b. of a and b by $a \cap b$. These are sometimes read "a cup b" and "a cap b," respectively.

If we examine the four examples of a partially ordered set which we gave in the second paragraph, it can be seen that these are all lattices. In the case of the ordinary integers with the usual relation $\geq$, it is clear that $a \cup b$ is the larger of the two numbers, while $a \cap b$ is the smaller. With $a \geq b$ defined in I to be $a|b$, $a \cup b$ will be the g.c.d. of a and b, while $a \cap b$ will be the least common multiple or l.c.m. of these numbers. In the example of the subsets of a set, which is basic in any study of lattices, the meanings of $A \cup B$ and $A \cap B$ will be set-theoretic union and intersection, respectively. It is probably to this example that the symbolism for "cup" and "cap" owes its origin. In the case of the subgroups of a group, $A \cap B$ will be the usual intersection, for we know that the intersection of two subgroups of a group is a subgroup, but $A \cup B$ will be interpreted as the subgroup generated by A and B, i.e., $A \cup B = [A,B]$. Of the diagrams shown in Figure 6, the first two are illustrative of lattices, while the other two are not.

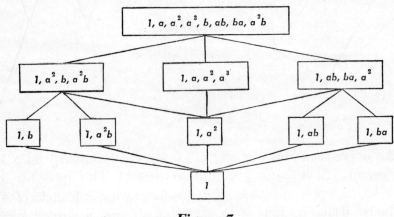

Figure 7

As an example of a lattice of subgroups consider the "dihedral" group $\{1, a, a^2, a^3, b, ab, ba, a^2b\}$ of order eight, where $a^4 = b^2 = 1$ and $a^3b = ba$. This group contains three subgroups of order four, and five subgroups of order two, as well as the identity subgroup. Each of the subgroups of order two is contained in one or more of the subgroups of order four, while the identity subgroup is contained in every one of the subgroups. The diagram of the lattice of subgroups of this dihedral group is shown in Figure 7.

Problems 7–1

*1. Give a complete definition of the greatest lower bound (g.l.b.) of a subset of a partially ordered set.

*2. Explain why the least upper bound and the greatest lower bound of a subset of a partially ordered set are unique elements of the set.

*3. Explain why $a \cup b \geq a$ and $a \geq a \cap b$, for elements a, b of a partially ordered set.

**4. If a and b are elements of a partially ordered set such that $a \geq b$, prove that $a \cap b = b$.

5. Draw diagrams of two different partially ordered sets which (a) are lattices; (b) are not lattices.

6. Draw diagrams for the following partially ordered sets:
   (a) the set of subsets of a set of four elements;
   (b) the set of subgroups of the cyclic group of order six (see **Problem 6 of Problems 4-5**);
   (c) the set of subgroups of S_3

7. Let S be the set of all continuous functions on R^*. If we define $f \geq g$ to mean that $xf \geq xg$, for each $x \in R^*$ and arbitrary functions f and g in S, show that S is partially ordered by $\geq$.

8. Make suitable definitions of $f \cup g$ and $f \cap g$ so that the set S of **Problem 7** is a lattice.

7.2 AN ALTERNATE DEFINITION

It was a major part of the definition of a lattice, which we gave in the preceding section, that this system has a partial ordering. In this section, however, we shall see that order is not really essential, and that it is possible to give an equivalent definition of a lattice without any specific mention of any type of ordering. In this setting, a lattice can be considered more like the other members of the family of algebraic systems which we have discussed before. But first we must establish several almost trivial results of our earlier definition.

Theorem 7.21 If a, b, c are arbitrary elements of a lattice, the following equalities hold:
1. $a \cup b = b \cup a$; $a \cap b = b \cap a$;
2. $(a \cup b) \cup c = a \cup (b \cup c)$; $(a \cap b) \cap c = a \cap (b \cap c)$;
3. $a \cup a = a$; $a \cap a = a$;
4. $(a \cup b) \cap a = a$; $(a \cap b) \cup a = a$.

Proof. Since there are only "language" differences between the l.u.b. of a and b and the l.u.b. of b and a, it is clear that $a \cup b = b \cup a$. A similar reflection shows that $a \cap b = b \cap a$, and 1 is verified. In order to establish **2**, we first note that $(a \cup b) \cup c \geq a \cup b$ and $(a \cup b) \cup c \geq c$, so that $(a \cup b) \cup c \geq a$, $(a \cup b) \cup c \geq b$, and $(a \cup b) \cup c \geq c$. Also if x is any element of the lattice such that $x \geq a$, $x \geq b$, $x \geq c$, then $x \geq (a \cup b)$ so that $x \geq (a \cup b) \cup c$. It follows that $(a \cup b) \cup c$ is the l.u.b. of a, b, c while a similar argument shows that $a \cup (b \cup c)$ is also the l.u.b. of a, b, c so that $(a \cup b) \cup c = a \cup (b \cup c)$. A similar argument shows that either $(a \cap b) \cap c$ or $a \cap (b \cap c)$ is the g.l.b. of a, b, c and so these two representations are equal, thus completing the verification of **2**. The definition of l.u.b. requires that $a \cup a = a$, while the definition of g.l.b. requires that $a \cap a = a$, stated in **3**. Finally, since $a \cup b \geq a$ (See **Problem 3 of Problems 7-1**), we have $(a \cup b) \cap a = a$; and since $a \geq a \cap b$, it follows that $(a \cap b) \cup a = a$. This establishes **4** and completes the proof of the theorem.

We shall now show that these properties are not only characteristic of any lattice, but that they are sufficient to define this type of system. This result is embodied in the following theorem.

Theorem 7.22   Let $\mathcal{L}$ be a set in which are defined two binary operations $\cup$ and $\cap$, and which possess the properties listed in **Theorem 7.21**. It is then possible to define a partial ordering $\geq$ in $\mathcal{L}$, such that $\mathcal{L}$ is a lattice in which $\cup$ and $\cap$ are the l.u.b. and g.l.b., respectively.

Proof.   We must define a partial ordering $\geq$ in $\mathcal{L}$, and show that (i) $a \geq b$ and $b \geq a$ if and only if $a = b$; (ii) if $a \geq b$ and $b \geq c$, then $a \geq c$. The definition of the partial ordering can be made as follows: $a \geq b$ if and only if $a \cup b = a$. The two required properties of this partial ordering can now be derived. For suppose that $a \geq b$ and $b \geq a$. Then $a \cup b = a$ and $b \cup a = b$, so that by **1** it follows that $a = b$. Conversely, if $a = b$, by **3** we have $a \cup b = a$ and so $a \geq b$. In like manner, we can show that $b \geq a$ if $a = b$, thus completing the verification of (i). Now suppose that $a \geq b$ and $b \geq c$. Then $a \cup b = a$ and $b \cup c = b$, so that $a \cup c = (a \cup b) \cup c = a \cup (b \cup c) = a \cup b = a$. Hence $a \geq c$ and (ii) is established. There remains only to show that $\cup$ and $\cap$ play the respective roles of least upper bound and greatest lower bound. Since $(a \cup b) \cap a = a$, by 4, we have $a \cup b \geq a$; and a similar argument leads to $a \cup b \geq b$. Now let c be any element of $\mathcal{L}$ such that $c \geq a$ and $c \geq b$. Then $a \cup c = c$ and $b \cup c = c$, and hence $(a \cup b) \cup c = a \cup (b \cup c) = a \cup c = c$. Thus $c \geq a \cup b$ and so $a \cup b$ is the l.u.b. of a and b. In like manner we can show that $a \cap b$ is the g.l.b. of a and b, thus completing the proof of the theorem.

We remark that the alternate postulates 1, 2, 3, 4 for a lattice are symmetric in the sense that like requirements have been imposed on the two operations $\cup$ and $\cap$. Hence any conclusions which we may derive will remain valid if $\cup$ and $\cap$ are interchanged, and this is the important *Principle of Duality: Any statement which has been deduced from the axioms of a lattice remains valid if $\cup$ and $\cap$ are interchanged in the statement.*

For example, if we assume that $a \cup b = a$, it follows that $a \cap b = (a \cup b) \cap b = b$, i.e., $a \cup b = a$ implies that $a \cap b = b$. We are then able to assert, on the strength of the Principle of Duality without any further argument, that $a \cap b = a$ would imply that $a \cup b = b$. If a statement is dualized, it is also necessary to replace any such assertion as $a \geq b$ by its dual $b \geq a$. For if $a \geq b$, we have $a \cup b = a$, and the dual of this latter statement is $a \cap b = a$ or $b \cap a = a$. It then follows that $b \cup a = b \cup (b \cap a) = b$, so that $b \geq a$, as asserted.

Problems 7–2

*1. Give the proof, omitted in our verification of **Theorem 7.22**, that $a \cap b$ is the g.l.b. of a and b.

**2. Prove that if a and b are elements of a lattice such that $a \cup b = a \cap b$, then $a = b$.

3. Prove that if a, b, c are elements of a lattice such that $a \cup b \cup c = a \cap b \cap c$, then $a = b = c$.

4. Let $\circ$ designate a binary operation in a set, and suppose that this operation is idempotent ($x \circ x = x$, for any x in the set), commutative, and associative. Then if we define $a \geq b$ to mean that $a \circ b = a$, for elements a, b in the set, show that the set is partially ordered with $a \circ b$ the l.u.b. of a and b.

7.3 SUBLATTICES AND ISOMORPHISM

It is usually the case that an algebraic system has subsystems of the same kind. Lattices are no exception to this, and it is customary to define a subset of a lattice $\mathcal{L}$ as a *sublattice* if it is closed with respect to the compositions $\cup$ and $\cap$ of $\mathcal{L}$. In other words, a sublattice of $\mathcal{L}$ is a subset which contains the l.u.b. and g.l.b. of every pair of elements of the subset. On the other hand, it is possible for a subset of a lattice $\mathcal{L}$ to be a lattice without being a sublattice of $\mathcal{L}$. In such a case, the compositions in the subset are not the same as those defined for the same elements when these are considered to be elements of $\mathcal{L}$. For example, Figure 8 may designate a portion of a lattice, with the "starred" elements belonging to a subset. Then, if a and b are considered elements of $\mathcal{L}$, $a \cup b = c \in \mathcal{L}$, whereas the corresponding l.u.b. in the subset is d. An example of this occurs when we consider the lattice $\mathcal{L}$ of subsets of a group $\mathcal{G}$, along with

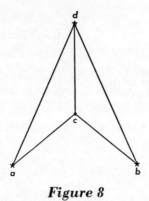

Figure 8

the lattice $\mathcal{L}'$ of subgroups of $\mathcal{G}$. Since every subgroup of $\mathcal{G}$ is a subset of $\mathcal{G}$, it is clear that $\mathcal{L}' \subseteq \mathcal{L}$. However, if H_1 and H_2 are arbitrary subgroups of $\mathcal{G}$, the subset $H_1 \cup H_2$ is not in general a subgroup of $\mathcal{G}$, and so is not a member of $\mathcal{L}'$. As we have already seen, it is necessary to define $H_1 \cup H_2$ to be the subgroup generated by H_1 and H_2, if $\mathcal{L}'$ is to be a lattice. While $\mathcal{L}'$ is a lattice, with this definition of $\cup$ and the same definition of $\cap$ as for $\mathcal{L}$, it is clear that $\mathcal{L}'$ is not a sublattice of $\mathcal{L}$.

In view of our alternate definition of a lattice, which made no specific mention of order, we can apply the usual notions of homomorphism and isomorphism to lattices. To wit, a mapping $a \to a'$ of a lattice $\mathcal{L}$ onto a lattice $\mathcal{L}'$ is a *homomorphism* if

$$(a \cup b)' = a' \cup b' \text{ and } (a \cap b)' = a' \cap b',$$

where $a, b \in \mathcal{L}$ and $a', b' \in \mathcal{L}'$. If the mapping is bijective, the homomorphism is an *isomorphism*. It is sometimes easier to apply the following theorem as a criterion for deciding whether a given mapping is an isomorphism.

Theorem 7.31   Let $a \to a'$ be a bijective mapping of a lattice $\mathcal{L}$ onto a lattice $\mathcal{L}'$. Then the mapping is an isomorphism if and only if $a \geq b$ in $\mathcal{L}$ implies and is implied by $a' \geq b'$ in $\mathcal{L}'$, i.e., if and only if both the mapping and its inverse are "order preserving."

Proof.   First, let us suppose that the mapping $a \to a'$ is an isomorphism, and that $a \geq b$, for elements $a, b \in \mathcal{L}$. Then, $a \cup b = a$, and since the mapping is an isomorphism $(a \cup b)' = a' \cup b' = a'$. Hence $a' \geq b'$, so that the mapping of $\mathcal{L}$ onto $\mathcal{L}'$ is order preserving. In a similar manner, it can be shown **(Problem 3)** that the inverse mapping is also order preserving. Conversely, let us suppose that $a \to a'$ is a bijective mapping of $\mathcal{L}$ onto $\mathcal{L}'$ which, along with its inverse, is order preserving. Then if $a \cup b = c$, for elements $a, b, c \in \mathcal{L}$, we must show that $a' \cup b' = c'$. But if $a \cup b = c$, we know that $c \geq a$ and $c \geq b$, so that $c' \geq a'$ and $c' \geq b'$, by our assumption on the preservation of order under the mapping. Now let d' be any element of $\mathcal{L}'$ such that $d' \geq a'$ and $d' \geq b'$, and suppose that d is an element of $\mathcal{L}$ such that $d \to d'$. Then $d \geq a$ and $d \geq b$, so that $d \geq a \cup b = c$, and $d' \geq c'$. Hence c' is the l.u.b. of a' and b', which means that $c' = a' \cup b'$, as desired. In like manner **(Problem 4)**, we can show that $(a \cap b)' = a' \cap b'$, and the theorem is established.

Problems 7–3

**1. If b is any element of a lattice $\mathcal{L}$, prove that the set of all elements $x \in \mathcal{L}$, such that $x \geq b$, is a sublattice of $\mathcal{L}$.

2. If a and b are elements of a lattice $\mathcal{L}$, where $a \geq b$, show that the set of all elements $x \in \mathcal{L}$, such that $a \geq x \geq b$, is a sublattice of $\mathcal{L}$.

*3. Prove the point, omitted in the proof of **Theorem 7.31**, that the mapping $a' \to a$ is order preserving.

*4. Prove the point, omitted in the proof of **Theorem 7.31**, that $(a \cap b)' = a' \cap b'$, under the assumption that the mapping and its inverse are order preserving.

5. Prove that the set of invariant subgroups of a group G comprises a sublattice of the lattice of subgroups of G, with l.u.b. and g.l.b. as in our discussion above.

7.4 TYPES OF LATTICES

It is usually possible to enlarge the set of postulates of an algebraic system, and thereby obtain a special system with properties not characteristic of the general system. In the case of groups, for example, we obtained the subclass of abelian groups by including the postulate of commutativity; and in Chapter 5 we gave some brief discussion to Noetherian rings, a subclass of rings with some properties not possessed by rings in general. In this section we shall consider some special kinds of lattices.

By the definition of l.u.b. and g.l.b., $a \cup b$ and $a \cap b$ are *unique* elements of a lattice containing a and b. In the proof of 2 of **Theorem 7.21** this result was extended to take care of any three elements, and it can be shown by induction **(Problem 1)** that the l.u.b. and g.l.b. of *any finite* subset of elements of a lattice $\mathcal{L}$ is a unique element of $\mathcal{L}$. However, this result may, or may not, be true for infinite subsets of elements, a fact which leads us to the next definition.

> **Definition.**   A lattice $\mathcal{L}$ is *complete* if any (finite or infinite) subset of $\mathcal{L}$ has a l.u.b. and a g.l.b.

The lattice of subsets of a set is clearly complete, for, in this case, the l.u.b. of any subset of the lattice is the set-theoretic union of the elements of the subset and so is an element of the lattice; while the g.l.b. of any such subset is the set-theoretic intersection of the elements of the subset which, as a subset, is also an element of the lattice. It is not difficult to show that the lattice of subgroups of a group is also complete **(Problem 2)**. On the other hand, the lattice of rational numbers with the usual definition of $\geq$, is not complete: for example, the subset of rational numbers x such that $x^2 < 3$ has no l.u.b.

If there exists in a lattice $\mathcal{L}$ an element 1 such that $1 \geq a$, for every $a \in \mathcal{L}$, then 1 is known as the *all* or *identity* element of the lattice. If an element 0 exists in $\mathcal{L}$ such that $a \geq 0$, for every $a \in \mathcal{L}$, the element 0 is known as the *zero* element of the lattice. The elements 1 and 0 do not necessarily exist in a lattice, but if they exist they are unique **(Problem 3)**.

If we consider $\cup$ to be the analogue of addition and $\cap$ to be the analogue of multiplication in a ring, the following definition will appear to be quite natural.

> **Definition.** A lattice $\mathcal{L}$ is said to be *distributive* if $a \cap (b \cup c) = (a \cap b) \cup (a \cap c)$, for arbitrary elements $a, b, c \in \mathcal{L}$.

There are many examples of a distributive lattice, one of the most familiar being the lattice of subsets of a set, with the usual compositions of set-theoretic union and intersection **(Problem 6)**. However, while many lattices are distributive, there are also many important ones which are not. For example, the lattice of ideals of a ring is not a distributive lattice **(Problem 12)**. This leads us to the definition of another type of lattice, called "modular," which satisfies a somewhat less stringent condition than distributivity.

> **Definition.** A lattice $\mathcal{L}$, such that $a \cap (b \cup c) = b \cup (a \cap c)$, for elements $a, b, c \in \mathcal{L}$ such that $a \geq b$, is said to be *modular*.

Since $a \geq b$ implies that $a \cap b = b$, the condition for modularity is precisely the distributive law for this somewhat special triplet of elements a, b, c. Hence any distributive lattice is modular, so that the class of distributive lattices is a subclass of the class of modular lattices. The great importance of modular lattices is due in part to the following result.

Theorem 7.41 The lattice of invariant subgroups of a group is modular.

Proof. We recall, for this lattice, that we identify $\geq$ with set inclusion, i.e., $H_1 \geq H_2$ means that $H_1 \supseteq H_2$, for elements (subgroups) H_1 and H_2 of the lattice. Moreover, $H_1 \cup H_2$ is the subgroup generated by H_1 and H_2, while $H_1 \cap H_2$ is the subgroup whose elements comprise the set-theoretic intersection of H_1 and H_2.

In any lattice we have the one-sided distributive law for arbitrary elements a, b, c of the lattice: $a \cap (b \cup c) \geq (a \cap b) \cup (a \cap c)$. For it is clear that $a \cap (b \cup c) \geq a \cap b$ and $a \cap (b \cup c) \geq a \cap c$, with the elements in an arbitrary lattice. In the present environment, this means that $H_1 \cap (H_2 \cup H_3 \geq (H_1 \cap H_2) \cup (H_1 \cap H_3)$, where H_1, H_2, H_3 are arbitrary (invariant) subgroups in the given lattice. If we now suppose that $H_1 \geq H_2$, as required in the definition of a modular lattice, the above property gives us immediately that $H_1 \cap (H_2 \cup H_3) \geq H_2 \cup (H_1 \cap H_3)$. It remains to show that $H_2 \cup (H_1 \cap H_3) \geq H_1 \cap (H_2 \cup H_3)$, and to this end let h be an arbitrary element of $H_1 \cap (H_2 \cup H_3)$. Since $H_2 \cup H_3 = [H_2, H_3]$, and these subgroups are invariant in the group of the theorem, it follows from **Theorem 4.91** that $h = h_2 h_3 = h_1$, where $h_1 \in H_1$, $h_2 \in H_2$, $h_3 \in H_3$. Then $h_3 = h_2^{-1} h_1 \in H_1$, since $h_2 \in H_2 \subseteq H_1$, and so $h = h_2 h_3 \in H_2 \cup (H_1 \cap H_3)$. We have shown that $H_2 \cup (H_1 \cap H_3) \geq H_1 \cap (H_2 \cup H_3)$, and this result combined with the reversed inequality obtained before implies that $H_1 \cap (H_2 \cup H_3) = H_2 \cup (H_1 \cap H_3)$. Hence the lattice of invariant subgroups is modular, as asserted.

Our final general type of lattice is now described in the following definition.

Definition. A lattice $\mathcal{L}$ with 0 and 1 is said to be *complemented* if there is associated with each element $a \in \mathcal{L}$ an element $a' \in \mathcal{L}$, such that $a \cup a' = 1$ and $a \cap a' = 0$. Either element a or a' is then said to be the *complement* of the other.

The lattice of subsets of a set S is complemented. For we identify the whole set S with 1 and the empty set with 0, and then define the complement of any subset of S as the collection of all elements of S which are not in the subset. It is clear that this definition satisfies the requirements of a complement.

Let $\mathcal{L}$ be a complemented modular lattice, with $a \geq b$, for elements $a, b \in \mathcal{L}$. Then there exists an element $b' \in \mathcal{L}$ such that

$b \cup b' = 1$ and $b \cap b' = 0$; and the modularity property gives
$a = a \cap (b \cup b') = b \cup (a \cap b') = b \cup b_1$, where $b_1 = a \cap b'$.
Since $b \cap b_1 = b \cap (a \cap b') = (b \cap b') \cap a = 0$, and $b \cup b_1 = a$,
the element b_1 is what is known as a *relative complement* of b with
respect to a. We have shown that if a and b are elements of a complemented modular lattice such that $a \geq b$, there exists a *relative
complement* of b with respect to a, i.e., an element b_1 such that
$b \cap b_1 = 0$ and $b \cup b_1 = a$.

Problems 7–4

*1. Give the inductive proof that any finite subset of elements of
a lattice has a l.u.b.

**2. Prove that the lattice of subgroups of a group is complete.

*3. Why can there be at most one zero and one identity element in a
lattice?

*4. If a lattice $\mathcal{L}$ has an identity 1, prove that $a \cap 1 = a$ and $a \cup 1$
$= 1$, for an arbitrary element $a \in \mathcal{L}$.

*5. If a lattice $\mathcal{L}$ has an element 0, prove that $a \cap 0 = 0$ and $a \cup 0$
$= a$, for an arbitrary element $a \in \mathcal{L}$.

6. Use a diagram to verify that $a \cap (b \cup c) = (a \cap b) \cup (a \cap c)$,
where a, b, c are overlapping point sets on a plane.

7. If we define $a \geq b$ to mean that $a|b$, prove that the lattice of posi-
tive integers with this partial ordering is distributive. (In this case,
$\cup$ is the g.c.d. and $\cap$ is the l.c.m.)

8. Write down the dual equivalent of the definition which we gave for
a distributive lattice.

9. Prove that $a \cap (b \cup c) \geq (a \cap b) \cup (a \cap c)$, where a, b, c are
arbitrary elements of any lattice.

10. Prove that the lattice of rational numbers, with the usual ordering,
is not complete.

11. Prove that any linearly or "simply" ordered lattice (i.e., a chain)
is distributive.

12. Prove that the lattice of ideals in a ring is modular but not distributive.

7.5 A BRIEF SURVEY

In this section we shall indicate a few further results which can
be obtained for certain lattices.

A lattice is said to satisfy the *descending chain condition* if it
contains no infinite set of elements $a_1, a_2, a_3, \cdots$ such that $a_1 > a_2$

$> a_3 > \ldots$, while the *ascending chain condition* has an analogous meaning. It is easy to see that if a lattice satisfies the descending chain condition and is also known to be complemented, there exist elements of the lattice which cover 0. These elements, sometimes called *atoms*, play an important part in the theory of complemented lattices.

A *composition chain* connecting two elements a and b of a lattice, with $a > b$, is a finite chain $a = a_1 > a_2 > a_3 > \cdots > a_{n+1} = b$, in which each a_i is a cover for a_{i+1}. The *length* of such a chain is n. It is possible to prove a theorem, which is comparable to the Jordan-Hölder theorem of group theory, and which states in part that any two composition chains in a *modular* lattice have the same length if they connect the same elements of the lattice. It is beyond the scope of this book, however, to prove this theorem.

A study of modular lattices which satisfy the ascending chain conditions may be considered the lattice abstraction of a portion of the theory of ideals in a Noetherian ring. An element a of such a lattice $\mathcal{L}$ is said to be *reducible* if $a = a_1 \cap a_2$, for elements a_1, a_2, $\in \mathcal{L}$, where $a_1 > a$ and $a_2 > a$. It is then easy to see that any element of $\mathcal{L}$ can be represented as the intersection of a finite number of irreducible elements, where the meaning of "irreducible" is clear. If we define such a representation as *irredundant* when no one of its components can be omitted from the representation, it can be shown that the following theorem is true.

Theorem 7.51 Let $\mathcal{L}$ be a modular lattice in which the ascending chain condition is holding. Then if an element $b \in \mathcal{L}$ is represented as an irredundant intersection of irreducible elements of $\mathcal{L}$, the number of such elements is uniquely determined by b.

We shall not prove this theorem or pursue our study of general lattices any further. The final topic of this chapter is a special type of lattice known as a *Boolean algebra*.

7.6 BOOLEAN ALGEBRAS

In recent years much interest has arisen in what are known as "Boolean algebras." The principal reason for this great interest is that many applications of this discipline have been found in connection with various systems of automation. We have already noted that the basic ideas of Boolean algebra were first introduced by George Boole, in an attempt to formalize a study of the calculus of propositions. For many years this type of algebra was considered to be essentially different from any of the more conventional algebraic systems, and it has been in only relatively modern times that the true position of Boolean algebra as an algebraic structure has been recognized. The connection between Boolean algebras and lattices is made apparent by the following definition.

Definition. A *Boolean algebra* is a complemented and distributive lattice.

It may be well to repeat, of course, that Boolean algebras were not defined in this way by Boole, because the study of lattices is much more modern. A brief discussion of a Boolean algebra of propositions will be made later, however, so that the above definition may not seem so far removed from the ideas of Boole as it does at the outset.

It is easy to see that the set of all subsets of a set, with the usual compositions of intersection, union, and complementation is a Boolean algebra **(Problem 1)**. In fact, this example is so basic, that a Boolean algebra is sometimes defined as an abstraction of this algebra of sets. Some of the most important elementary propositions of Boolean algebra are described in the following theorem.

Theorem 7.61 The complement a' of any element a of Boolean algebra $\mathcal{B}$ is unique. The mapping $a \to a'$ of $\mathcal{B}$ onto $\mathcal{B}$ is bijective, $(a')' = a$, and the following equalities are satisfied for arbitrary elements $a, b \in \mathcal{B}$: $(a \cup b)' = a' \cap b'$; $(a \cap b)' = a' \cup b'$.

Proof. Suppose a' and a_1 are both complements of an element $a \in \mathcal{B}$. Then $a \cup a' = a \cup a_1 = 1$, and $a \cap a' = a \cap a_1 = 0$. Moreover, $a_1 = a_1 \cap 1 = a_1 \cap (a \cup a') = (a_1 \cap a) \cup (a_1 \cap a') = 0 \cup (a_1 \cap a') = a_1 \cap a'$; and similarly $a' = a' \cap 1 = a' \cap (a \cup a_1) = (a' \cap a) \cup (a' \cap a_1) = 0 \cup (a' \cap a_1) = a' \cap a_1$. Since $a_1 \cap a' = a' \cap a_1$, it follows that $a' = a_1$, and so a has a *unique* complement, which we shall designate a'. In view of the definition of a complement, and the uniqueness just established, the complement of a' is a, i.e., $(a')' = a$. Furthermore, it follows from this that the mapping $a \to a'$ is bijective. Finally, suppose $a \geq b$, for elements $a, b \in \mathcal{B}$. Then since $a' \cap b \leq a' \cap a$, we have $a' = a' \cap 1 = a' \cap (b \cup b') = (a' \cap b) \cup (a' \cap b') = 0 \cup (a' \cap b') = a' \cap b'$. Hence $b' \geq a'$, and we have shown that the mapping $a \to a'$ inverts the partial ordering of the lattice. Now let $d = a \cup b$, so that $d \geq a$ and $d \geq b$, whence $a' \geq d'$ and $b' \geq d'$. If c' is any element of $\mathcal{B}$ such that $a' \geq c'$ and $b' \geq c'$, and c is the inverse image of c' under the mapping, it follows that $c \geq a$ and $c \geq b$. Hence $c \geq d$ and so $d' \geq c'$, i.e., d' is the g.l.b. of a' and b'. This means that $(a \cup b)' = a' \cap b'$, as desired in the theorem. The proof that $(a \cap b)' = a' \cup b'$ is similar **(Problem 3)**.

The relation between a Boolean algebra and other algebraic systems is made clear by our next theorem.

Theorem 7.62   Any Boolean algebra is a ring if the ring operations of addition and multiplication are suitably defined.

Proof.   In order to make a Boolean algebra $\mathcal{B}$ into a ring, we first define the "product" ab of any two elements $a, b \in \mathcal{B}$ to be the same as $a \cap b$. The "sum" or "symmetric difference" of a and b is defined as follows: $a + b = (a \cap b') \cup (a' \cap b)$. It is a consequence of the distributive property of a Boolean algebra that $(b' \cup a') \cap (b \cup a) = [(b \cup a) \cap b'] \cup [(b \cup a) \cap a'] = [0 \cup (a \cap b')] \cup [(b \cap a') \cup 0] = (a \cap b') \cup (a' \cap b) = a + b$. In the case of the Boolean algebra of subsets of a set, the symmetric difference of two subsets is the set of elements which belong to either but not both of the subsets. It is now possible to verify that $\mathcal{B}$ is a ring with these two operations of addition and multiplication. Our definition of $a + b$ implies that $a + b = b + a$, so that the system is commutative under addition. If we note that $(a + b)' = (a \cap b')' \cap (a' \cap b)' = (a' \cup b) \cap (a \cup b') = [(a' \cup b) \cap a] \cup [(a' \cup b) \cap b'] = (a \cap b) \cup (a' \cap b')$, it is easy to verify that addition is associative **(Problem 4)**. Since $a + 0 = (a \cap 1) \cup (a' \cap 0) = a$, the element 0 is the zero of the additive system of $\mathcal{B}$; and since $a + a = (a \cap a') \cup (a' \cap a)$ $= 0$, each element a is its own additive inverse. Hence $\mathcal{B}$ is an additive abelian group. The operation of multiplication, which we identified with $\cap$, is associative, and it is elementary to check that $(a + b)c = ac + bc$. Since it is a postulate of any lattice that $\cap$ is commutative, it follows that $c(a + b) = ca + cb$, and this completes the proof that $\mathcal{B}$ is a ring with the given compositions.

Since $a1 = a \cap 1 = a$, for any element a in the ring of **Theorem 7.62,** we see that 1 serves as the identity element of this ring. We have already remarked that this ring is commutative, and it also follows immediately from the definition of multiplication that $aa = a^2 = a$, so that each element of the ring is idempotent. We have seen earlier, however, that any ring of idempotent elements is commutative (**Problem 10 of Problems 5-1**) so that the essential properties of the above ring are that it has an identity and that its elements are idempotent. This leads us to the next definition.

Definition.   A ring is said to be *Boolean* if all of its elements are idempotent.

A partial converse to **Theorem 7.62** is provided by the following theorem.

Theorem 7.63   Any Boolean ring with an identity element is a Boolean algebra, after suitable definitions have been made for $\cup$ and $\cap$.

Proof.   We first give definitions for $\cup$ and $\cap$ as follows: $a \cup b = a + b - ab$ and $a \cap b = ab$, for arbitrary elements a, b in the ring. It is a matter for direct verification that the composition $\cup$ is associative, and it may be of interest to note that this is the "circle" composition that was introduced in I in **Problem 4 of Problems 3-1.** We have noted earlier that the property of commutativity is always a consequence of the idempotency of the elements of a system, and so our present system is commutative under multiplication. The other characteristic properties of a lattice, as given in our alternate definition in §**7.2,** are immediate consequences of our definitions of $\cup$ and $\cap$ **(Problem 6).** There

remains to show that our lattice is distributive and comple-
mented. Now $(a \cup b) \cap c = (a + b - ab)c = ac + bc - abc = ac + bc - abc^2 = ac + bc - acbc = (a \cap c) \cup (b \cap c)$, for arbitrary elements a, b, c in the ring, and so the distributive property is established for the lattice. Finally, if 1 and 0 are the respective identities of multiplication and addition for the ring, we have $a \cup 1 = a + 1 - a1 = 1$, and $a \cap 0 = a + 0 - a0 = a$, for any ring element a. Hence, if we define $\geq$ as was done in **Theorem 7.22**, it follows that $1 \geq a$ and $a \geq 0$, so that 1 is the identity element and 0 is the zero element of the lattice. We now define $a' = 1 - a$, for any a in the ring, and so $a \cup a' = a + (1 - a) - a(1 - a) = 1$, while $a \cap a' = a(1 - a) = 0$. Hence the Boolean ring, with $\cup$ and $\cap$ defined as above is a Boolean algebra.

Problems 7–6

*1. Prove that the set of all subsets of a set is a Boolean algebra with the usual compositions of this system.

2. With reference to the proof of **Theorem 7.61, why does the fact that $(a')' = a$ imply that the mapping $a \rightarrow a'$ is bijective?

*3. Prove that $(a \cap b)' = a' \cup b'$, for arbitrary elements a, b of a Boolean algebra.

*4. Prove that the "symmetric difference" is an associative operation in a Boolean algebra.

*5. Prove that multiplication, as defined in **Theorem 7.62**, is distributive with respect to the operation of "symmetric difference" in a Boolean algebra.

*6. Prove that the properties listed in **Theorem 7.21** are valid for the system described in **Theorem 7.63**, so that this system is a Boolean algebra.

7. Prove that if there exists a prime natural number p such that $pa = 0$ and $a^p = a$, for each a in a ring, the ring is commutative.

7.7 THE BOOLEAN ALGEBRA OF PROPOSITIONS

A Boolean algebra, as a complemented distributive lattice, is an algebraic system with three operations $\cup$, $\cap$, and $'$, two relations $=$ and $\leq$, as well as two special elements 1 and 0. In order to prove that a certain system is actually a Boolean algebra, it is not always

necessary to verify that all the properties of such an algebra are possessed by the system. For it is possible to give a much smaller list of
postulates for a Boolean algebra than is the case if we define it as a
complemented distributive lattice. This smaller list of postulates is,
of course, much easier to use than a large list. In fact it can be
shown—though we omit the proof—that if a nonempty set has had
defined in it an equivalence relation (=) and two operations $\cap$
and $'$ which satisfy the seven postulates below, the system is a
Boolean algebra. These seven postulates are now stated, wherein
x, y, z are arbitrary elements of the set.

1. x' and $x \cap y$ are well-defined elements of the set.
2. $x \cap y = y \cap x$.
3. $(x \cap y) \cap z = x \cap (y \cap z)$.
4. There exists an element 0 such that $x \cap x' = 0$.
5. If $x \cap y' = 0$, then $x \cap y = x$.
6. If $x \cap y = x$, then $x \cap y' = 0$.
7. If $x = y$, then $x' = y'$ and $x \cap z = y \cap z$.

If we wish to check the usual properties of a Boolean algebra,
we must define the operation $\cup$, the partial ordering $\geq$, and the
identity element 1 as follows:

$$1 = 0'; x \cup y = (x' \cap y')'; x \geq y \text{ if } x \cup y = x.$$

As an example of a Boolean algebra which may appear to be
quite different from the algebra of sets, consider the set of all integral divisors of 110, i.e., the set $\{1, 2, 5, 10, 11, 22, 55, 110\}$. If x
and y are any two elements of this set, let us define $x \cap y$ to be the
g.c.d. of x and y, and x' to be the quotient when 110 is divided by x.
It can be shown that this set of integers, with the usual definition
of equality and the definitions just given for $\cap$ and $'$ comprises a
Boolean algebra. To establish this, one merely has to check the
seven postulates given above for this system. For instance, the
fourth postulate asserts the existence of an element 0, such that for
each integral divisor x of 110, the g.c.d. of x and the quotient
$110/x$ is 0. In the system under observation, the natural number 1
plays the role of the zero of the Boolean algebra. Also, postulate 5
asserts that if x and y' have no common factor except 1, then x

divides y. It can be readily checked that this requirement is indeed satisfied by all numbers of the given set. The other five postulates for a Boolean algebra can be similarly verified for our present system **(Problem 1)**.

Probably the simplest system which satisfies the postulates of a Boolean algebra contains only the two elements 0 and 1, and we shall refer to this algebra as $\mathcal{B}(0, 1)$. The complete operation table for this system is given in Table 2 below, in which due recognition should be given to the heading of each column.

Table 2

x	y	$x \cup y$	$x \cap y$	x'
1	1	1	1	0
1	0	1	0	0
0	1	1	0	1
0	0	0	0	1

Let us now consider the Boolean algebra of propositions. A proposition is a declarative statement of some fact such as, "A circle is round" or, "A stone is soft." While the truth of some propositions may be in doubt, let us consider only those propositions which can be labeled definitely true or definitely false. We shall say that a statement has the truth value T if it is true, and the truth value F if it is false.

If p and q are propositions, the *disjunction* of p and q is the proposition "p or q" and is denoted by $p \cup q$; this compound statement is true if *at least* one of p or q is true, and false if both these statements are false. For example, if p is the statement above concerning a circle and q is the statement about a stone, the proposition $p \cup q$ is "A circle is round or a stone is soft," and is a true statement. The *conjunction* of p and q is the proposition "p and q," and is denoted by $p \cap q$; this compound statement is true if *both* p and q are true, and otherwise false. To continue the meanings just assigned to p and q, it is clear that $p \cap q$ is false since the statement, "A circle is round and a stone is soft" is false. The *negation* of a proposition p is "not p," and is denoted by p'; p' is true when

p is false, and false when p is true. For example, if p is the statement, "A circle is round," p' is the statement "A circle is not round." In this case, p is true while p' is false. In Table 3 below we have exhibited the truth values for the propositions $p \cup q$, $p \cap q$, and p', for all possible combinations of truth values for p and q. Such a table is known as a *truth table* for the various compound propositions.

Table 3

p	q	p∪q	p∩q	p'
T	T	T	T	F
T	F	T	F	F
F	T	T	F	T
F	F	F	F	T

A quick comparison of Table 3 with Table 2 reveals that these two tables are very much alike. In fact if we set up a correspondence between the two systems in which propositions p and q correspond, respectively, to the elements x and y of $\mathcal{B}(0, 1)$, and further let T and F correspond to 1 and 0, respectively, the two systems become indistinguishable. Hence our "Algebra of Logic" or "Propositional Calculus" is equivalent to the Boolean algebra $\mathcal{B}(0, 1)$. It is for this reason that Boolean algebra is sometimes called the "Algebra of Logic," and it was somewhat in this form that George Boole invented it.

It would take us far beyond the scope of this book to include a discussion of the present-day applications of Boolean algebra, but we do make mere mention of one. A relay is a set of switches, controlled by an electromagnet, which opens or closes certain contacts as it is energized. Thus, there is associated with each relay X of an electric circuit the proposition "Relay X is energized," which we can indicate by x. At any given instant this proposition is either true or false. If we now define our operations as for the general propositional calculus, which we have just discussed, it is easy to see that the set of all x-propositions associated with a given network of relays comprises a Boolean algebra, with the same operation table as $\mathcal{B}(0, 1)$. It is possible to use the discipline of Boolean algebra to simplify complicated electrical networks, and to design new and unusual circuits. However, we do not pursue this matter further, but rather invite the interested student to consult the references listed at the close of the chapter.

Problems 7–7

1. With reference to the discussion of this section, verify that the other five postulates for a Boolean algebra hold for the system of integral divisors of 110.

*2. Verify that the five postulates for a Boolean algebra which were not verified in this section are satisfied by the algebra of propositions.

3. Decide whether the following systems, with the designated operations, form Boolean algebras.
   (a) The set of integral divisors of 15, $x \cap y$ the l.c.m. of x and y, and x' identified with $15/x$.
   (b) The set of integral divisors of 24, $x \cap y$ the g.c.d. of x and y, and x' identified with $24/x$.
   (c) The set of natural numbers, $x \cap y$ the smaller of x and y, and $x' = 1$ for any x.

4. Let p and q be declaratory statements, as in the Boolean algebra of propositions discussed in this section. Define p' as usual, but give $p \cap q$ the meaning of "p if and only if q" as described in the following table:

p	T	T	F	F
q	T	F	T	F
$p \cap q$	T	F	F	T

Verify whether this algebra of propositions is a Boolean algebra.

*5. If p and q are propositions, show that $p' \cup q$ means "p implies q" (in symbols, $p \rightarrow q$) in the algebra of propositions. (Hint: $p \rightarrow q$ means that q must be true unless p is false.)

6. A *tautology* is a statement which is true regardless of the nature of the components of the statement, as for instance $(p \cap p')'$. Use the result of **Problem 5 to see which of the following are tautologies in the algebra of propositions: (a) $p \rightarrow p'$; (b) $(p \rightarrow q') \rightarrow (q' \rightarrow p)$; (c) $(p \rightarrow q) \rightarrow (q' \rightarrow p')$.

REFERENCES

BIRKHOFF, G.: *Lattice Theory* (New York, A.M.S., Colloquium Publication, Vol. 25, 1948).

HERMES: *Einfuhrung in die Verbandstheorie* (Berlin, Springer-Verlag).

HOHN, F.: *Applied Boolean Algebra* (New York, Macmillan, 1960).

HOHN, F.: "Some Mathematical Aspects of Switching," *Amer. Math. Monthly*, Vol. 62 (1943), pp. 75–90.

JACOBSON, N.: *Lectures in Abstract Algebra*, Vol. 1, Chap. 7 (Princeton, N.J., Van Nostrand, 1951).

WHITESITT, J.: *Boolean Algebra and Its Applications* (Addison-Wesley, Reading, Mass., 1961).

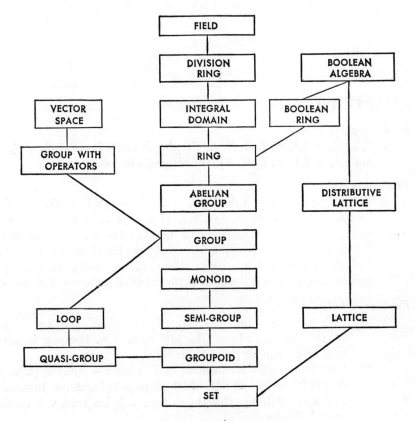

Some Algebraic Systems

APPENDIX

CHAPTER 1

Problems 1–1

1. $S_1 \cup S_2 = \{A, E, I, L, N, R, T\}$, the elements in *either* S_1 or S_2.
$S_1 \cap S_2 = \{A, E, L, R, T\}$, the elements in *both* S_1 and S_2.

Problems 1–2

2. Let $S_1 = \{a_1, a_2, \cdots, a_m\}$ and $S_2 = \{b_1, b_2, \cdots, b_n\}$, so that $S_1 \cup S_2 = \{a_1, a_2, \cdots, a_m, b_1, b_2, \cdots, b_n\}$. If we let $a_1 \to 1$, $a_2 \to 2$, $\cdots$, $a_m \to m$, $b_1 \to m + 1$, $b_2 \to m + 2$, $\cdots$, $b_n \to m + n$, we have established a one-to-one correspondence between the elements of $S_1 \cup S_2$ and $\{1, 2, \cdots, m + n\}$. Hence, the cardinal number of $S_1 \cup S_2$ is $m + n$, and $m + n$ is the sum of the cardinal numbers of S_1 and S_2.

Problems 1–3

5. (a) Suppose $s_1 \alpha = s_2 \alpha$, for $s_1, s_2 \in S$. Then $(s_1 \alpha)\beta = (s_2 \alpha)\beta$, $s_1(\alpha\beta) = s_2(\alpha\beta)$, $s_1 1_S = s_2 1_S$, and so $s_1 = s_2$. Hence α is injective, and a similar proof holds for β.

   (b) Let t be an arbitrary element of T. Then $t = t(\beta\alpha) = (t\beta)\alpha$, so that $t\beta$ is an element of S which maps onto t under α. Inasmuch as t was arbitrary, this shows that α is surjective. A similar proof holds for β.

(c) Let t be an arbitrary element of T. Then $t = t(\beta\alpha) = (t\beta)\alpha$ and $t\beta = t\beta(\alpha\alpha^{-1}) = [t(\beta\alpha)]\alpha^{-1} = t\alpha^{-1}$. Hence $\beta = \alpha^{-1}$.

Problems 1–4

2. Since $a\alpha = a\alpha$, for any $a \in S$, it follows that $a\mathcal{R}a$. Let $a\mathcal{R}b$, so that $a\alpha = b\alpha$, for $a, b \in S$. Then also $b\alpha = a\alpha$, so that $b\mathcal{R}a$. Finally, suppose $a\mathcal{R}b$ and $b\mathcal{R}c$, so that $a\alpha = b\alpha$ and $b\alpha = c\alpha$, for arbitrary elements $a, b, c \in S$. Then $a\alpha = c\alpha$, and so $a\mathcal{R}c$. Hence $\mathcal{R}$ is reflexive, symmetric, and transitive, and so is an equivalence relation.

CHAPTER 2

Problems 2–1

3. Since 1 is a nonsuccessor, $1^+ \neq 1$ and so $1 \in S$. Assume $k \in S$, i.e., $k^+ \neq k$. Then if $(k + 1)^+ = k + 1 = k^+$, it follows from the injective property of the mapping that $k + 1 = k^+ = k$. But this contradicts our inductive assumption, and so $(k + 1)^+ \neq k + 1$ and so $k + 1 \in S$. Hence, by the First Principle of Induction, $S = N$, and so $n^+ \neq n$ for every $n \in N$.

Problems 2–2

2. If $m^+ \not\leq n$, $m^+ > n$, i.e., $n < m^+$, so that $n = m + k$, for some $k \in N$. If $k = 1$, $m^+ = n$; while if $k \neq 1$, $k = 1 + h$, for some $h \in N$, so that $n = (m + 1) + h$ whence $m^+ < n$. In either case, we can assert that $m^+ \leq n$.

Problems 2–3

4. Let $x = \overline{(m, n)}$ and $0 = \overline{(r, r)}$. Then $0 + x = \overline{(r, r)} + \overline{(m, n)} = \overline{(r + m, r + n)} = \overline{(m, n)} = x$, by definition of equality. Similarly, $x + 0 = x$.

Problems 2–4

1. Since b is a positive integer, $b \geq 1$. It follows that $b|a| \geq |a|$, and so $a + b|a| \geq a + |a| \geq 0$.

CHAPTER 3

Problems 3–1

4. Since $a \circ b$ is an integer, for arbitrary $a, b \in I$, the "circle" composition is defined in I. This implies that $(a \circ b) \circ c = (a + b - ab) \circ c = (a + b - ab) + c - (a + b - ab)c = a + b + c - ab - ac - bc + abc$. Also $a \circ (b \circ c) = a + (b \circ c) - a(b \circ c) = a + b + c - bc - a(b + c - bc) = a + b + c - ab - ac - bc + abc$. Hence $(a \circ b) \circ c = a \circ (b \circ c)$, and I is a semi-group under the "circle" composition.

Problems 3-2

4. Let $G = \{a_1, a_2, \cdots, a_n\}$ be a finite monoid, and suppose that any solution of $ax = b$, for $a, b \in G$, is unique if it exists. If a is an arbitrary element of G, the elements $aa_1, aa_2, \cdots, aa_n$ are all distinct, by our assumption of uniqueness. Hence these elements comprise the complete set of G, so that if b is any element of G, there exists an element $a_k \in G$ such that $aa_k = b$. But this means that $x = a_k$ is a solution of $ax = b$, as asserted. A similar argument applies to the equation $ya = b$.

Problems 3-3

1. Let G and G' be isomorphic groupoids, with a' and b' arbitrary elements of G'. The definition of an isomorphism implies the existence of elements $a, b \in G$ such that $a \to a'$, $b \to b'$, $ab \to a'b'$, and $ba \to b'a'$. Since $ab = ba$, it follows that $a'b' = b'a'$, and so G' is commutative.

Problems 3-4

4. Let a_1, a_2 be arbitrary elements of A. Then, the definition of the product of two mappings, along with the properties of a homomorphism, imply that $(a_1a_2)(\alpha\beta) = [(a_1a_2)\alpha]\beta = [(a_1\alpha)(a_2\alpha)]\beta = [(a_1\alpha)\beta][(a_2\alpha)\beta] = [a_1(\alpha\beta)][a_2(\alpha\beta)]$. Hence $\alpha\beta$ is a homomorphism of A into C.

Problems 3-5

2. (b) Suppose $a_1\psi = a_2\psi = 1$ and $b_1\psi = b_2\psi = -1$, for integers a_1, b_1. Then $a_1 + b_1$ is odd so that $(a_1 + b_1)\psi = -1$, and $a_2 + b_2$ is also odd so that $(a_2 + b_2)\psi = -1$. It follows that $a_1 + b_1$ and $a_2 + b_2$ are in the same equivalence class, and the partition is regular.

CHAPTER 4

Problems 4-1

2. Let $ab = ac$, for elements a, b, c in the semi-group. If we designate a' as a left inverse of a with respect to a left identity e', then $a'(ab) = a'(ac)$, $(a'a)b = (a'a)c$, $e'b = e'c$, whence $b = c$.

Problems 4-2

1.

	1	−1
1	1	−1
−1	−1	1

Problems 4–3

7. (a) $\beta\gamma = \begin{pmatrix} 1 & 2 & 3 & 4 & 5 & 6 \\ 3 & 1 & 5 & 6 & 4 & 2 \end{pmatrix}$. Hence $\alpha(\beta\gamma) = \begin{pmatrix} 1 & 2 & 3 & 4 & 5 & 6 \\ 6 & 1 & 3 & 5 & 4 & 2 \end{pmatrix}$

$$= \begin{pmatrix} 1 & 2 & 4 & 5 & 6 \\ 6 & 1 & 5 & 4 & 2 \end{pmatrix}.$$

(c) $\alpha^2 = \begin{pmatrix} 1 & 3 & 4 \\ 3 & 4 & 1 \end{pmatrix}$. Hence $\alpha^2\beta = \begin{pmatrix} 1 & 2 & 3 & 4 & 5 & 6 \\ 1 & 6 & 4 & 3 & 5 & 2 \end{pmatrix}$

$$= \begin{pmatrix} 2 & 3 & 4 & 6 \\ 6 & 4 & 3 & 2 \end{pmatrix}.$$

Problems 4–4

7. Since the sum of two continuous functions is a continuous function, the set of continuous functions is closed under addition. Now let f, g, h be any three continuous functions on R^*, and consider $f + (g + h)$ and $(f + g) + h$. If x is any real number, $x(\overline{f + g + h})$ $= xf + x(g + h) = xf + (xg + xh)$, whereas $x(\overline{f + g} + h) =$ $x(f + g) + xh = (xf + xg) + xh$. Inasmuch as addition is associative in R^*, we have $xf + (xg + xh) = (xf + xg) + xh$, so that $f + (g + h) = (f + g) + h$, which establishes the associative law. The zero of the set is the function which has the value 0 for every real x, and we can designate this function 0. For it is clear that $x(f + 0)$ $= x(0 + f) = xf$, for any function f of the set. Finally, we define $-f$, for any f of the set, so that $x(-f) = -(xf)$, and this function is easily seen to be continuous. That it has the characteristic property of an inverse follows from $x[f + (-f)] = xf + x(-f) = xf$ $- (xf) = 0$, so that $f + (-f) = 0$. This shows that the set of continuous functions is a group under the given composition.

Problems 4–5

3. Let a and b be arbitrary elements of N_g. Then $gb = bg$, $(gb)b^{-1}$ $= (bg)b^{-1}$, $g(bb^{-1}) = b(gb^{-1})$, and $b^{-1}g = gb^{-1}$, so that $b^{-1} \in N_g$. But then $g(ab^{-1}) = (ga)b^{-1} = (ag)b^{-1} = a(gb^{-1}) = a(b^{-1}g) = (ab^{-1})g$, from which we see that $ab^{-1} \in N_g$. It follows by **Theorem 4.51** that N_g is a subgroup.

Problems 4–6

8. $G = \{0, 1, 2, 3\}$. On multiplication of the elements of G on the right by 0, 1, 2, 3, respectively, we obtain: $\pi_0 = \begin{pmatrix} 0 & 1 & 2 & 3 \\ 0 & 1 & 2 & 3 \end{pmatrix}$,

$\pi_1 = \begin{pmatrix} 0 & 1 & 2 & 3 \\ 1 & 2 & 3 & 0 \end{pmatrix}$, $\pi_2 = \begin{pmatrix} 0 & 1 & 2 & 3 \\ 2 & 3 & 0 & 1 \end{pmatrix}$, $\pi_3 = \begin{pmatrix} 0 & 1 & 2 & 3 \\ 3 & 0 & 1 & 2 \end{pmatrix}$.

The right regular realization of G is then the group whose elements are $\{\pi_0, \pi_1, \pi_2, \pi_3\}$.

Problems 4–7

2. Since every permutation is either even or odd, the set S of odd permutations and the even permutations in A_n comprise all elements of S_n. If we multiply every element of S_n on the right by an arbitrary transposition π_t, the even permutations become odd and the odd permutations become even. Since S_n is a group, all these transformed permutations are distinct, and so the number of elements in S must be the same as the number in A_n. Hence the number of each is $n!/2$.

Problems 4–8

4. By the result of **Problem 2** of **Problems 4-5**, a subset of a finite group is a subgroup if the subset is closed under the group operation. We see that $(123)(123) = (132)$, $(132)(132) = (123)$, and $(123)(132) = (1)$, so that the given subset is closed, and therefore a subgroup. The coset decomposition of S_3, with respect to this subgroup is $S_3 = \{(1), (123), (132)\} \cup (12)\,\{(1), (123), (132)\}$ or $S_3 = \{(1), (123), (132)\} \cup \{(12), (13), (23)\}$.

Problems 4–9

5. Since K is normal in $\mathcal{G}$, $aK = Ka$ for any $a \in \mathcal{G}$. But every element of H is an element of $\mathcal{G}$, so that $hK = Kh$ for any $h \in H$. Hence K is normal in H.

Problems 4–10

2. In order to show that a subgroup H is *not* normal in a group $\mathcal{G}$, we need simply exhibit an element $a \in \mathcal{G}$ such that $aH \neq Ha$. Now $(123) \in S_3$, but $(123)\{(1), (12)\} = \{(123), (23)\}$ whereas $\{(1),(12)\}$ $(123) = \{(123), (13)\}$. Hence $\{(1), (123)\}$ is not normal in S_3.

CHAPTER 5

Problems 5–1

9. Let $x = a + bi$ and $y = c + di$ be arbitrary Gaussian integers. Then $x - y = (a + bi) - (c + di) = a - c + (b - d)i$ and also $xy = (a + bi)(c + di) = ac - bd + (bc + ad)i$. Since both $x - y$ and xy are seen to be Gaussian integers, an application of **Theorem 5.11** shows that the Gaussian integers form a subring of the ring of complex numbers.

Problems 5–2

3. By the distributive laws for a ring, $(a + b)(c + d) = a(c + d) + b(c + d) = ac + ad + bc + bd$.

Problems 5–3

3. Let a be an arbitrary element of the integral domain. Then $ae^2 = ae$, and $(ae - a)e = 0$. Since $e \neq 0$, and an integral domain contains no divisors of 0, we must have $ae - a = 0$, and so $ae = a$. Similarly, $ea = a$, and e must be the identity element.

Problems 5–4

6. Since u is a solution of the given equation, $u^3 = -4u^2 + 2u - 3$, and $u^4 = -4u^3 + 2u^2 - 3u = -4(-4u^2 + 2u - 3) + 2u^2 - 3u$ $= 18u^2 - 11u + 12$. Hence $(2u^2 + 1)(3u^2 - 2u - 1) = 6u^4 - 4u^3$ $+ u^2 - 2u - 1 = 108u^2 - 66u + 72 + 16u^2 - 8u + 12 + u^2$ $- 2u - 1 = 125u^2 - 76u + 83$. If u is transcendental, the product is $6u^4 - 4u^3 + u^2 - 2u - 1$.

Problems 5–5

1. Since $ab = ba$, we have $(a, b) \sim (a, b)$, so the relation is reflexive. If $(a, b) \sim (c, d)$, we have $ad = bc$ and also $cb = da$, whence (c, d) $\sim (a, b)$. Hence $\sim$ is symmetric. If $(a, b) \sim (c, d)$, and $(c, d) \sim$ (e, f), then $ad = bc$ and $cf = de$, so that $dafc = cbed$. Hence $af = be$, $(a, b) \sim (e, f)$ and the relation is transitive.

Problems 5–6

6. Suppose E is an ideal in a field F. If $a \neq 0$ is an element of E, $a^{-1} \in F$ and so $aa^{-1} = 1 \in E$. Hence $b1 = b \in E$, for arbitrary $b \in F$, and so $E = F$. It follows that either $E = 0$ or $E = F$.

Problems 5–7

1. The prescribed mapping is $a \rightarrow a + E$, for each $a \in A$. Then if $b \rightarrow b + E$, we have $a + b \rightarrow a + b + E$ and $ab \rightarrow ab + E$. But $a + E + b + E = a + b + E$, since A is commutative under addition; and also $(a + E)(b + E) = ab + aE + Eb + EE = ab + E$, since E is an ideal. Hence $a + b \rightarrow a + b + E$ and $ab \rightarrow ab + E$, and so the mapping is a homomorphism.

Problems 5–8

9. Let U be the set of units in the ring. If u and v are units, then $(uv)(v^{-1}u^{-1}) = u(vv^{-1})u^{-1} = uu^{-1} = 1$, and so uv is a unit, so that U is closed under addition. Associativity of multiplication is automatic in U as a subset of a ring. Since $1^{-1} = 1$, $1 \in U$. Finally, since $u^{-1}u = uu^{-1} = 1$, for any $u \in U$, $(u^{-1})^{-1} = u$ and so $u^{-1} \in U$. Hence U is a multiplicative group.

Problems 5–9.

5. (a) Since $(2)(4) = 8$, $\bar{2} \cdot \bar{4} = \bar{1}$, and so $(\bar{2})^{-1} = \bar{4}$.

(b) As in (a), $(\bar{4})^{-1} = \bar{2}$

(c) Since $(5)(3) = 15$, $\bar{5} \cdot \bar{3} = \bar{1}$, and so $(\bar{5})^{-1} = \bar{3}$.

Problems 5–10

5. If a is a unit, there exists an element a' in the domain such that $a'a = 1$. Then, for any b in the domain, $b\delta = [a'(ab)]\delta \geq (ab)\delta$. But always in a Euclidean domain $(ab)\delta \geq b\delta$, so that $(ab)\delta = b\delta$. In particular, if we put $b = 1$ in the equation, we obtain $(a1)\delta = a\delta = 1\delta$.

Problems 5–11

5. The radical Z of a ring A is the set of elements z in A such that $z^n = 0$, for some integer n. Let a and b be in the radical, with $a^r = b^s = 0$, for integers r, s. Then if $t = r + s$, $(a - b)^t = 0$, and so $a - b \in Z$. It follows from **Theorem 4.51** that Z is an additive subgroup of A. If $x \in A$, $(ax)^r = a^r x^r = 0$, and so $ax \in Z$. Hence Z is an ideal in A.

CHAPTER 6

Problems 6–1

1. $(a_1, b_1) + (a_2, b_2) = (a_1 + a_2, b_1 + b_2) = (a_2 + a_1, b_2 + b_1) = (a_2, b_2) + (a_1, b_1)$.

$[(a_1, b_1) + (a_2, b_2)] + (a_3, b_3) = (a_1 + a_2, b_1 + b_2) + (a_3, b_3) = ((a_1 + a_2) + a_3, (b_1 + b_2) + b_3)) = (a_1 + (a_2 + a_3), b_1 + (b_2 + b_3)) = (a_1, b_1) + [(a_2, b_2) + (a_3, b_3)]$.

Problems 6–2

4. **(a)** $\xi + 2\eta - 3\zeta = (1, -2, 3) + 2(-3, -2, 5) - 3(2, -5, 6) = (1, -2, 3) + (-6, -4, 10) + (-6, 15, -18) = (-11, 9, -5)$.

(b) $4(1, -2, 3) + 2x - 3(2, -5, 6) = 0 = (0, 0, 0)$. Hence $2x = (6, -15, 18) + (-4, 8, -12) = (2, -7, 6)$, and so $x = (1, -7/2, 3)$.

Problems 6–3

7. **(a)** Let $X_1 = (x_1, x_2, x_3, x_4)$ and $X_2 = (y_1, y_2, y_3, y_4)$, with the components integers. Then $X_1 + X_2 = x_1 + y_1, x_2 + y_2, x_3 + y_3, x_4 + y_4)$, and we note that the components are integers. Also $cX_1 = (cx_1, cx_2, cx_3, cx_4)$, for any real number c, but cx_i is not necessarily an integer when x_i is an integer. Hence the system in **(a)** is not a subspace.

(b) Let $X_1 = (x_1, x_2, x_3, x_4)$ and $X_2 = (y_1 y_2, y_3, y_4)$ where $x_2 = 2x_1$, $x_3 = x_1 + x_2$, $y_2 = 2y_1$, $y_3 = y_1 + y_2$. Then $X_1 + X_2 = (x_1 + y_1, x_2, + y_2, x_3 + y_3, x_4 + y_4)$ and $x_2 + y_2 = 2x_1 + 2y_1 = 2(x_1 + y_1)$, $x_3 + y_3 = (x_1 + x_2) + (y_1 + y_2) = (x_1 + y_1) + (x_2 + y_2)$, so that $X_1 + X_2$ is in the set. Also $cX_1 = (cx_1, cx_2, cx_3, cx_4)$, where $cx_2 = c(2x_1) = 2(cx_1)$ and $cx_3 =$

$c(x_1 + x_2) = cx_1 + cx_2$, for any $c \in R^*$. Hence cX_1 is in the set, and so by **Theorem 6.32** the set comprises a subspace.

Problems 6-4

7. The vectors (a_1, b_1), (a_2, b_2) are linearly dependent if and only if there exist nonzero scalars c_1, c_2 such that $c_1(a_1, b_1) + c_2(a_2, b_2) = (0, 0)$. But this vector equation is equivalent to the two equations

$$c_1 a_1 + c_2 a_2 = 0$$
$$c_1 b_1 + c_2 b_2 = 0,$$

and these equations have a nontrivial solution for c_1 and c_2 if and only if $\begin{vmatrix} a_1 & a_2 \\ b_1 & b_2 \end{vmatrix} = 0 = a_1 b_2 - a_2 b_1$.

Problems 6-5

3. **(a)** Since the equation $c_1 + c_2 x + c_3 x^2 = 0$ has at most two real solutions for x, for arbitrary scalars c_1, c_2, c_3, it follows that the equation can not be identically 0. Hence 1, x, x^2 are linearly independent.

   (c) Since $(-1)1 + (1) \sin^2 x + (1) \cos^2 x = 0$, for every real x, it is clear that $1, \sin^2 x, \cos^2 x$ is a linearly dependent set. In this case, $c_1 = -1, c_2 = 1, c_3 = 1$.

Problems 6-6

3. There can be only 3 basis elements in the set, so consider the vectors $(-1, 2, 2)$, $(2, 2, -1)$, $(2, -1, 2)$. The equation $c_1(-1, 2, 2) + c_2(2, 2, -1) + c_3(2, -1, 2) = 0$ is equivalent to the three equations

$$-c_1 + 2c_2 + 2c_3 = 0$$
$$2c_1 + 2c_2 - c_3 = 0$$
$$2c_1 - c_2 + 2c_3 = 0,$$

and these equations have a nontrivial solution if and only if

$$\begin{vmatrix} -1 & 2 & 2 \\ 2 & 2 & -1 \\ 2 & -1 & 2 \end{vmatrix} \neq 0.$$

Since this determinant is -27, we see that the vectors $(-1, 2, 2)$, $(2, 2, -1)$, $(2, -1, 2)$ comprise a basis.

It is clear from inspection that $(3, 0, -3) = (2, 2, -1) - (-1, 2, 2)$.

Problems 6-7

1. By definition of T, $(c_1, c_2, c_3) + (d_1, d_2, d_3) = (c_1 + d_1, c_2 + d_2, c_3 + d_3)$ $\rightarrow (c_1 + d_1)\lambda + (c_2 + d_2)\mu + (c_3 + d_3)\nu = (c_1\lambda + c_2\mu + c_3\nu) + (d_1\lambda + d_2\mu + d_3\nu) = (c_1, c_2, c_3)T + (d_1, d_2, d_3)T$. Also $c(c_1, c_2, c_3) =$

$$(cc_1, cc_2, cc_3) \rightarrow (cc_1)\lambda + (cc_2)\mu + (cc_3)\nu = c[c_1\lambda + c_2\mu + c_3\nu] = c[(c_1, c_2, c_3)T].$$ Hence T is linear.

Problems 6–8

9. By definition of T, $\epsilon_1 T = [-(-1, 1) + (0,1)] T = -(1, -2) + (0, 1) = (-1,3) = -\epsilon_1 + 3\epsilon_2$, while $\epsilon_2 T = 0\epsilon_1 + 1\epsilon_2$.

Hence the matrix of T is $\begin{bmatrix} -1 & 3 \\ 0 & 1 \end{bmatrix}$.

Problems 6–9

2. $A(cX) = A\begin{bmatrix} cx_1 \\ cx_2 \\ \cdot \\ \cdot \\ cx_n \end{bmatrix} = \begin{bmatrix} ca_{11}x_1 + ca_{12}x_2 + \cdots + ca_{1n}x_n \\ ca_{21}x_1 + ca_{22}x_2 + \cdots + ca_{2n}x_n \\ \cdots\cdots\cdots\cdots \\ \cdots\cdots\cdots\cdots \\ ca_{n1}x_1 + ca_{n2}x_2 + \cdots + ca_{nn}x_n \end{bmatrix} =$

$$c\begin{bmatrix} a_{11}x_1 + a_{12}x_2 + \cdots + a_{1n}x_n \\ a_{21}x_1 + a_{22}x_2 + \cdots + a_{2n}x_n \\ \cdots\cdots\cdots\cdots \\ \cdots\cdots\cdots\cdots \\ a_{n1}x_1 + a_{n2}x_2 + \cdots + a_{nn}x_n \end{bmatrix} = c(AX).$$

Problems 6–10

6. By Cramer's rule, $x = \begin{vmatrix} 19 & -3 & 8 \\ 6 & -1 & 1 \\ 7 & 4 & -3 \end{vmatrix} \Big/ \begin{vmatrix} 2 & -3 & 8 \\ 3 & -1 & 1 \\ 2 & 4 & -3 \end{vmatrix} = \dfrac{154}{77} = 2.$

Similarly $y = \begin{vmatrix} 2 & 19 & 8 \\ 3 & 6 & 1 \\ 2 & 7 & -3 \end{vmatrix} \Big/ \begin{vmatrix} 2 & -3 & 8 \\ 3 & -1 & 1 \\ 2 & 4 & -3 \end{vmatrix} = \dfrac{231}{77} = 3,$ and

$z = \begin{vmatrix} 2 & -3 & 19 \\ 3 & -1 & 6 \\ 2 & 4 & 7 \end{vmatrix} \Big/ \begin{vmatrix} 2 & -3 & 8 \\ 3 & -1 & 1 \\ 2 & 4 & -3 \end{vmatrix} = 3.$

If $A = \begin{bmatrix} 2 & -3 & 8 \\ 3 & -1 & 1 \\ 2 & 4 & -3 \end{bmatrix}$, then $A^{-1} = \dfrac{\text{adj } A}{|A|} = \dfrac{\begin{bmatrix} -1 & 23 & 5 \\ 11 & -22 & 22 \\ 14 & -14 & 7 \end{bmatrix}}{77}.$

The solution of $AX = B$ is

$$X = A^{-1}B = \dfrac{\begin{bmatrix} -1 & 23 & 5 \\ 11 & -22 & 22 \\ 14 & -14 & 7 \end{bmatrix}}{77}\begin{bmatrix} 19 \\ 6 \\ 7 \end{bmatrix} = \begin{bmatrix} 2 \\ 3 \\ 3 \end{bmatrix}.$$

Hence, as before, $x = 2$, $y = 3$, and $z = 3$.

Problems 6–11

3. We shall refer to rows 1, 2, 3, respectively, by (1), (2), (3). Then, applying the elementary row operations in succession, we obtain

$$\begin{bmatrix} 1 & 1 & -5 & 26 \\ 1 & 2 & 1 & -4 \\ 1 & 3 & 7 & -34 \end{bmatrix} \xrightarrow{(2)-(1)} \begin{bmatrix} 1 & 1 & -5 & 26 \\ 0 & 1 & 6 & -30 \\ 1 & 3 & 7 & -34 \end{bmatrix} \xrightarrow{(3)-(1)}$$

$$\begin{bmatrix} 1 & 1 & -5 & 26 \\ 0 & 1 & 6 & -30 \\ 0 & 2 & 12 & -60 \end{bmatrix} \xrightarrow{(1)-(2)} \begin{bmatrix} 1 & 0 & -11 & 56 \\ 0 & 1 & 6 & -30 \\ 0 & 2 & 12 & -60 \end{bmatrix} \xrightarrow{(3)-2(2)}$$

$$\begin{bmatrix} 1 & 0 & -11 & 56 \\ 0 & 1 & 6 & -30 \\ 0 & 0 & 0 & 0 \end{bmatrix}.$$

Hence $x = 56 + 11z$, and $y = -30 - 6z$, and so in vector from

$$X = \begin{bmatrix} x \\ y \\ z \end{bmatrix} = \begin{bmatrix} 56 + 11c \\ -30 - 6c \\ 0 + c \end{bmatrix} = \begin{bmatrix} 56 \\ -30 \\ 0 \end{bmatrix} + c \begin{bmatrix} 11 \\ -6 \\ 1 \end{bmatrix},$$

where c is an arbitrary real number.

CHAPTER 7

Problems 7–1

4. Since $a \geq b$ and $b \geq b$, it follows that b is a lower bound for a and b, whence $a \cap b \geq b$. But by **Problem 3**, $b \geq a \cap b$, so that $b = a \cap b$.

Problems 7–2

2. By definition of l.u.b., $a \cup b \geq a$ and $a \cup b \geq b$; and also $a \geq a \cap b$, $b \geq a \cap b$. Hence $a \cup b \geq a \geq a \cap b$ and $a \cup b \geq b \geq a \cap b$. If $a \cup b = a \cap b$, it then follows that $a = a \cup b = a \cap b = b$.

Problems 7–3

1. We must show that the set S of elements $x \in \mathcal{L}$, such that $x \geq b$, is closed under $\cup$ and $\cap$. Let x_1 and x_2 be elements of S, i.e., $x_1 \geq b$

and $x_2 \geq b$. Then $x_1 \cup x_2 \geq b$, by definition of l.u.b. and so $x_1 \cup x_2 \in S$. Also, b is a lower bound of x_1 and x_2, so that $x_1 \cap x_2 \geq b$, by definition of g.l.b. It follows that $x_1 \cap x_2 \in S$, and so S is a sub-lattice of $\mathcal{L}$.

Problems 7–4

2. The l.u.b. of any set of subgroups of a group is a subgroup, by definition of $\cup$, and so is in the lattice. Also, the g.l.b. of the set is a subgroup and so is in the lattice. Hence the lattice is complete.

Problems 7–6

2. Suppose $a \rightarrow a'$ and $b \rightarrow a'$, for elements a, b of $\mathcal{B}$. Then, $(a')' = a$ and $(a')' = b$, and since complements are unique it follows that $a = b$. Hence the mapping is injective. But also, since $(a')' = a$, each element $a \in \mathcal{B}$ is the complement of an element $a' \in \mathcal{B}$, so that the mapping is surjective. Hence the mapping $a \rightarrow a'$ is bijective.

Problems 7–7

6. (a) By **Problem 5**, $(p \rightarrow p') = p' \cup p' = p'$, which asserts that p is not true. This is not a tautology, for its truth depends on the nature of p.

(c) The assertion here, with the help of **Problem 5**, is $(p' \cup q)' \cup (q \cup p')$. Since any statement or its denial is true, this assertion is a tautology.

INDEX

Absolute value, 27
Adjoint, 159
Algebraic, 96
Appendix, 190 ff.
Arithmetic
  Fundamental Theorem of, 31
  Laws of, 19
Ascending chain condition
  for lattices, 179
  for rings, 118
Associate, 109
Atom, 180
Automorphism, 44, 76, 81
  inner, 77
  ring, 90

Basis of
  ideal, 104
  vector space, 138 ff.
Boole, George, 167
Boolean algebra, 7, 188 ff.

Cancellation Law, 61
Cardinality, 4
Cayley theorem, 67
Center, 66 (Probs)
Centralizer, 66 (Probs)
Chain, 168
Class, 1
  equivalence, 13
Cofactor, 158
Collection, 1

Commutator, 78 (Probs)
Comparable, 168
Component, 128
Composition, 9
  chain, 180
  series, 81
Congruence, 58
Conjugate, 76
Conjunction, 186
Consistency condition, 157 (Probs)
Correspondence (one-to-one), 4
Coset, left and right, 72 ff.
Cover, 168
Cramer's rule, 158
Cycle, 68
  disjoint, 68

Degree, 57
  polynomial, 96
Descending chain condition, 179
Determinant, 158
Dimension, 127, 135, 141
Direct product, 81
Disjunction, 186
Division algorithm, 28
Divisor of zero, 92
Duality principle, 173

Element, 1
Elementary operations, 161
Endomorphism, 45, 90
Equivalent (solutions), 161

Euclidean domain, 114 ff.
Euclidean g.c.d., 29
Euler ϕ-function, 111 (Probs)

Factor, 81
Factor group, 61
Factor groupoid, 48
Factor set, 47
Fermat theorem, 75 (Probs)
Field, 93
Function, 7
  domain of, 8
  linear, 146
  range of, 8
  value of, 7

Galois, 81
Gauss reduction, 160
Gaussian domain, 114 ff.
Gaussian integer, 89 (Probs)
Generator, 65
  subspace, 134
Graph, 8
Greatest common divisor, 29
Group, 4, 40, 50 ff.
  abelian, 50
  alternating, 72, 80
  commutative, 50
  cyclic, 64
  derived, 78
  hamiltonian, 80
  maximal, 80
  simple, 80
  solvable, 81
  symmetric, 57, 66
Group with operators, 131
Groupoid, 3, 35 ff.

Hamilton, 95
Homogeneous system, 154
Homomorphism, 44 ff., 78 ff.
  lattice, 175
  natural, 48
  ring, 90

Ideal, 101 ff.
  difference, 105 ff.
  maximal, 112, 118
  primary, 120
  prime, 110, 111
  principal, 104
  proper, 102
Idempotent, 89 (Probs)
Identity, 39
  lattice, 177
Inconsistent, 163
Index, 73

Induction
  Axiom of, 18
  First Principle of, 18
  Second Principle of, 21 ff.
Inner product, 127
Integer
  rational, 24 ff.
  prime, 29
Integral domain, 92
Intersection, 3
Inverse
  element, 51
  operation, 39
  permutation, 57
Irreducible, 115
Irredundant, 121, 180
Isomorphic, 41
Isomorphism, 41 ff.
  lattice, 175
  ring, 90
  vector space, 143

Jordan-Hölder theorem, 81

Kernel, 79, 107

Lagrange theorem, 73
Lattice, 7, 169
  complemented, 178
  complete, 176
  distributive, 177
  modular, 177
Linear combination, 133
Linear dependence, 135
Linear transformation, 145 ff.
Linearly ordered, 168
Locally infinite, 63
Loop, 40
Lower bound, 169

Mapping, 1, 6 ff.
  bijective, 8
  equal, 9
  injective, 8
  inverse, 9
  natural, 14
  surjective, 8
Matrix, 85
  augmented, 161
  coefficient, 154
  inversion of a, 159
Member, 2
Minor, 158
Monoid, 39 ff.

Negation, 186
Nilpotent, 94 (Probs)
  ideal, 122 (Probs)
  operator, 153 (Probs)

Nonhomogeneous system, 154
Norm, 97 (Probs)
Normalizer, 66
Number
  cardinal, 4
  complex, 33, 34
  natural, 16 ff.
  rational, 32 ff.
  real, 33, 34

Operation, 9
  commutative, 36
Order of
  group, 50
  group element, 62
  integer, 26
  matrix, 86
  natural number, 21 ff.

Partially ordered, 168
Partition, 13
  regular, 47, 78
Peano, 17, 18
Periodic, 62
Permutable (sets), 77
Permutation, 56
  even, 72
  group, 57, 66 ff.
  odd, 72
Polynomial, 95 ff.
  monic, 97
  prime, 97
Prime, 110
Proposition, 184 ff.

Quasi-group, 40
Quaternion, 95
Quotient
  field, 98
  group, 61
  groupoid, 47
  ring, 105 ff., 111 ff.
  set, 14

Radical, 120
Radical ideal, 111 (Probs)
Rank (of matrix), 165
Realization (right and left regular), 67
Recursive, 18
Reduced echelon, 162
Reducible, 180
Relation, 10 ff.
  equivalence, 12
Relative complement, 179
Representative, 14, 58
Ring, 5, 83 ff.
  Boolean, 183

commutative, 91
division, 93
Noetherian, 118 ff.
simple, 102

Scalar multiplication, 124
Semi-group, 3, 37 ff.
Set
  countable, 5
  denumerable, 5
  disjoint, 3
  empty, 3
  finite, 4
  index, 13
  infinite, 5
  power, 3 (Probs)
  product, 6
  quotient, 14
Skew field, 93
Solution, 154
  complete, 155
Subgroup, 50, 64 ff.
  invariant, 76
  normal, 76
  self-conjugate, 76
Subgroupoid, 37
Subinvariant series, 81
Sublattice, 174
Submonoid, 39
Subring, 84
Subsemi-group, 38
Subset, 2
  closed, 36
  proper, 3
Subspace, 133
Successor, 18
Symmetric group 57, 66
System of equations, 154 ff.

Tautology, 188 (Probs)
Torsion-free, 63
Totient, 111 (Probs)
Transcendental, 96
Transformation, 9
Transposition, 68
Trichotomy, 21
Truth table, 187

Union, 3
Unit, 109
Upper bound, 169

Vector, 123 ff.
Vector space, 6
  abstract, 129

Well-ordering principle, 21